RIVER POLLUTION
I. CHEMICAL ANALYSIS

RIVER POLLUTION
I. CHEMICAL ANALYSIS

by

LOUIS KLEIN
M.Sc., Ph.D.(Lond.), F.R.I.C., M.Inst.S.P.
Chief Chemist, Mersey River Board

LONDON
BUTTERWORTHS

ENGLAND: BUTTERWORTH & CO. (PUBLISHERS) LTD.
LONDON: 88 Kingsway, W.C.2
AUSTRALIA: BUTTERWORTH & CO. (AUSTRALIA) LTD.
SYDNEY: 20 Loftus Street
MELBOURNE: 343 Little Collins Street
BRISBANE: 240 Queen Street
CANADA: BUTTERWORTH & CO. (CANADA) LTD.
TORONTO: 14 Curity Avenue, 16
NEW ZEALAND: BUTTERWORTH & CO. (NEW ZEALAND) LTD.
WELLINGTON: 49/51 Ballance Street
AUCKLAND: 35 High Street
SOUTH AFRICA: BUTTERWORTH & CO. (SOUTH AFRICA) LTD.
DURBAN: 33/35 Beach Grove

Published 1959
Reprinted 1964
Reprinted 1967
Reprinted 1968

10931   b5904767

©
Butterworth & Co. (Publishers) Ltd.,
1959

Set in Monotype Baskerville type
Made and printed in Great Britain by William Clowes and Sons, Limited
London and Beccles

16.8.93

CONTENTS

PREFACE

FOLLOWING the appearance of my book 'Aspects of River Pollution', it was suggested in some quarters that Chapters 9 and 10 of that book, reviewing methods of detecting and determining the various forms of pollution and discussing the interpretation of the results, might well form the theme of a separate publication. The present volume represents, therefore, a revised version of those chapters which it is hoped will appeal to all interested in chemical analysis as applied to river pollution problems, sewage and trade wastes. The importance of analysis in helping to safeguard the purity of our rivers can hardly be overstressed.

Since the larger work was written, two important practical handbooks on the analysis of effluents have appeared in this country. First, late in 1956, H.M. Stationery Office issued the Ministry's 'Methods of Chemical Analysis as applied to sewage and sewage effluents', a thorough revision of the original edition of 1929. Secondly, in 1958, there appeared for the first time in this country 'Recommended Methods for the analysis of trade effluents' prepared by a Joint Committee of the Association of British Chemical Manufacturers and the Society for Analytical Chemistry; these methods have also been published individually in 'The Analyst' from January 1956 to April 1958. Advantage has been taken during the preparation of this book of incorporating the recommendations of these two publications.

A bibliography of nearly 600 references has been appended, of which no less than 87 cover work published during 1957 and 1958, but many more would be needed for a complete literature survey. In this connection, it may be apt to point out that the 'Bibliography on water and sewage analysis' by B. H. Weil, P. E. Murray, G. W. Reid and R. S. Ingols, published in 1948 as Special Report No. 28, State Engineering Experiment Station, Georgia Institute of Technology, Atlanta, Georgia, U.S.A., contains 2560 references. This useful and invaluable indexed guide carries the literature up to the end of 1947 but even then does not include every paper on water and effluent analysis. Other first-rate sources of analytical methods are the 'Analyst', the American 'Analytical Chemistry', the excellent 'Water Pollution Abstracts' published monthly for the Water Pollution Research Laboratory by H.M. Stationery Office, 'Chemical Abstracts' issued by the American Chemical Society, and

'Analytical Abstracts' published since 1954 by the Society for Analytical Chemistry.

My thanks are due to Dr. B. A. Southgate, C.B.E., Director of the Water Pollution Research Laboratory, for allowing me to reproduce a table showing the solubility of oxygen in water based on work carried out by that laboratory. A similar table for sea-water from a paper by G. A. Truesdale and A. L. H. Gameson has been reproduced by courtesy of the Secretary General of the Bureau du Conseil International pour l'Exploration de la Mer in whose Journal it was published.

I am also greatly indebted to Mrs S. M. Rawson, B.Sc., Assistant Chemist, Mersey River Board, for reading and criticising the manuscript.

L. KLEIN

Manchester,

November, 1958.

ABBREVIATIONS

ABCM—SAC Joint Committee. Association of British Chemical Manufacturers and Society for Analytical Chemistry Joint Committee for the analysis of trade effluents

A.P.H.A. American Public Health Association

B.D.H. British Drug Houses

B.O.D. Biochemical Oxygen Demand

EDTA Ethylene diamine tetra-acetic acid (sodium salt)

M Molar, i.e. a solution containing the molecular weight in grams of a substance per litre of solution

N Normal, i.e. a solution containing 1 gram equivalent of substance, or amount of substance equivalent to $1 \cdot 008$ grams of hydrogen, per litre of solution

p.p.m. parts per million (i.e. grams per million millilitres,* or milligrams per litre)

‰ parts per thousand (grams per kilogram)

$<$ less than

$>$ greater than

mg/l. milligrams per litre

h hours

ml millilitres

gr grains

µg micrograms (i.e. millionths of a gram)

The abbreviations appearing in the Bibliography are taken from *World List of Scientific Periodicals* (Butterworths, London)

---

* Definition given by Ministry of Housing and Local Government in Circular No. 8/54, 1954. In British units, it is for all practical purposes approximately equal to lb. per million lb. or lb. per 100,000 gal.

CHAPTER 1

INTRODUCTION

MUCH pollution of the rivers of this country by sewage and trade wastes has been going on since the days of the Industrial Revolution over 150 years ago. The Rivers Pollution Prevention Act, 1876, did something to improve the position, especially because it led to the formation of River Authorities in certain industrial areas (e.g. the Mersey and Irwell Joint Committee, the Ribble Joint Committee and the West Riding of Yorkshire Rivers Board). Since the Second World War, there has been a renewed interest in pollution problems owing to the expansion of industry, the growing scarcity of sources of water, and the ever-increasing usage of water for domestic and industrial purposes. Evidently new legislation was needed to replace the existing law so that better control over pollution could be exercised. The establishment by the River Boards Act, 1948, of River Boards covering all the watersheds of England and Wales and dealing with land drainage, fisheries, and pollution prevention was an important step in this direction. This was followed by the passing of the Rivers (Prevention of Pollution) Act, 1951, which gave up-to-date legal powers to these new Boards. A similar Act for Scotland, the Rivers (Prevention of Pollution) (Scotland) Act, 1951, set up and also provided legislation for Scottish River Authorities which were termed 'River Purification Boards' since, unlike the English Boards, they dealt with pollution prevention only.

It is obvious that since most pollutions are of a chemical or physical nature, chemical analysis supplemented by physical and physico-chemical procedures must play a vital part in the detection and measurement of river pollution. Many excellent handbooks giving practical details of analytical methods suitable for water, sewage, trade wastes and river waters have appeared in recent years (see references 1–25) and it is not the purpose of this book to encroach upon the ground covered by these publications. Rather is it the intention to provide a chemical background for, and supplement to, the information on analytical methods and in addition to review critically other methods which, though not officially recommended, may nevertheless be useful in certain circumstances for research, control work and field tests.

Before commencing analytical work it is essential to have a clear idea about the purpose of the analysis. It may be conducted

1

for research purposes or for the control and management of a sewage disposal works or of trade premises. The determination of the strength of a sewage or trade waste may be needed to gain an idea of the capacity of the various treatment units and, for trade wastes discharging to sewers, to decide what pre-treatment is required. It may be vital to determine impurities likely to affect adversely sewers, men working in sewers, or the treatment and disposal of sewage. It may be necessary to assess the effect of discharges upon a river, to determine whether these discharges satisfy certain standards and to carry out river surveys for these purposes.

River surveys are carried out for a number of reasons. The surveys may be merely of a routine character conducted to obtain an idea of the quality of the stream water at various points and under varying weather conditions, and if possible to assess the effect of the many pollutions. In this way, valuable data can be obtained providing a basis for a comparison of the state of the stream at different seasons and in different years. Surveys may also be undertaken for research purposes, or with the intention of formulating by-laws or taking legal proceedings under the Rivers (Prevention of Pollution) Act, 1951, or with the object of investigating some complaint such as mortality amongst fish, odour nuisance, or unsuitability of the river water for industrial and other uses. Whatever the purpose in view, the detection and identification of the particular pollution or pollutions followed by the application of quantitative methods to determine the extent of the pollution must constitute a fundamental feature of the survey. For this purpose, various procedures are available making use of hydrological, physical, chemical, bacteriological and biological techniques. In this book only the chemical and physical methods are discussed.

It is rarely necessary to undertake an elaborate survey using all the methods and techniques reviewed here, and often a simple field survey utilizing a limited number of tests and methods suffices. The choice and number of methods used will depend to a large extent upon the purposes in view, on the nature of the problems encountered, on the staff and funds available, on the periods of time over which observations are taken, and on local circumstances. In making a choice amongst a number of available procedures for a particular constituent, such factors as accuracy, the time taken to perform the test, the limitations of the method, the interferences likely to be encountered, and the concentration of the desired constituent must all be considered.

The sampling for a physical and chemical examination of discharges of sewage effluents and trade effluents and of stream waters forms an important feature of a river survey (see references 26–35A). Samples should be taken in clean, colourless glass bottles provided with ground-in glass stoppers; half-Winchester bottles holding one quart (or about 1 l.) are convenient for this purpose but the amount of sample required may be more or less than this quantity depending upon the nature and composition of the sample and upon the completeness of the analysis. Certain determinations (e.g. dissolved oxygen, oil, sulphide) must be performed on a separate sample taken specially for the purpose in another bottle. It is a wise precaution when sampling to rinse the bottle once or twice with the sample. Care should be taken to see that a representative sample containing the true proportion of suspended matter to liquid is obtained and it is obvious that any deposit on the bottom of the stream, sewage fungus growing on the bed, etc., should not normally be included (such extraneous matter should be separately collected and examined).

The taking of a sample in a bottle of absolutely clear and colourless glass facilitates a general description of the appearance of the sample. The description of the settled sample should include the smell, the colour, and the degree of turbidity of the supernatant liquid as well as the colour, apparent quantity and general characteristics of the sediment (e.g. whether finely divided, flocculent, sandy, etc.). The sediment, which may include dead and living material, frequently has a characteristic appearance under the microscope, consequently a microscopic examination should rarely be omitted. Dead material may be chiefly of mineral origin (e.g. sand granules from the river bed or from a sand washery) or it may be predominantly organic (e.g. coal-dust, cotton fibres, wool, paper pulp, starch granules). Living material can include algae, filamentous organisms (e.g. 'sewage fungus'), yeast cells (from brewery wastes), protozoa, crustacea, etc., and the identification of these by biological methods frequently yields valuable information. Sewage sludges, if present, may contain dead as well as living material.

The observations of WEBBER [26] are of particular relevance in connection with sampling:

'The actual collection of the water sample is a matter of considerable importance, more especially as this is often done by laymen with little knowledge of such matters. There can be few responsible chemists who have not received a grubby bottle filled with dirty water late on a Friday afternoon, accompanied by a vague note dated the previous Saturday. On opening the "sample", it may reek to high heaven of cough mixture, "Evening in Paris", or gin. Such efforts are completely useless.'

The label on the sample bottle should include such information as the type of sample (e.g. stream water, sewage effluent, trade effluent, etc.), the source (e.g. name of stream, firm, or local authority), the exact position of the sampling point (an Ordnance map reference may be necessary), the date, the time, the temperature of the sample, the weather and particulars of recent weather conditions, the visible state of the river (e.g. whether above or below normal flow, whether in spate), the state of the tide if the river is tidal, whether taken in the middle, left or right bank, and at what depth, and any other relevant data which might assist the analyst. The signature of the person taking the sample should also appear on the label and if possible the name of the person in whose presence the sample is taken, and the label should bear a reference number.

If a bacteriological analysis is required, a special sample should be taken under aseptic conditions in a sterilized glass bottle (capacity about 200–250 ml.) provided with a ground-in dust-proof stopper; if a river water is being sampled, the stopper is removed below the stream surface and against the flow. Precautions to be observed and other recommendations in connection with sampling for bacteriological tests are given in a Ministry of Health report[5].

River samples are often taken at a point halfway between the surface and the bed of the stream, carefully avoiding the disturbance of sediment at the bottom. Since, however, the mean velocity of a stream on any vertical is usually found at approximately $0.6\ h$ from the surface (where $h =$ depth) it has been suggested that sampling should be done at that depth. Much depends upon local circumstances and it may be necessary in some cases (especially near effluent outfalls) to take samples at different depths. For a fuller discussion of the precautions to be taken when sampling and of the most suitable sampling positions, the reader is referred to the literature (see especially references 1, 2, 3, 6, 7, 14 and 27). When it is necessary to take river, sewage and trade samples at frequent intervals during the day, the use of automatic sampling devices is often desirable[29, 31-33], and is particularly useful at large sewage works receiving discharges of trade wastes[33]. Samples should be kept in a refrigerator at about 4° C if the analysis cannot be carried out immediately, since it has been shown in the case of sewage and sewage effluents[34] that considerable changes in composition may take place on storage at ordinary temperatures owing to biochemical action.

Section 15 of the River Boards Act, 1948, specifies that where it is desired to use an analysis of a sample as evidence in legal proceedings, the occupier of the land or the local authority must be notified of the fact that an analysis is to be carried out. The person taking the sample must divide the sample into three parts each of which must be placed in a bottle or container and sealed. One part is handed to the occupier of the land or the local authority, another part is kept for court inspection, and the third part is analysed.

When a river board wishes to make an application to the Minister under the Rivers (Prevention of Pollution) Act, 1951, for consent to take proceedings in respect of pollution of a stream by sewage effluent or trade effluent the stream water should be sampled, according to a Ministry circular[35A], both above and below the alleged source of pollution, and, if at all possible, a sample of the effluent itself should be taken.*

HANEY and SCHMIDT[35A] have pointed out that many forms or indications of pollution are not readily susceptible to precise quantitative determination but nevertheless may sometimes figure prominently in legal actions involving river pollution. Examples are odours, froth, scum, oil, discoloration, floating masses of putrefying sludge, objectionable solids or slimes on the stream bed, and dead fish. In many of these instances photography can be a useful and intelligible aid as a record of pollution and far more persuasive than masses of figures. The position is well put by these authors:

'One carefully composed well-documented photograph, particularly if it is in colour, may be worth a hundred dissolved oxygen samples in so far as securing public support or influencing a jury is concerned.'

It may not be amiss to add a few words on the question of the accuracy of the methods used in the chemical examination of samples. The degree of accuracy normally attainable in chemical work of this kind is of the order ±5 per cent and this is sufficient for most routine work. For research work, a higher degree of accuracy is desirable and for this purpose lengthy proceedures are often necessary involving the use of expensive apparatus and equipment and careful attention to detail. For most routine work and field tests, time is a most important consideration and it is desirable to use quick straightforward methods. There is a tendency in some of the newer methods of today to use complex procedures and expensive equipment where a simpler and more direct approach might be sufficient for the purpose. A modern method is not always better than an older well-tried one; indeed, the word 'modern' is often applied to justify something that has little other merit. It must be remembered, too, that the accuracy of a method is limited by the accuracy of the sampling which is generally not of a very high order. The position is well summarized by LOVETT and FISH[18]:

'Frequently, extreme accuracy is not essential in routine testing, and providing the limitations of a particular procedure are fully

_____

* It may not be feasible to get a sample of the effluent if the outlet is submerged or if the discharge takes place in a culvert.

appreciated, it may be a great advantage to make some sacrifice regarding accuracy, particularly if appreciable saving in time results therefrom.'

It is important, however, to emphasize that this does *not* mean that slipshod work is condoned or that it matters little if an end-point be overstepped by several drops of titrant.   In general, then, it is better to be prudent and use a simple straightforward method whose errors and limitations are known rather than a so-called 'improved' procedure of doubtful soundness. Let us, therefore, adopt towards these newer but insufficiently tested methods a somewhat cautious attitude of mind.

Needless to say, arithmetical calculations involved in analytical and survey work should be carefully checked either by means of a slide rule, or by the use of books of mathematical tables[41-44]. Although the metric system of weights and measures is used wherever possible and chemical results are now generally expressed in parts per million (p.p.m.)*, i.e. grams per million millilitres, or milligrams per litre, large scale data are frequently determined in the imperial system and conversion from the one system to the other is often required.   A few common conversion factors are given in the Appendix but a more complete list is to be found in a publication of the British Standards Institution[37] and in handbooks of chemical and physical constants[38-40].

In the analysis of sea water[287, 288], results for chlorinity, salinity and the major constituents are generally expressed in parts per 1000 (grams per kilogram of sea water).   Another unit, however, is coming into use in the literature, especially for the minor constituents, viz milligram-atoms or microgram-atoms per litre of sea water at 20° C.

---

* In the U.S.A., the latest edition of the A.P.H.A. *Standard Methods*[2] recommends the use of the more precise term 'mg. per litre' (instead of p.p.m.) and this is also recommended by the ABCM—SAC Joint Committee

CHAPTER 2

PHYSICAL METHODS

A DISCUSSION of physico-chemical methods with full details of their practical application to all kinds of problems is given in the standard works by REILLY and RAE [45], and GIBB [46], to which the reader is referred for further information.

TEMPERATURE

It is usually sufficiently accurate to take the temperature of a stream water or an effluent to the nearest half degree centigrade. For more accurate work, especially in connection with the calculation of the percentage saturation of dissolved oxygen, a standardized thermometer graduated in tenths of a degree centigrade should be used.

COLOUR AND TURBIDITY

The purest natural river waters are generally colourless and the presence of any colour at all is usually an indication of the presence of organic matter, which may impart a straw, yellow or brownish tint to the water. It is possible in these cases to express the colour in terms of the Hazen standard unit, i.e. the colour given by 1 p.p.m. of platinum in the form of chloroplatinic acid modified by the addition of 2 p.p.m. of cobaltous chloride hexahydrate [2, 4]. This determination is much simplified by using the B.D.H. Lovibond nesslerizer and a disc with nine permanent glass standards ranging from 5 to 70 Hazen units [139, 140]. If much suspended matter is present, the estimation of colour should be made after settlement or centrifuging.

With many polluted waters containing highly coloured wastes (e.g. textile dye wastes), the colour may be green, blue, purple, black, etc., and so cannot be determined by the simple procedure just outlined. In such cases, use can be made of the Lovibond tintometer in which the colour is matched by a suitable combination of graded red, yellow, and blue glass filters and expressed in terms of the internationally used Lovibond units.

RUDOLFS and HANLON [47, 48] have described accurate spectrophotometric and filterphotometric methods of determining colour in waters and industrial wastes in terms of the dominant wavelength (which defines the hue or kind of colour), luminance (which defines the degree of brightness) and purity (which defines saturation, i.e. pastel, pale, etc.). The procedure is given in the latest edition of the A.P.H.A. *Standard Methods*[2]. For most purposes, however, it is sufficient to express the colour of a river water or trade waste in purely qualitative terms.

PALIN[49] has proposed a standard definition of colour in water in terms of optical density. The Unit* ('Absorptiometric Colour Unit') is that of a clear water having an optical density of 0·001 per cm depth to violet light (peak wavelength 425 mμ, i.e. the wavelength at which the yellow-brown colour of most natural waters shows a maximum absorbance). When a water is both coloured and turbid, the colour reading must be corrected for the influence of turbidity (see p. 9). Various commercial turbidimeters, visual and photoelectric, are available for the measurement of turbidity and they are generally calibrated against standards made up from fuller's earth, a correction being made for any colour in the sample[14]. In the U.S.A., the unit of turbidity was, until recently, the turbidity imparted to a water by 1 p.p.m. of fuller's earth. This unit has now been abandoned in favour of arbitrary turbidity units fixed in relation to a standard Jackson candle turbidimeter[2]. This change has evidently been made because, as experience in this country also shows, standards prepared from fuller's earth vary somewhat with the source and grade of material used and so do not give reproducible results.

A submersible photoelectric absorptiometer specially suitable for the measurement of high turbidities in river waters was used in the survey of the Thames estuary by SCRAGG, BRIGGS and KNOWLES[50]. To obtain the calibration curve, the instrument was placed in water free from turbidity (i.e. water of 100 per cent transmission) and by the use of various neutral density filters, dial readings were obtained corresponding to a particular optical density or percentage transmission. Curves showing the relation between the optical density and various types of suspended matter of differing nature and particle size were also constructed.

The use of the Zeiss–Pulfrich nephelometer for determining the turbidity of river waters has been described by RIES[51].

For rapid routine work, an inexpensive visual apparatus [1, 3, 52] for measuring approximately the clarity or transparency of a sample (which is inversely related to its degree of turbidity) can be constructed from a colourless glass tube, 620 mm long, and of internal diameter about 25 mm with a plane glass bottom on the outside of which a black cross (with lines 1 mm in width) is pasted. A side tube near the bottom connects, via rubber tubing, with a glass reservoir, and the depth of liquid in the tube is adjusted by raising

* This Unit is 2·5 times the Hazen unit.

or lowering the reservoir until on looking down the tube, preferably in north daylight, the black cross just disappears from sight. The length of the liquid column in millimetres is measured or read off from graduations on the tube. If the test is performed on the settled as well as shaken sample, the difference gives a good idea of the amount of suspended matter present. With good effluents or river waters, the black cross may still be visible even at a depth of 600 mm, in which case the result is recorded as >600 mm. Most satisfactory sewage effluents and good trade effluents give settled transparency figures of 300 mm or more. Poorly clarified sewage or trade effluents may give readings of less than 100 mm.

Palin[49] has proposed a new Absorptiometric Unit of turbidity which is that of a suspension having an optical density of 0·001 per cm depth to yellow light (peak wavelength 580 mμ)*. Turbidity and colour can thus be determined photometrically using two different light filters. Colour can be corrected for turbidity and vice versa by determining the values of the ratio

$$\frac{\text{Optical density to violet light}}{\text{Optical density to yellow light}}$$

at the two wavelengths for both colour and turbidity. Palin found that this ratio is 4·7 for natural colour in water and 1·2 for turbidity (using relatively coarse fuller's earth suspensions).

pH VALUE[53-57]

Wide-range and narrow-range test-papers for the approximate estimation of pH values ranging from 2·0 to 10·5 are available commercially.† These papers are convenient for rough work and for field tests. The use of the British Drug Houses universal indicator is also convenient for obtaining an approximate idea of the pH value of a sample, the colour obtained at various pH values being indicated in *Table 1*.

Table 1. Colours obtained at various pH values with B.D.H. universal indicator

pH value	Colour	pH value	Colour
3·0	Red	8·0	Green
4·0	Deeper red	8·5	Bluish–green
5·0	Orange–red	9·0	Greenish–blue
5·5	Orange	9·5	Blue
6·0	Orange–yellow	10·0	Violet
6·5	Yellow	10·5	Reddish–violet
7·0–7·5	Greenish–yellow	11·0	Deeper reddish–violet

* This Unit is almost identical with the arbitrary APHA turbidity unit[2]. For practical purposes, the difference is negligible.

† For instance from the British Drug Houses, Poole, Dorset; and from Johnsons, Hendon, London, N.W.4.

More accurate determinations of pH (usually to within 0·1 pH unit over the range 0·2–10·0) can be made with the Lovibond comparator* in which, with the aid of a series of suitable discs, the colour obtained with 10 ml. of sample plus an appropriate amount of a suitable indicator (usually 0·5 ml.) is matched against Lovibond permanent glass colour standards. With many pure river waters and other samples which are poorly buffered (e.g. samples having a methyl orange alkalinity, expressed as $CaCO_3$, of less than about 20 p.p.m.), an appreciable error can be introduced due to the pH value exerted by the indicator itself. In such cases, it is preferable to use the B.D.H. Lovibond nesslerizer in which 50 ml. Nessler tubes replace the 10 ml. tubes of the comparator and a much smaller

Table 2. *Selected list of indicators suitable for the colorimetric determination of* pH *in the range* 0·2–14·0 *with the Lovibond comparator or the B.D.H. Lovibond nesslerizer*

Indicator	pH range of colour disc (in steps of 0·2 unless otherwise indicated)	Instrument C = Comparator N = Nesslerizer		Colour change acid→alkaline
Cresol red (acid range)	0·2–1·8	C		red—orange—yellow
Thymol blue (acid range)	1·2–2·8	C	N	purple–red—orange—yellow
Bromophenol blue	2·8–4·4	C	N	yellow—purplish-grey—purple-blue
B.D.H. '3046' indicator	3·0–4·6	C	N	purple—grey—green
Bromocresol green	3·6–5·2	C	N	yellow—green—blue
B.D.H. '4460' indicator	4·4–6·0	C	N	red—orange—yellow—green
Bromocresol purple	5·2–6·8	C	N	yellow—grey-purple—violet
Bromothymol blue	6·0–7·6	C	N	yellow—green—blue
Cresol red (alkaline range)	7·2–8·8	C	N	yellow—orange—pink—violet-red
Thymol blue (alkaline range)	8·0–9·6	C	N	yellow—greenish—blue
B.D.H. '8610' indicator	8·6–10·0	C		yellow—orange—pink—red
B.D.H. '9011' indicator†	9·0–11·0	C	N	yellow—grey—violet-grey
B.D.H. '1014' indicator‡	11·0–14·0	C	N	green—brownish-grey—pink—orange

† 5 standards in steps of 0·5.
‡ 9 standards in steps of 0·5. Unsuitable in presence of lime.

* Obtainable from Tintometer Ltd., Salisbury, or from the British Drug Houses, Poole, Dorset.

proportion of indicator solution (0·2 ml.) is taken. With this instrument, the colour is matched looking vertically down the column of liquid and not, as in the case of the comparator, horizontally through the liquid. Some useful indicators suitable for use with these two instruments are given in *Table 2*.

The colorimetric determination of pH can also be carried out accurately by comparing the colour produced by the sample plus a specified amount of indicator with that of buffer solutions of known pH containing the same amount of indicator. Lists of suitable indicators are given by SNELL[53], BRITTON[55] and TOMICEK[58].

When samples are coloured or very turbid, and generally when greater accuracy is required, the electrometric method utilizing the glass electrode is to be preferred. The calibration of the glass electrode is carried out using buffer solutions whose pH value is known with a high degree of accuracy. *Table 3* gives the pH values of aqueous solutions of standards that have been recommended for this purpose.

Table 3. Calibration of glass electrode for pH *determinations:* pH *values of standard solutions at various temperatures* (° C)

Standard substance	Formula	Composition of solution M=Molar	pH					Refer- ence
			14°	15°	20°	25°	26°	
Potassium tetroxalate	$KH_3(C_2O_4)_2 \cdot 2H_2O$	0·1 M	—	—	—	1·48	—	56, 59
Potassium tetroxalate	$KH_3(C_2O_4)_2 \cdot 2H_2O$	0·01 M	—	—	—	2·15	—	61
Potassium bitartrate	$KHC_4H_4O_6$	Saturated	3·55	—	—	3·56	—	60, 61
Potassium hydrogen phthalate	$C_6H_4{<}^{COOH}_{COOK}$	0·05 M	4·000	4·000	4·001	4·005	—	56
Borax . . .	$Na_2B_4O_7 \cdot 10H_2O$	Saturated	9·40	—	—	—	9·34	60
Borax . . .	$Na_2B_4O_7 \cdot 10H_2O$	0·05 M	—	—	9·18	—	—	62
Lithium carbonate .	Li_2CO_3	Saturated	11·51	—	—	—	11·36	60
Trisodium phosphate	Na_3PO_4	0·01 M	—	—	—	11·72	—	61
Calcium hydroxide	$Ca(OH)_2*$	Saturated	—	—	—	12·45	—	63

* Prepared from CaO obtained by igniting pure $CaCO_3$. Recommended by the U.S. National Bureau of Standards for measurements in the strongly alkaline range.

OIL AND OTHER IMMISCIBLE LIQUIDS

According to KIRSCHMAN and POMEROY[64], oil is the 'relatively non-volatile liquid component that contributes to the formation of oil films and deposits'. This definition excludes oils that evaporate rapidly at ordinary temperatures; such oils are usually of minor importance in river pollution, since owing to their volatility, they do not often contribute to the formation of oily films on the surface of a stream. In the normal procedures for determining oil based on extraction with a volatile solvent and evaporation of the extract, volatile oils would, of course, not be included since they would be lost by volatilization. There may be instances (e.g. discharges to sewers) when relatively volatile oils may be of some importance and an ingenious method for their determination has been described by SHERRATT [65, 66]. The method involves removal of the volatile oil by a current of air, adsorption of the oil on activated carbon and extraction with acetone; dilution of the acetone extract with acid Teepol gives a turbidity which can be compared with a series of standards containing petrol or other suitable volatile oil.

Oil is usually determined by extracting the acidified sample with a suitable organic solvent (e.g. light petroleum, hexane, ethyl ether, or chloroform), removing the solvent from the extract by evaporation or distillation, drying the residual oil at 100–105° C, and weighing. The method is only approximate since it gives not only oil but also fat, tar, and any grease associated with the suspended solids. Kirschman and Pomeroy [64] describe a wet extraction procedure for determining oil in oilfield waste waters using commercial hexane as solvent; the latter was removed by distillation on the water-bath and the oil obtained was finally dried at room temperature. More reproducible but slightly lower results were obtained by these authors by a flocculation method using zinc acetate and sodium carbonate, the precipitated zinc carbonate trapping the oil very effectively; after filtering and air-drying the precipitate, the adsorbed oil was extracted with hexane. Small amounts of oil can be estimated by flocculation with iron salts [67]. Ferric chloride is added to the sample which is then heated to boiling and precipitated with ammonia. The precipitated ferric hydroxide, which entrains all the oil, is filtered, washed with water and dried, and the oil is then extracted from the precipitate with ether.

A flocculation method, using magnesium sulphate and lime (or other suitable flocculents), followed by acidification of the precipitate and extraction with light petroleum is recommended by the ABCM-SAC Joint Committee [66].

A sub-committee of the American Petroleum Institute [67A] examined several methods for determining oil in refinery effluents and concluded that the best was a procedure involving extraction of the oil with CCl_4 and measurement of the infra-red absorption at 3·42 μ and 3·50 μ. Almost as good, and using much cheaper equipment, was an extraction-pycnometer procedure in which the density of the CCl_4 extract was compared with that of the pure solvent.

PRINGLE [68] has described a method suitable for very small quantities (up to 10 p.p.m.) of oil. The sample (2½ litres) acidified with hydrochloric acid is shaken with benzene and to prevent emulsion formation hydrogen is generated by introducing magnesium wire. The benzene layer is distilled and the residual oil is dried at 100° C.

POMEROY [69] has devised a useful test for the estimation of the floatable oil and grease present in waste waters discharging to sewers.

The estimation of very slight traces of oil is difficult by ordinary methods but HOLLAENDER[70] has determined as little as 0·02 p.p.m. of oil in steam condensate by comparing the fluorescence under ultra-violet light with that of standards.

Oil often consists of motor fuel oil or lubricating oil derived from petroleum.   Such oils dissolve in light petroleum giving a brown solution exhibiting a greenish fluorescence.   Standard methods for testing such oils are given in a recent publication[71]; important characteristics of these oils are specific gravity, distillation range, flash point, viscosity, and behaviour on heating and ignition.   If coal-tar oils are present, they should show the special reactions for phenols and will give a strong phenolic odour on ignition.   The Standardisation of Tar Products Tests Committee have published standard methods for testing tar and its products[72].

A special sectional sampling tube has been recommended for the taking of representative oil-water samples[52].

ELECTRICAL CONDUCTIVITY[2, 7, 45, 73]

GUSTAFSON and BEHRMAN[74] have recommended the determination of electrical conductivity as a rapid means of checking results of the determination of total dissolved solids as obtained by the evaporation method which is often slow and not always very accurate owing to losses of certain mineral constituents.   It may be necessary to dilute the sample first and it is essential to remove any free carbon dioxide by aeration with air free from carbon dioxide.

Although the determination of electrical conductivity is useful in the analysis of potable waters in showing changes in the concentration of total ionizable salts, its application to river survey work is somewhat limited.   Nevertheless, it can be used to indicate alterations in the content of ionizable salts in river waters due to such discharges as brine, oil-field waste waters, and chemical wastes.   A convenient commercial instrument (the dionic water tester*) is available for this purpose and this can easily be checked from time to time against a standard solution of potassium chloride.

An instrument has been described for measuring the salinity of estuaries by a conductivity determination with an accuracy of +0·33 parts per 1000 over the range 0·2–50 parts per 1000; the temperature and electrical conductivity having been determined, the salinity is estimated from a nomogram[75].

The unit used for expressing conductivity is the reciprocal of 1 megohm per centimetre-cube.   Results should be corrected to a standard temperature (generally 20° or 25° C).   Conductivity increases very markedly with rise in temperature, usually approximately 2 per cent per degree centigrade.

* Made by Messrs. Evershed and Vignoles, London.

MACKERETH[76] has made use of determinations of electrical conductivity for measuring the cation concentration (Ca, Mg, Na and K) and the anions of strong and weak acids in diluted river waters after the latter have been passed through columns of strongly basic and acidic ion exchange resins.

SUSPENDED SOLIDS, SETTLEABLE SOLIDS, DISSOLVED SOLIDS AND TOTAL SOLIDS[1-3, 14, 16, 77-87]

Two standard methods are in use in this country for the determination of suspended solids.

The Gooch crucible method involves the filtration by suction of a known volume of the shaken sample through a specially prepared asbestos mat in a Gooch crucible, which is then dried at 100–105° C. The preparation of a series of such crucibles for routine work is rather laborious and filtration is sometimes very slow particularly with polluted samples containing much colloidal matter and greasy suspended matter. Moreover, it is difficult to prepare a standard mat and the suspended solids figure obtained will depend to some extent upon the thickness of this mat. Studies of the method by DEGEN and NUSSBERGER[77] showed that to reduce errors to a minimum the following points were important:

(1) the crucible should have *small* perforations,
(2) soluble salts should be washed from the filter mat after filtration,
(3) the asbestos should be of good quality,
(4) filtration should be carried out at a lower vacuum than that used in the preparation of the mat, and
(5) loss of fine asbestos particles should be avoided during filtration and washing.

Several workers have reported favourably on the use of a glass fibre filter disc in place of an asbestos mat in the Gooch crucible method[77A, 77B].

In the alternative centrifuge method, which the writer prefers, a known volume of the shaken sample (usually 50–200 ml.) is centrifuged under standardized conditions using special conical-end centrifuge tubes. After pouring off the separated liquid, the suspended matter at the bottom of the tubes is washed with distilled water, re-centrifuged, the separated water is again removed, and the suspended matter is transferred to a weighed platinum or other suitable basin by means of a jet of water from a wash bottle and dried at 100–105° C. In general, this method is much quicker than the Gooch crucible method, especially when large numbers of samples are being examined, but gives slightly lower results as it does not include any colloidal matter that tends to be retained by the Gooch mat. Indeed, the work of RUDOLFS and BALMAT[78] has definitely shown that the so-called 'suspended solids' determination as carried out by the filtration of raw sewage through a Gooch crucible does include a portion of the colloidal fraction. Another advantage of the centrifuge method lies in the ease with which a determination of volatile solids can be subsequently carried out by ignition of the platinum basin containing the suspended solids; during this ignition, valuable information about the nature of the suspended solids can be obtained by noting any blackening, darkening or colour changes, any odours produced, evolution of fumes, appearance of sparks, flame, etc. The mineral residue remaining after ignition should be subjected to a qualitative analysis for the commoner cations and anions, especially calcium, magnesium, iron, chromium, copper, zinc, lead, sulphate, chloride and phosphate.

The filtrate from the Gooch crucible, or the separated liquid in the centrifuge, can be used for a determination of 'dissolved solids' or 'soluble solids' by evaporating a known volume to dryness. Any colloidal matter present will also be included in this determination.

FRASCHINA[81] prefers to estimate suspended solids in sewage by filtration through a weighed filter paper on a Buchner funnel, and considers that this method is quicker and easier for plant control than the Gooch crucible method. Correction is made for moisture absorbed by the filter paper during weighing.

A rapid photoelectric method for suspended solids estimation suitable for the control of sewage plant operations is described by SETTER and his co-workers[82] and involves the measurement of the percentage light transmission of the sample after homogenization for 30 sec in a Waring Blendor. The suspended solids can then be estimated from calibration curves which are different for raw sewages and final effluents. It is stated that 10 samples can be tested by the method within half an hour.

For plant control purposes, it is convenient, especially at small sewage plants with limited laboratory facilities, to estimate settleable solids rather than suspended solids. This can be done by a simple volumetric method using an Imhoff Cone[1, 2] which consists of an inverted glass cone (1 litre capacity) having the apex part graduated in millilitres. A litre of the sample is settled (usually for 1 hour) and the volume of settled sludge is read and expressed as ml. per litre. Domestic sewages usually give readings of about 3–15 ml. of settleable solids and tank effluents a reading around 0·5 ml. Final effluents from the humus tanks at biological filtration plants should give much smaller values whilst activated sludge plant effluents should yield practically no settleable solids. The test can be used to give a rough idea of the efficiency of sedimentation tanks and, in the case of filter effluents, to indicate the amount of sludge settling in the humus tanks and the rate at which unloading of solids by the filters is occurring.

Total solids can be determined by evaporating a known volume of the well-shaken sample to dryness on the water bath and drying at 100–105° C. In the case of potable waters, however, it is customary in this country[14] to dry at 180° C, since at this temperature calcium sulphate is anhydrous and magnesium sulphate contains one molecule of water of crystallization. When hygroscopic salts (e.g. calcium and magnesium chlorides and nitrates) are present, the final weighing is likely to be somewhat inaccurate.

The determination of total solids in sewage sludges and river muds is usually carried out by evaporating a known weight or volume of sample to dryness on the water bath and drying in a oven at 100–105° C. The method is only approximate since volatile inorganic and organic compounds are lost by volatilization. The principle of the well-known Dean and Stark moisture determination has been applied by LUMB[83, 84] to the determination of moisture (and hence total solids) in various sludges. A weighed amount of sludge (enough to yield about 15–19 ml. of water) is distilled with perchloroethylene, C_2Cl_4, (a non-inflammable solvent boiling at 120° C and having a specific gravity of 1·63) in a flask connected to a special distillation apparatus with a graduated measuring tube arranged to collect the distillate. The latter separates into an upper water layer and a lower layer of organic liquid, excess of which automatically passes back to the flask via a syphon tube. The volume of water is read to ±0·01 ml. giving an error of only ±0·06% in the moisture figure. A result can be obtained in half an hour. An improved form of the Dean and Stark apparatus has been described by BARR and YARWOOD[85].

A rapid filtration method useful for activated sludge and aeration tank 'mixed liquor' has been described by SMITH[86] and is given in the A.P.H.A. *Standard Methods*[2]. A known volume of sludge is poured on to a weighed filter paper in a perforated circular aluminium dish fitted by means of a rubber gasket to a Buchner funnel. Gentle suction rapidly removes the liquid portion, and the dish is then dried and re-weighed. A test can be completed within half an hour if drying is done at 120° C for 10 minutes. Results by this method are slightly lower than those obtained by the much slower evaporation method[87] since the latter method also includes dissolved solids.

RADIOACTIVITY

The detection and measurement of radioactivity require the use of specialized and expensive equipment as well as staff specially trained for the purpose. Commercial instruments are now available which permit the detection of α-, β- and γ-radiation. Since some form of protection is necessary for personnel handling radioactive wastes, a radiological laboratory must include a number of special features not to be found in an ordinary laboratory. The testing of radioactive effluents in this country is at present in the hands of the Ministry of Housing and Local Government, and it is unlikely that for some considerable time river boards, sewage works or trade premises will be called upon to determine radioactivity. The reader who is interested in radioactive techniques and in the design of radiological laboratories is referred to the extensive literature on the subject. (See references 88–97.)

FROTHING TEST

The growing use of synthetic detergents for domestic and industrial purposes is causing considerable froth to appear on the surface of many rivers in this country. It is very desirable, therefore, to have some test which can be used to determine the extent to which a river water shows a tendency to froth when shaken or aerated.

A simple empirical test of this kind is in use in the laboratories of the Mersey River Board. A 48-oz. or 50-oz. glass-stoppered bottle of colourless glass is half filled with the sample, shaken vigorously for 30 sec, and the breaking time of the froth noted as well as observations on the time taken for large bubbles, fine scum and all other bubbles to disappear.

Table 4. Classification of river waters by frothing test. Sample shaken vigorously in half-full 48-oz. Winchester stoppered bottle for 30 sec and breaking time of froth and other observations made

Description of water	Remarks on froth	Breaking time of froth	Time taken for large bubbles to disappear	Phantom froth (fine scum)	Approx. time for total disappearance of all bubbles
Non-frothy.	—	nil	up to 3 sec	nil	up to 3 sec
Almost non-frothy	—	up to 1 sec	3 to 5 sec	slight trace	1 h
Slightly frothy	—	up to 10 sec	up to 30 min	trace	4 h
Rather frothy	½ in. layer	about 5 min	—	—	¼ of surface still covered in 18 h
Frothy	½–¾ in. layer	2 to 4 h	—	—	¾ of surface still covered in 18 h
Very frothy	1 in. layer	18 h or more	—	—	—

Table 4 shows a classification of river waters based upon this test and used in the Mersey River Board laboratories.

It is found in practice that those river waters belonging to the categories of 'non-frothy' and 'almost non-frothy' do not cause foaming troubles or give rise to complaints of froth.

OKURA[98] uses a foam test as a rapid field method of estimating the content of paper manufacturing wastes (e.g. sulphite cellulose wastes) in water since such wastes tend to stabilize froth. The sample is shaken in a stoppered bottle for 5 seconds and the time taken for the froth to disappear is measured. The content of waste is then estimated from a standard curve. A laboratory apparatus for determining the frothing tendency of a sample by measuring the maximum frothing height during 30 seconds is described by MUNRO and his associates[99].

OTHER PHYSICAL METHODS

Many instrumental methods[100-104] are finding increasing application in pollution problems in cases where purely chemical methods have hitherto been used. Some of the more important of these newer techniques will now be briefly discussed.

Chromatography[103-105]

This is a method of separating substances (especially mixtures of complex closely related organic materials) by passage of the sample in a suitable solvent through a vertical column of an adsorbent (e.g. alumina, cellulose, or silica gel). After washing with the pure solvent, there will be a series of zones ranging from the most easily absorbed compounds at the top to the least adsorbed substances towards the bottom. After drying the column by gentle suction with a water pump, the zones are isolated by cutting and are then extracted ('eluted') with a suitable solvent or mixture of solvents.

For detecting and following the separation of colourless substances, physical methods are useful. GRANT[106] has described an apparatus for the detection of substances (e.g. amino-acids) in the effluent from a chromatographic column by the continuous measurement of the dielectric constant which changes with the composition of the solution.

There are variants of the chromatographic technique using paper as an adsorbent. Paper chromatography has been used as a means of detecting and identifying compounds causing tastes and odours in water[107].

Chromatography was used by Wedgwood and Cooper for separating traces of polynuclear hydrocarbons (e.g. pyrene, fluoranthene, and 3:4-benzpyrene) in sewage, sewage humus, and industrial effluents. The hydrocarbons were subsequently identified and determined by absorption spectroscopy (see under Hydrocarbons, p. 95, also references 444–447).

Chromatography has also found application in the determination of volatile acids in digesting sludges (see Acidity, p. 49).

Absorption spectroscopy[108, 109]

It is possible to measure the optical density of a substance at different wavelengths, generally in the ultra-violet region, by using a spectrophotometer. The absorption spectrum, or curve obtained by plotting wavelengths against optical density, often shows well-defined maxima and minima which may be characteristic of the absorbing substance and so be of value not only in its identification but also, by application of the Beer–Lambert law, in its quantitative determination.

The spectrophotometer was used by HOATHER[109A] to assess the carbonaceous impurity of waters. He showed that for a number of waters (including river waters) the optical density measured in a 4 cm cell in the ultra-violet at 275 mμ is roughly proportional to the permanganate value. The determination can be quickly and accurately performed and requires only a small amount of the sample.

Emission spectrography[110–112]

It has long been known that an element yields a characteristic emission spectrum which affords a good criterion of the identity of the element in question. The spectrum can be a flame, arc, or spark spectrum, and the intensity of the spectral lines on a photographic plate depends upon the quantity of the element present. This intensity can be measured by means of a microphotometer, or visually by comparison with standard spectra in a series containing known and gradually increasing amounts of the element to be determined. The method is particularly useful for determining traces of the alkali metals (e.g. sodium and potassium) and the alkaline earth metals (e.g. calcium, strontium and barium) for which suitable chemical methods are scarce and lacking in sensitivity and specificity.

Flame photometry[3, 113–115]

In this comparatively recent technique, the sample solution is atomized, sprayed into a specially designed burner, and the intensity of the light emitted by a particular spectral line is measured with the aid of a suitable light filter, a photoelectric cell and a galvanometer. Commercial instruments for the determination are available at a reasonable price, and the method is a particularly useful and rapid one for traces of sodium and potassium.

Polarography[116, 117]

Polarographic procedures are particularly useful for the simultaneous determination of small amounts of metallic ions for which diffusion current–voltage curves are obtained using a cell containing mercury as anode and a cathode consisting of a dropping mercury electrode (i.e. a glass capillary tube from which a drop of mercury falls about once every few seconds). In the presence of a sample containing several metals of different reduction potential, a series of steps is obtained on the curve, the voltage indicating the particular metal and the height of the step indicating the concentration of the metal.

The method has been applied by BUTTS and MELLON[118] to the determination of metals in industrial wastes but is restricted to metal concentrations down to about 3–5 p.p.m. and consequently is not so sensitive as most colorimetric procedures.

Physical titration methods[15, 101, 102, 104]

Titrations by instrumental methods frequently have advantages over the ordinary chemical titrations when indicators fail to give satisfactory results, for instance in many oxidation–reduction titrations and when highly coloured solutions are being tested.

In potentiometric titrations, the equivalence point is indicated by an abrupt change in potential when the E.M.F. or rate of change of E.M.F. with volume of titrant is plotted against the volume of titrant.

In conductometric titrations, the end-point is shown by a sudden change in conductivity when the conductance is plotted against the volume of titrating solution.

In amperometric titrations, the end-point is indicated on a curve in which the current passing through the titration cell, between a dropping mercury electrode and a standard calomel electrode, is plotted against the volume of titrant.

Commercial apparatus is available for carrying out these various titrations.

CHAPTER 3

CHEMICAL METHODS

THE chemical methods used for the quantitative determination of pollution are mainly volumetric (titrimetric) and colorimetric; gravimetric methods involving the conversion of the constituent to be estimated to a suitable insoluble form for weighing (e.g. the determination of sulphate by precipitation as insoluble barium sulphate) are less frequently used on account of their tedious nature and much lower sensitivity (see references 15, and 119–140).

Volumetric methods, unlike gravimetric methods which are mainly confined to precipitation reactions, are applicable to almost every type of chemical reaction, for instance precipitation reactions, neutralizations, complex ion formation, and oxidation–reduction reactions. The sensitivity of volumetric methods is increased by the use of more dilute standard solutions (e.g. N/40, N/80, N/100 or even N/1000) than those generally employed in ordinary analysis. In some cases, for instance, the estimation of traces of ferrous iron by titration with N/1000 potassium dichromate (pages 69–70), or the titration of cyanide with N/1000 silver nitrate in the modified Liebig method (page 85), the use of a micro-burette may be desirable to increase the accuracy. In these and similar cases indicator blanks should be determined experimentally using the reagents and distilled water instead of the sample and the appropriate correction made to the titration when the sample is being titrated.

Colorimetric methods are, in general, of a still higher order of sensitivity than volumetric methods. For example, as little as 0·01 p.p.m. of ammoniacal nitrogen can be estimated by means of the yellow–brown colour given with Nessler's reagent whereas an ordinary titration method can scarcely determine with accuracy less than 1 p.p.m. of ammoniacal nitrogen unless the specialized micro-diffusion techniques due to CONWAY[25] are used.

A colorimetric method involves the determination of the concentration of a coloured substance in solution and this can be done either visually in Nessler tubes,* or photoelectrically by measuring the effect of the transmitted light on a photoelectric cell. The photoelectric procedure is more accurate but necessitates the use of

---

* The use of the visual Duboscq colorimeter for this purpose has now become rare.

an expensive instrument (an absorptiometer or a spectrophoto-meter). Visual methods, involving comparison of the intensity of the colour of the unknown solution with that of the colour produced under the same conditions in a series of standard solutions in Nessler glasses, are in general satisfactory for most colorimetric work, especially for occasional determinations. Where it is necessary to extract a coloured substance with an immiscible organic solvent, for instance in methods involving the use of carbon tetrachloride solutions of dithizone, it is preferable to use a photoelectric method as the extraction of a whole series of standards every time the deter-mination is carried out is very tedious.

Although photoelectric methods have many advantages where large numbers of determinations are to be performed, for research work and in other cases where a high degree of accuracy is required, it must be remembered that they may be affected by errors due to impurities in every new batch of reagents, by mechanical and other defects in the apparatus, by fluctuations in temperature and in the mains voltage, and by any turbidity* or 'off-tints' in the solutions. In routine work, a limited staff does not always have the time needed to test and check the instrument or to prepare a new calibration curve frequently.

There is indeed much to be said for the two slogans used by Tintometer Ltd of Salisbury:

(1) 'Measure colour with colour and *see* what you are doing.'
(2) 'If you want to know what a colour looks like, *look* at it.'

The preparation of a set of standards for a visual method can be avoided and much time saved by the use of permanent colour standards; discs containing a series of graded coloured glasses suitable for a particular determination have become very popular in recent years. Discs for most of the common colour tests are now available for use with either the Lovibond comparator (which utilizes 10 ml. tubes) or the larger B.D.H. Lovibond nesslerizer (which utilizes 50 ml. Nessler tubes). When using these visual instruments, it is essential that the method described in the Tinto-meter books[139, 140] should be precisely followed. It is desirable that with every new batch of reagents the colour discs should be checked against standards; this is not necessary when the ordinary standard series method is used since any errors due to impurities in the reagents are compensated for.

Important requirements for any reaction used in colorimetric analysis are that the reaction should be highly sensitive, specific,

---

* CHAMBERLIN[141] has well said the 'no electronic device is capable of doing what the eye does, namely to separate out the difference between colour and turbidity.'

if possible, or at least fairly selective, and that the colour should be reasonably intense, stable, reproducible, and not too sensitive towards light, and finally it is desirable that the colour system should conform to Beer's law, i.e. the intensity of the colour should be proportional to the concentration of the substance being determined.

Many methods require the use of organic reagents which if used carelessly may cause skin trouble (e.g. β-naphthylamine and benzidine which are carcinogenic). This is no reason why the chemist should abandon their use if reasonable care is taken.

PREPARATION OF SAMPLE FOR ANALYSIS

No preliminary treatment is required for the sample in the case of such determinations as acidity, alkalinity, dissolved oxygen, suspended and total solids, and 3 minutes and 4 hours permanganate values. Such processes as centrifuging, or less satisfactorily filtration, may be desirable when the suspended solids content of the sample is sufficiently high to cause interference with colorimetric methods, for instance in determinations of pH, nitrite, nitrate, phenols and cyanides. When the sample is cloudy and coloured, clarification with aluminium hydroxide cream, or with aluminium sulphate and sodium carbonate, and colour removal with activated carbon, may be necessary. Distillation is sometimes used to separate volatile compounds from interfering substances, for example, in the determination of ammonia, phenols and hydrogen cyanide. When a method is not sufficiently sensitive, concentration of the desired constituent, if non-volatile, may often be achieved by evaporation of the sample. Extraction with an immiscible solvent (e.g. ether, chloroform, benzene, carbon tetrachloride, amyl alcohol) is another useful procedure for removing interfering substances and it finds application in the Fox–Gauge method for the determination of phenols, where chloroform is used to separate vegetable phenolic bodies from 'tar acids' (page 91). Ion exchange methods of separation have not often been used in the past but are finding increasing application; for instance an ion-exchange resin was used by RUSH and YOE [394] (page 81) for the separation of zinc from interfering metals.

When metallic constituents are to be determined colorimetrically, it must be remembered that the metal may be present partly in solution and partly in the sediment. In such cases, the metal is determined in the centrifuged or settled sample and a second determination is performed on the shaken sample (i.e. the sample including its sediment). In the latter case, the sample is evaporated to dryness and ignited at a low red heat to destroy organic matter;

the residue is treated with hydrochloric acid, again evaporated to dryness and heated to 105–110° C in the usual way to render any silica insoluble, and the metal finally extracted with hot hydrochloric acid. Alternatively, for greater accuracy, BUTTS, GAHLER and MELLON[322] recommend destruction of organic matter by evaporating the sample first with nitric acid to a small volume, then with a mixture of nitric and sulphuric acids until dense white fumes of sulphur trioxide appear. If lead is present, insoluble lead sulphate may separate out in the last procedure and can be dissolved in hot 40 per cent ammonium acetate. The destruction of organic matter in solid and semi-solid materials (e.g. river muds, sludges) can be carried out in a similar way. In the presence of difficultly oxidizable organic matter or when lead is to be determined, destruction of organic matter is best carried out with nitric and perchloric acids[1, 322]. Care should be taken when using perchloric acid as explosions sometimes occur.

The ABCM-SAC Joint Committee recommend destruction of organic matter by digestion with nitric and sulphuric acids in an all-glass apparatus[325] but certain metals (e.g. chromium) require special treatment.

When total chromium is to be determined in a sample containing both trivalent chromium and hexavalent chromium, there may be loss of chromium as volatile chromyl chloride if the sample contains chloride and is evaporated with sulphuric acid. In such cases, pretreatment with sodium sulphite and sulphuric acid is necessary to reduce chromate to chromic sulphate[334].

A sample containing ferrous iron must not, of course, be evaporated or treated with any oxidizing reagent, otherwise oxidation to the ferric state will take place (see page 67).

CHAPTER 4

DISSOLVED OXYGEN, OXYGEN DEMAND TESTS, ORGANIC CARBON, STABILITY

DISSOLVED OXYGEN

THE dissolved oxygen content of a river water can be expressed in any of the following ways:

(i) parts by weight of oxygen per 100,000 parts by volume of sample (i.e. mg per 100 ml. or parts per 100,000);

(ii) parts by weight of oxygen per million parts by volume of sample (i.e. mg per litre or p.p.m.);

(iii) ml. (or c.c.) of oxygen (at 0° C and 760 mm of mercury pressure) per litre of sample (i.e. ml. per litre); and

(iv) as a percentage of saturation, in relation to the maximum amount dissolved by water at the same temperature and salinity as the sample. It is necessary for this purpose to know the solubility of oxygen at various temperatures and salinities, and this is given in the Appendix, *Table 34*, page 180.

The following formulae show the relation between these various ways of expressing dissolved oxygen:

(a) parts per 100,000 of
 dissolved oxygen × 10 = p.p.m. of dissolved oxygen

(b) ml. of dissolved oxygen
 per litre × 1·43 = p.p.m. of dissolved oxygen

(c) p.p.m. of dissolved
 oxygen × 0·7 = ml. of dissolved oxygen per litre

(d) dissolved oxygen, per cent of saturation

$$= \frac{\text{p.p.m. of dissolved oxygen found experimentally in sample} \times 100}{\text{p.p.m. of oxygen under observed conditions of temperature and salinity obtained from } Table\ 34 \text{ in Appendix}}$$

A review of various methods which have been used for determining dissolved oxygen in waters is given by the Water Pollution Research Laboratory[142]. The most accurate titration method for the determination of dissolved oxygen is that due to WINKLER[143] and generally carried out in glass-stoppered bottles completely filled with the sample in such a manner as to avoid aeration. Winkler's method

25

is based upon the formation of a white precipitate of manganous hydroxide by the action of alkaline potassium iodide on manganous chloride or sulphate and the conversion of this white precipitate by the dissolved oxygen to a brown precipitate of manganic hydroxide; the latter dissolves upon addition of sulphuric acid giving manganic sulphate which immediately liberates iodine from potassium iodide in amount equivalent to the quantity of dissolved oxygen originally present:

$$MnSO_4 + 2KOH = Mn(OH)_2 + K_2SO_4$$
$$2Mn(OH)_2 + O_2 = 2MnO(OH)_2$$
$$MnO(OH)_2 + 2H_2SO_4 = Mn(SO_4)_2 + 3H_2O$$
$$Mn(SO_4)_2 + 2KI = MnSO_4 + K_2SO_4 + I_2$$

The liberated iodine is then estimated by titration with a standard solution of sodium thiosulphate, using starch as indicator.

Several modifications of the Winkler method are used when interfering substances are present.

In the Rideal–Stewart, or permanganate, modification[1, 2, 3, 144] which is used when ferrous salts, sulphides, or nitrites are present, a preliminary oxidation of these interfering substances is carried out with potassium permanganate and sulphuric acid, the excess of permanganate being removed by addition of the minimum amount of potassium oxalate. In the presence of ferrous or ferric salts (e.g. stream water containing mine drainage), potassium fluoride should be added to form a complex iron fluoride which does not liberate iodine from potassium iodide, or alternatively the iron can be complexed by carrying out the final acidification with phosphoric acid instead of sulphuric acid.

When sulphites, thiosulphates and polythionates are present (e.g. in certain paper mill wastes), THERIAULT and McNAMEE[2, 145] recommend a preliminary oxidation for a few seconds with alkaline sodium hypochlorite to oxidize these sulphur compounds completely to sulphates; the excess of hypochlorite is then removed by acidification with sulphuric acid, treatment with potassium iodide and neutralization of the liberated iodine with sodium sulphite. The Winkler procedure is then followed, using a slight excess of the alkaline iodide reagent. The above procedure (omitting the treatment with alkaline hypochlorite) can also be used for samples containing hypochlorites or free chlorine.

When the only interference is due to nitrites, it is customary nowadays to use the simple azide procedure due to ALSTERBERG[146] rather than the longer Rideal–Stewart method. In the azide method[1, 2, 147], nitrites are destroyed by addition of sodium azide (incorporated in the alkaline iodide reagent) which in the presence of sulphuric acid (used later for the acidification) reacts with nitrites according to the equations:

$$2NaN_3 + H_2SO_4 = 2HN_3 + Na_2SO_4$$
$$HNO_2 + HN_3 = N_2 + N_2O + H_2O$$

Sulphamic acid[148] has also been suggested as a means of destroying nitrites but it has not come into general use.

The Winkler method has been adapted to semi-micro work[149] and to micro-work[22] by the use of small or very small sample bottles. The Winkler technique has also been used by POTTER and WHITE[150] for the micro-determination of dissolved oxygen in water at the 0·001 p.p.m. level; to obtain accurate results at these low concentrations a new design of water sampler is used and the titration of the liberated iodine is performed amperometrically.

BRIGGS and his co-workers[151] have described a continuous recording apparatus for dissolved oxygen based on the Winkler method which is adapted to automatic working by determining the liberated iodine photometrically. A modification of the Winkler titration method was used by TRUESDALE and his associates[152] in a recent re-determination of the solubility of oxygen in water when exposed to air. As a check on the accuracy of this titrimetric procedure, WHEATLAND and SMITH[153] have compared determinations of the dissolved oxygen content of waters using the Winkler method and a new gasometric reference method, and the values obtained by the two methods agreed remarkably well, the mean difference between the results by these two methods being only about 0·01 p.p.m. of oxygen.

Another titration method for dissolved oxygen, finding occasional application in field and control tests, is that due to MILLER[16, 154, 155] and depends upon the oxidation of ferrous salts at a high pH value to ferric salts, tartrate being present to prevent any precipitation of ferric hydroxide. The sample containing alkali, Rochelle salt, and a drop or two of an indicator (phenosafranine or methylene blue) is titrated with a standard solution of ferrous sulphate or ferrous ammonium sulphate until the colour of the indicator is discharged. Another method depending upon the oxidation of ferrous salts was originally described by MOHR[156] and later modified by other workers[157, 158]. The method is based on the oxidation of ferrous hydroxide to ferric hydroxide by dissolved oxygen; the mixture of ferrous and ferric hydroxides is then dissolved in dilute sulphuric acid and the excess of unoxidized ferrous salt determined by titration with potassium permanganate.

Russian workers[159] have described an interesting titration method for dissolved oxygen depending upon the oxidation of cerous hydroxide in alkaline medium to ceric hydroxide, which, after solution in acid, is determined by titration with standard ferrous ammonium sulphate using N-phenylanthranilic acid as internal indicator.

GAD[160] uses a method based on the oxidation of manganous hydroxide to manganic hydroxide but avoids the use of expensive potassium iodide by dissolving the precipitate in a mixture of sulphuric acid and phosphoric acid and titrating the manganic sulphate with standard ferrous sulphate using diphenylamine as indicator.

Many colorimetric methods have been suggested for the estimation of dissolved oxygen. For example, amidol buffered to pH 5·1 gives a reddish colour with dissolved oxygen and this reaction has been made the basis for a colorimetric method by ISAACS[161], GILCREAS[162] and ELLIS and ELLIS[163], and a simple procedure for use as a field test has been given by ELLIS, WESTFALL and ELLIS[7]. Various adaptations of the Winkler method to colorimetric work have been proposed. For instance, the colour intensity of the iodine can be measured with a spectrophotometer[164], or by comparison with standards for which purpose colour discs are available for use with the Lovibond comparator and the B.D.H. Lovibond nesslerizer[139, 140]. A highly sensitive colorimetric method for the determination of dissolved oxygen in water utilizes the yellow colour produced when manganic hydroxide, formed by the action of dissolved oxygen on manganous hydroxide, is treated with an acid solution of o-tolidine. The method will estimate accurately dissolved oxygen concentrations of the order 0·02–0·1 p.p.m. Interference by iron is prevented by using phosphoric acid in place of hydrochloric acid[165, 166]. BANKS[167] estimates traces of dissolved oxygen (as little as 0·007 p.p.m.) in boiler water by applying Winkler's method and measuring the liberated iodine absorptiometrically by means of the purple–red colour it gives with 3:3'-dimethyl-naphthidine in the presence of a sodium acetate buffer.

Electrical methods for the determination of dissolved oxygen involving the use of the dropping mercury electrode (polarography) have been proposed and are proving useful for the continuous recording of dissolved oxygen in river waters (see references 168–173).

OXYGEN DEMAND TESTS

3 minutes and 4 hours permanganate values[1, 3, 14, 16, 190]

The determination of the amount of oxygen taken up by a sample in 4 hours from a dilute sulphuric acid solution of N/80 potassium permanganate when maintained in a stoppered bottle at a temperature of 80° F* is one of the most important tests used in this country

---

* This temperature equals 26·7° C but has been standardized by the Ministry[1] at exactly 27° C.

for assessing the quantity of oxidizable matter in the sample. The test, which in the past has been called the '4 hours oxygen absorption' or more briefly the 'O.A.', is completed by adding excess of potassium iodide, which reacts with the unused permanganate to give iodine, and titrating the liberated iodine with standard sodium thiosulphate. A determination is also generally performed in 3 minutes. The significance of these two tests is discussed in Chapter 11.

In the presence of other oxidizing agents, for instance, free chlorine or hypochlorites, chromates, manganese dioxide (from some lime sludges), a low or even 'negative' result may be obtained. In such cases, a 'blank' determination is carried out with the sample + dilute sulphuric acid + potassium iodide in order to estimate the iodine equivalent of the oxidizing agent and so enable a correction to be applied. Interference due to the presence of iron salts (e.g. if mine water is present) is best circumvented by adding syrupy phosphoric acid just before the potassium iodide when a complex ferri-phosphate is formed which does not liberate iodine from potassium iodide. If nitrites are present, they will, of course, be included in the figure obtained for the permanganate value, but many workers have in the past corrected the result. If the permanganate value is corrected in this way, the fact should be stated.

Hydrogen peroxide, which may be present in peroxide kier liquors, behaves differently from other oxidizing agents and samples containing it give *high* permanganate values owing to the reduction of the permanganate according to the equation:

$$2KMnO_4 + 3H_2SO_4 + 5H_2O_2 = K_2SO_4 + 2MnSO_4 + 8H_2O + 5O_2$$

A correction can be applied by performing a blank determination with the sample + dilute acid + potassium iodide.

In the determination of the McGowan strength figure of sewages†, it should be remembered that the customary N/80 permanganate is replaced by N/8 permanganate which gives somewhat higher values than the weaker permanganate[1, 174]. There is no satisfactory way of converting N/80 values to N/8 values, for the conversion factor can vary with different sewages but usually lies between 1 and 1·2[1].

Waters having a high content of chloride tend to give high results with the Ministry acid permanganate test and ROBERTS[175]

---

† The McGowan formula for the strength of sewage is
$$4·5\,N + 6·5\,P$$
where N = ammoniacal nitrogen + organic nitrogen
and P = N/8 permanganate value
(all expressed in parts per 100,000)

has suggested that this interference is probably due to the action of the liberated chlorine on certain organic substances and not, as hitherto believed[14], to loss of chlorine. Roberts finds that errors due to the presence of chlorides can be very much reduced by substituting dilute phosphoric acid for the dilute sulphuric acid used in the test.

NIEDERCORN and his co-workers[176] have proposed the use of a simple and rapid alkaline permanganate procedure (carried out for 10 minutes at room temperature) for determining the organic content of industrial wastes containing high and fluctuating concentrations of chlorides.

Hypochlorite values (3 minutes and 4 hours)

These are determined in a somewhat similar manner to the corresponding permanganate values, the acid N/80 potassium permanganate being replaced by an N/80 solution of sodium hypochlorite[16, 177]. These determinations are mainly of importance in connection with problems involving the differentiation between animal pollution and vegetable pollution. GIBSON[177], following up earlier work of BUYDENS[178] and DIXON and JENKINS[179], showed that the determination of the ratio hypochlorite value : permanganate value could sometimes be of real significance in tracing a source of pollution since this ratio was shown to be less than 1·0 for organic matter of vegetable origin and greater than 1·0 for organic matter of animal origin. The method is further discussed in Chapter 11, page 115.

Values obtained by using other oxidizing agents

In addition to permanganate and hypochlorite, various other oxidizing agents have been proposed from time to time for assessing rapidly the organic content of a sample, for instance potassium dichromate (references 180–191), ceric sulphate[183], and potassium periodate[192]. The most popular of these is potassium dichromate[3], the use of which has been the subject of rather voluminous literature in the U.S.A., where the test is now generally called the 'Chemical Oxygen Demand' or C.O.D. test. In the U.S.A., potassium dichromate[2] has now replaced potassium permanganate as a chemical oxidizing agent for assessing organic pollution. The dichromate method involves refluxing the sample with potassium dichromate and 50% sulphuric acid for 2 hours and this results in more complete oxidation of organic matter than is obtained with other oxidising agents. With some organic wastes, the C.O.D. obtained in this way nearly equals the B.O.D. but in other cases it is greater or less.

Once the B.O.D.:C.O.D. ratio has been established for a particular waste, the determination of C.O.D. can replace the B.O.D. test for rough control in routine work. A standard procedure for performing the dichromate test is included under the name 'Dichromate value' amongst oxygen demand tests recommended by the ABCM-SAC Joint Committee[190, 191]. The old-established permanganate method, however, will probably continue to be used for routine determinations on large numbers of samples in view of its simplicity and convenience, and, moreover, it is suitable for samples of low or high oxygen demand whereas the dichromate test in its present form is not applicable to samples with an oxygen demand of less than about 50 p.p.m. It should be added that chlorides interfere with the dichromate test especially in the presence of nitrogenous compounds but an approximate empirical correction can be applied[191].

Biochemical oxygen demand (B.O.D.)

This test, the most important and widely used of all tests for organic pollution, is normally carried out for routine work by the 'dilution' method, which was originally described in the 8th Report of the Royal Commission on Sewage Disposal[193], and has since undergone certain modifications in the interests of ease of performance, elimination of interferences, and accuracy[1-3, 16, 190]. In outline, the test is carried out by preparing a suitable dilution of the sample with aerated water and dividing between two glass-stoppered bottles; the dissolved oxygen is determined at once on one bottle, and again when the second bottle has been incubated at a standard temperature for 5 days*. The B.O.D., expressed in p.p.m., is the amount of oxygen in milligrams taken up during the 5-day period by 1 l. of the sample. The dilution should be such that only about 50 per cent of the dissolved oxygen is taken up, therefore, with unknown samples several different dilutions should be prepared. The standard temperature originally selected by the Royal Commission[193] was 65° F (= 18·3° C) because it was unusual in this country for a river water in a non-manufacturing district to exceed this value even during the summer months. The Ministry of Housing and Local Government[1] have, however, now recommended that the incubator temperature for the B.O.D. test should be 20° C. The Ministry[1] have also recommended the use of a synthetic dilution water (distilled aerated water plus nutrient salts) in place of the aerated tap water hitherto used for dilution purposes,

---

* In special cases (e.g. deoxygenation and re-aeration studies of rivers, and work on B.O.D.—time curves) other incubation periods are used, such as 2 days, 4 days 6 days, 10 days, etc.

and this should result in better agreement in values obtained in different laboratories.

The azide modification[194-196] for the estimation of the dissolved oxygen is now used wherever possible in B.O.D. determinations but the older Rideal–Stewart modification should be employed when ferrous salts are present (cf. under Dissolved Oxygen, page 26) where other interfering substances are discussed). In the presence of hydrogen peroxide, incorrect B.O.D. results are obtained but interference can be obviated by adding a small amount of the enzyme catalase which decomposes hydrogen peroxide to water and oxygen (Private communication, Laporte Chemicals Ltd., Luton).

A useful check on the accuracy of the B.O.D. technique can be obtained by carrying out determinations on suitable standard organic compounds for which purpose SAWYER and his co-workers[197] recommend glucose and glutamic acid (see page 124). Data on the B.O.D. of a number of pure organic compounds are given in a report of a research committee of the Federation of Sewage and Industrial Wastes Associations[198].

The occurrence of nitrification during the B.O.D. test (i.e. bacterial oxidation of ammonia to nitrite and nitrate) can cause abnormally high B.O.D. values. This can be prevented either by flash pasteurization, or by acidification to pH $3·0$ followed by neutralization; the sample must then be seeded with fresh settled sewage (free from nitrifying bacteria) to supply the necessary organisms (see Chapter 11, page 125).

The B.O.D. of river waters containing algae can be misleadingly high if the test is carried out, as is usually the case, in the dark. The algae will exert an extra oxygen demand on account of respiration and possibly also their organic content. The test in such cases should be done on the centrifuged or filtered sample (compare Analyses in Appendix, *Table 46*).

The seeding of river waters, sewages, or sewage effluents is not usually necessary when carrying out a B.O.D. determination since the right types of bacteria should normally be present. In the case of trade wastes, however, care must be taken to see that they are neutralized, if necessary, and seeded with settled sewage or river water. According to the A.P.H.A. *Standard Methods*[2], the dilution should be such that the toxicity is removed and the maximum B.O.D. value obtained, but in practice this is not always feasible and some wastes will yield abnormally low values. Moreover, certain trade wastes containing toxic substances (e.g. phenols) may require specialized flora (not necessarily present in sewage) in order to get a true B.O.D. value but the use of properly acclimatized seeds for such wastes, although recommended by some workers[199], presents practical difficulties for routine work in laboratories dealing with a great variety of samples. It must be remembered, too, that the degree of acclimatization of a seed has an important influence on the rate of oxidation of an organic compound. Thus, different acclimatized sludges have been shown to give different rates of oxidation[200]. In all B.O.D. work with trade wastes, many of which are deficient in nitrogen, phosphorus and other nutrients, care must be taken to ensure that sufficient nutrient materials are present (cf. page 127).

For research purposes, manometric methods (see references 3, 190, 201–207) have much to commend them and a tentative method using the manometric technique is given in the latest edition of the A.P.H.A. *Standard Methods*[2].

BRYAN and ROHLICH[208] determine a 'chlorate oxygen demand' by incubating sewage for 5 days with excess of sodium chlorate, which is biochemically reduced to chloride equivalent to the oxidizable matter originally present. The 'chlorate oxygen demand' can be calculated from the difference between the final and initial chloride concentrations.

ORGANIC CARBON[1, 2, 3, 209, 210]

The determination of total organic carbon affords at first sight an attractive method of assessing the amount of organic or carbonaceous impurity in a sample. In practice, however, the method has its limitations in view of the following considerations:

(a) The procedures for organic carbon are tedious and time-consuming, requiring the use of a train of apparatus taking up considerable bench space, and necessitate the adoption of elaborate precautions in the presence of interfering substances (e.g. carbonates, oxalates, thiocyanates, volatile organic substances, etc.). Since only one determination at a time can be carried out, the method is only of value for research work and is unsuitable for routine work.

(b) The total amount of organic carbon is of lesser importance in pollution work than that portion of the carbonaceous matter which is relatively easily oxidized biologically by micro-organisms and which is much more simply evaluated by a B.O.D. test.

Nevertheless, for investigations on polluted estuaries, tidal waters and sea waters, where other methods of estimating oxygen demand tend to be unreliable on account of the presence of high salt concentrations, determinations of organic carbon may be of considerable value in assessing organic pollution.

The majority of methods for the estimation of organic carbon in sewage and effluents involve the wet oxidation of the sample by a mixture of chromic and sulphuric acids followed by the determination of the evolved carbon dioxide by a suitable gravimetric or volumetric procedure. For instance, MILLS[211], in his studies of mud obtained from river beds, absorbed the carbon dioxide in a solution of barium hydroxide and weighed the precipitated barium carbonate. JENKINS and ROBERTS[212], who describe a fairly straightforward method for determining organic carbon in sewage liquors and sludge, passed the carbon dioxide through acidified potassium iodide (to remove chlorine) and then through a solution of barium hydroxide, the amount of unused baryta being determined by titration. Recovery of carbon from a number of pure substances tested by this method was greater than 95 per cent.

STABILITY

The stability of a sample of river water or effluent is the ability of the sample to maintain itself in an oxidized state when kept out of contact with oxygen or air in an incubator at a specified temperature. Several forms of incubator test have been described and the most useful include the following:

Simple incubator test[213]

This involves incubation of the sample in a stoppered bottle (or bottle provided with a water seal) for 5 days at 80° F (26·7° C*), the appearance and odour being then noted. A smell of hydrogen sulphide and/or a black precipitate (due to ferrous sulphide) shows that the sample is unstable. In cases of doubt, traces of hydrogen sulphide can be detected in the air in the upper part of the bottle by means of a slightly moistened lead acetate paper.

Scudder's permanganate incubator test[213]

The 3 minutes acid permanganate value (corrected if necessary for nitrite) is determined on a sample before and after incubation for 5 days at 80° F (26·7° C*) If this value increases (due to sulphide) after incubation (allowing, of course, for a small margin due to experimental error), the sample may be regarded as unstable.

Stoddart's incubator test[214]

In this modification, the sample is incubated for 3–6 days and any hydrogen sulphide formed is detected (or even estimated colorimetrically) by adding a solution of lead chloride.

Scudder's indigo carmine test[215]

In this test 4 bottles containing a 1:1 dilution of the sample with aerated tap water are incubated at 65° F (18·3° C) for 5 days.

* A temperature of 27° C is now generally employed.

Reduced indigo carmine (prepared in a special apparatus) is used to indicate after 2, 3, 4 and 5 days whether dissolved oxygen is still present; the reduced indigo carmine turns blue if dissolved oxygen is still present but remains yellow if none is present.

Methylene blue stability test[1, 2, 216, 219]

This test, involving incubation of the sample in a stoppered bottle (or a bottle provided with a water seal to exclude air) at 20° C for 5 days in the presence of 1·33 p.p.m. of methylene blue,* is undoubtedly the simplest and most convenient form of incubator test. The sample is considered to have failed the test if the dye is decolorized within 5 days. The test has the advantage over the other tests mentioned above, in the case of unstable samples, of yielding information before the end of the incubation period since in such cases the colour of the dye may disappear quite early. Very grossly polluted samples decolorize the methylene blue immediately, very bad samples in ½–several hours, and bad or unsatisfactory samples in 18 hours–2 days. The presence of nitrates tends to delay the decolorization time. After the 5 days incubation period, tests may be made for sulphide (with lead acetate paper) and for nitrate (with diphenylamine reagent on a spot plate).

The test is a valuable one for determining the keeping quality of effluents and of polluted river waters. A river water failing the test within 5 days with formation of hydrogen sulphide is liable to cause odour nuisance, especially in warm weather.

Other dyes have been proposed to replace methylene blue in this test, for instance brilliant cresyl blue[218], but in the author's experience, methylene blue is superior.

In the American form of the methylene blue stability test[2], the incubation is carried on until the dye is decolorized, or at any rate for 20 days, and the stability is then expressed as a percentage ('relative stability number') which is given by the equation

$$S = 100 \ (1 - 0.794^t)$$

where S = stability in per cent

and t = decolorization time in days (at 20° C)

A sample retaining its colour for 20 days is 99 per cent stable.

The American modification has the disadvantage of requiring much more incubator space than the English form of the test.

It must be pointed out that the methylene blue stability test, being dependent upon the activities of bacteria, is vitiated by the presence of germicidal substances.

---

* LEDERER[217] has shown that higher concentrations of this dye have a bactericidal action.

CHAPTER 5

COMBINED NITROGEN

AMMONIACAL NITROGEN[1, 3, 221]

('Free and saline ammonia')

ALTHOUGH many methods have been suggested from time to time for the estimation of ammonia[133], the colorimetric determination based upon the yellow–brown coloration (colloidal in nature) given by traces of ammonia and ammonium salts with Nessler's reagent (a solution of potassium mercuri-iodide, K_2HgI_4, in excess of potassium hydroxide) is still the most widely used procedure. The reaction which is generally referred to as 'nesslerization' takes place according to the equation:

$$2K_2HgI_4 + 2NH_3 = NH_2Hg_2I_3 + 4KI + NH_4I$$

Ammonia solutions to be nesslerized should not contain more than about 2 p.p.m. of ammoniacal nitrogen, and it is important to note that Nessler's reagent must always be added *to* the ammonia solution and never vice versa, otherwise turbidity will result.

When determinations of albuminoid nitrogen or organic nitrogen are not required, a saving in time can be obtained by estimating ammoniacal nitrogen by direct nesslerization without resorting to a preliminary distillation. Many substances, however, such as calcium salts, give a cloudy solution with Nessler's reagent. To obviate this difficulty, it is recommended in the U.S.A.[2] that the sample be first clarified with zinc sulphate and caustic soda and that Rochelle salt (sodium potassium tartrate) be added before nesslerization. A still simpler procedure for direct nesslerization is given by HOULIHAN[220] who uses a solution of sodium hexametaphosphate ('Calgon') to prevent development of cloudiness.

In general, however, it is more accurate to separate ammonia by distillation of the sample rendered alkaline with sodium carbonate and then determine ammonia in the distillate by nesslerization[1]. An excellent discussion of the interferences and factors affecting the Nessler method is given in the book edited by BOLTZ[134].

In gasworks practice, a distinction is made between the 'free' ammonia and the 'fixed' ammonia content of an effluent. The free ammonia is estimated by a straightforward distillation *without* addition of an alkaline reagent, and the residual liquor is then

36

treated with sodium carbonate[221], magnesium oxide[221] or caustic soda[20] and distilled to get the fixed ammonia. This differentiation is made because it is normal practice at a gasworks to remove 'free' ammonia from crude gas liquor by distillation in a concentrator plant so as to obtain a spent gas liquor which is easier to deal with at a sewage works by biological methods.

JENKINS[222] has described a new method of determining ammoniacal nitrogen involving distillation of the sample with light magnesia into a measured excess of N/140 sulphuric acid (containing a mixed methyl red–methylene blue indicator) and back-titration of the hot boiled distillate with N/140 sodium hydroxide to a green end-point. This method is said to be quicker, more precise, and more flexible than the usual procedure, and is given as a standard method in the Ministry's handbook[1].

JENKINS[223] has shown that urea in sewage is partly recovered as ammonia during distillation with magnesia or sodium carbonate. Fresh samples of sewage containing urea should, therefore, be allowed to stand for 24 hours at room temperature (which permits hydrolysis of urea to ammonia by the urease present) before analysis for ammoniacal nitrogen unless it is desired to determine the urea content.

Ammonia forms a blue colour at 100° C with a sodium phenoxide-sodium hypochlorite reagent[133] and this reaction can be used for the colorimetric estimation of ammonia. CROWTHER and LARGE[224] have improved the method by using a phenol reagent prepared with industrial methylated spirit and acetone, thus enabling the colour to develop at room temperature in 20 minutes.

KRUSE and MELLON[225] have described a new photometric method for the determination of traces of free ammonia (as little as 0·025 p.p.m.) in which the sample is treated with chloramine-T and then allowed to react with a pyridine-pyrazolone reagent containing 3-methyl-1-phenyl-5-pyrazolone and a trace of the bis-pyrazolone; a purple colour develops which can be extracted with carbon tetrachloride[134]. The method has been applied by ATKINS[226] to the direct estimation of ammonia in sea water.

ORGANIC NITROGEN AND ALBUMINOID NITROGEN[1, 3, 221, 227–231]

Sewage, farm drainage, piggery wastes, vegetable processing wastes, food wastes, tannery wastes, sewage sludges, river muds, and river waters into which these wastes discharge contain varying proportions of nitrogenous organic matter. Estimations of organic nitrogen or of albuminoid nitrogen provide a rough index of the amount of this nitrogenous organic material present in the sample. Although it is more scientific to determine the total organic nitrogen, it has

long been customary in this country to carry out the simpler estimation of albuminoid nitrogen; i.e. the proportion of the organically
combined nitrogen which is converted to ammonia when the sample,
after removal of ammoniacal nitrogen by distillation, is boiled and
distilled with an alkaline solution of potassium permanganate
under prescribed conditions[1]. As WATSON[227] has rightly stressed,
the ammonia collected in the distillate is formed by a chemical
reaction and it is therefore important, in order to obtain comparable
results, to standardize the amounts of sample and alkaline permanganate and the rate of the distillation.

The determination of total organic nitrogen by the well-known
Kjeldahl process is, however, gradually finding favour in this
country and tending to replace the albuminoid nitrogen procedure,
especially in research work.   For routine purposes, however, the
determination of albuminoid nitrogen is quicker.   Nevertheless, the
time taken to perform a Kjeldahl determination can be much
reduced by the adoption of semi-micro procedures[228, 229].

JENKINS[230] has described a reliable method for the routine determination of organic nitrogen involving treatment of the sample
with powdered Devarda's alloy, followed by boiling for not less than
20 minutes to remove ammoniacal nitrogen and oxidized nitrogen;
the organic nitrogen in the sample is then determined by Kjeldahl
digestion with concentrated sulphuric acid to give ammonia, which
is distilled from the alkaline solution into N/140 sulphuric acid and
nesslerized.

NITROGEN AS NITRITE (nitrous nitrogen)

Two methods are recommended by the Ministry[1] for the quantitative estimation of nitrites:

(*i*) *The Griess–Ilosvay method*[1-3, 6, 14-16, 221, 232], which is based
upon the diazotization of sulphanilic acid by nitrite in acid solution
and the coupling of the resulting diazonium compound with alpha-
naphthylamine to give a red azo-dye.   This extremely sensitive
method is satisfactory for the determination of very low concentrations of nitrite nitrogen, say less than 2 p.p.m.

(ii) *The meta-phenylene diamine method*[1], which depends upon the
formation of a yellowish–brown dye by the action of nitrite in acid
solution on meta-phenylene diamine.   This method is suitable for
the estimation of fairly high concentrations of nitrite nitrogen (2
p.p.m. or more) although it can be used for concentrations down
to about 0·5 p.p.m.

It has been shown by KLEIN[233] that there is good agreement between results obtained by these two methods but the meta-phenylene
diamine method is preferable for the higher nitrite concentrations

since it avoids the preparation of very high dilutions of the sample. Sodium chloride up to about 500 p.p.m. of Cl has little influence on the results obtained by either method but very large amounts of chloride (10,000 p.p.m. of Cl) cause slightly high results with the Griess–Ilosvay method and rather low results with the meta-phenylene diamine method, thus making these methods unsuitable for sea-water, or for estuary water high in chloride.

Another very sensitive method for the determination of nitrite has been described by SHINN[131, 134A, 234]. Sulphanilamide is used instead of sulphanilic acid whilst alpha-naphthylamine is replaced by the water-soluble N- (1-naphthyl)-ethylene diamine dihydro-chloride. The sulphanilamide undergoes diazotization in hydro-chloric acid by the nitrite in the sample and the diazonium compound then couples with the diamine to give a stable red azo-dye. The method is quite as sensitive as the Griess–Ilosvay method and has the further merit of giving a brighter colour, the intensity being almost independent of pH and of the amount of reagent added. The diamine is, however, much more expensive than alpha-naphthyla-mine. The method can be used for the determination of nitrite in estuary water or sea water as salinity has no effect upon the results[235].

NITROGEN AS NITRATE (nitric nitrogen)

A rapid qualitative test for oxidized nitrogen (nitrates and/or nitrites) depends upon the intense blue coloration given with a solution of diphenylamine in concentrated sulphuric acid. The reaction is conveniently carried out on a spot plate and the intensity of the colour is a rough guide to the quantity of oxidized nitrogen present[1].

The following are the more important methods suitable for the quantitative determination of nitrate:

Phenol disulphonic acid method[1, 2]

This method depends upon the reaction between phenol disulphonic acid and nitrate in sulphuric acid solution to give a nitro-derivative which develops a yellow colour when rendered alkaline with sodium hydroxide. Small amounts of chloride do not interfere but nitrite should be removed by treatment with sodium azide[1].

Sulphosalicylic acid method [236]

A method similar in principle to the phenol disulphonic acid method involves the use of a reagent containing salicylic acid; the filtered or settled sample is evaporated with a 2 per cent solution of salicylic acid in concentrated sulphuric acid, made alkaline with caustic soda, and the yellow colour matched with standards similarly treated[237]. Advantages of this procedure are that the reagent is easily prepared and chlorides do not interfere.

Reduction to ammonia by aluminium foil in alkaline solution[1, 2]

The sample is evaporated with a little sodium carbonate to remove ammonia and the oxidized nitrogen is reduced to ammonia by aluminium foil in a solution made alkaline with sodium hydroxide. After standing overnight, the ammonia formed is estimated in an aliquot by nesslerization. This gives the total oxidized nitrogen from which nitrate nitrogen is calculated by deducting the nitrite nitrogen figure.

Reduction to ammonia by zinc–copper couple in acetic acid solution[1]

The sample, after removal of ammonia, is reduced to ammonia with zinc–copper couple in dilute acetic acid solution and the ammonia produced is distilled and estimated in the distillate by nesslerization.

When the sample has a relatively high nitrite content, a preliminary treatment with acetic acid solutions of alpha-naphthylamine and sulphanilic acid is necessary to remove nitrite[1].

Devarda's alloy method

JENKINS[238] uses the residual liquid remaining in the distillation flask after ammoniacal nitrogen has been determined by distillation with magnesia (page 37) and treats it with Devarda's alloy to reduce oxidized nitrogen to ammonia. The ammonia produced is then estimated by distillation into excess of $N/140$ sulphuric acid followed either by back-titration with $N/140$ sodium hydroxide, or, if the oxidized nitrogen is low (less than 4 p.p.m.) by nesslerization.

Rapid method using brucine[134, 139, 140, 239]

This useful method, based upon an old procedure described by HAASE[240], is suitable as a rapid field test for the approximate estimation of nitrate in river water. A disc covering the range 1–9 p.p.m. of nitrate nitrogen has been prepared for this purpose by Tintometer Ltd. for use with the Lovibond comparator[139, 140]. The sample (1 ml.) is treated with 0·1 ml. of a 5 per cent solution of brucine in glacial acetic acid, then with 2 ml. of pure nitrogen-free sulphuric acid and the mixture is shaken and allowed to stand for 7 minutes. The yellow colour is matched against the colour standards of the Lovibond disc, using as a blank 1 ml. of distilled water plus the reagents in the left-hand compartment of the comparator. Chloride up to 1000 p.p.m. does not interfere but larger amounts should be removed with silver sulphate. Nitrite, if present, must be separately estimated and an appropriate correction applied.

m-xylenol method[13, 134A]

This method, originally used for estimating nitrate in soils and plants, has been proposed for the determination of nitrate in sewage effluents[241] as well as natural waters and boiler waters[242]. It depends upon the nitration of the reagent (*m-xylenol*, i.e. 2:4-xylen-1-ol) by the nitrate in the presence of excess of sulphuric acid to form 5-nitro-2:4-xylen-1-ol:

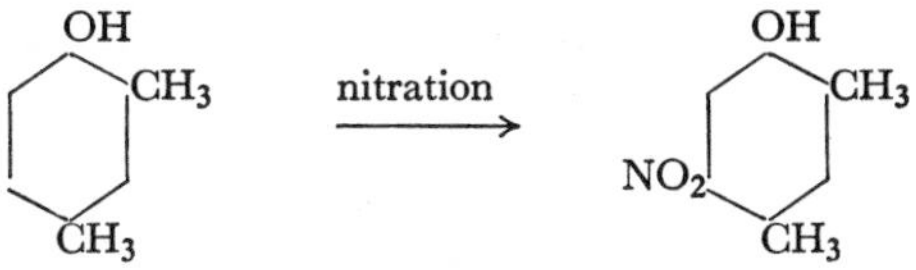

This compound is volatile in steam and can be distilled into dilute caustic soda to yield a brilliant yellow to orange-red colour which can be determined visually or absorptiometrically. The intensity of the colour increases with rise of temperature so colour comparison must always be carried out at the same temperature, preferably 20° C. No interference occurs with nitrites up to 10 p.p.m. and with sodium chloride up to 500 p.p.m. A B.D.H. Lovibond nesslerizer disc is available for use with this method.

Ferrous sulphate method

In this method[243], which is suitable for river waters and sewage effluents, the nitrate is reduced with alkaline ferrous sulphate and the ammonia produced is steam-distilled and determined absorptiometrically[225]. Nitrites interfere but can be separately determined and a correction made. Any ammonia in the sample should be removed with a cation exchange resin or by evaporation of the alkaline sample.

Methods for sea water[244–246, 287, 288]

A colorimetric method for oxidized nitrogen (nitrite + nitrate) suitable for use in the presence of very high concentrations of chloride (such as are found in sea water) utilizes the rose-red colour produced when a solution of reduced strychnine ('strychnidine') in concentrated sulphuric acid reacts with traces of nitrate or nitrite (up to about 50 microgram-atoms per litre)[244].

A solution of diphenylbenzidine in concentrated sulphuric acid[134A, 246] has also been used for the determination of nitrate in sea water and many workers consider this to be the best method. A blue colour is obtained which, unlike the colour given by the reduced strychnine reagent, is stable to light. The maximum development of colour occurs when the mixture of reagent and sea water contains 27·3% of water[288].

CHAPTER 6

SULPHUR COMPOUNDS

SULPHIDE

SULPHIDES are present in septic sewage, ammoniacal gas liquor, tannery wastes, sulphide dye liquors, viscose rayon wastes, oil refinery wastes, and in drainage from many tips. They may also occur in samples containing proteins which have been stored and have undergone anaerobic decomposition.

The accurate determination of small amounts of sulphide is difficult, and none of the published methods are entirely satisfactory or applicable to all types of samples. The determination is complicated by the property of hydrogen sulphide and other sulphides of undergoing oxidation to sulphur in the presence of air or oxygen. The presence of sulphides is usually shown by their characteristic odour of rotten eggs but this may not be apparent with insoluble sulphides or with strongly alkaline solutions of soluble sulphides.

The detection of sulphide is comparatively easy and can be carried out by putting the sample in a 100 ml. glass-stoppered conical flask, acidifying and suspending between the stopper and neck a slightly moistened lead acetate paper. A brown stain on the paper indicates the presence of sulphide; using a 50 ml. sample, as little as 0·01 p.p.m. of H_2S can be detected in this way. Another sensitive test for sulphides, detecting 0·1 p.p.m. or even less, is based on Raschig's azide–iodine reaction which was first utilized as a spot test for sulphides by FEIGL[136]. The test is particularly useful for testing a series of samples in river survey work and is carried out by MUELLER and RAND[247] as follows: The sample (1 ml.) is placed on a watch glass over black paper, 1 ml. of 30 per cent sodium azide is added followed by 1 ml. of N/10 iodine solution. In the presence of sulphide, bubbles of nitrogen develop on the surface of the glass within 2–5 minutes. The formation of these bubbles depends upon the fact that the reaction between sodium azide and iodine to give nitrogen gas, which is normally extremely slow, is catalytically accelerated by traces of soluble or insoluble sulphides:

$$2NaN_3 + I_2 \xrightarrow[\text{sulphide}]{\text{catalysed by}} 2NaI + 3N_2$$

The only interfering sulphur compounds are thiosulphates and thiocyanates which also catalyse the azide–iodine reaction.

The best and most sensitive colorimetric method for estimating sulphide is based upon the fact that hydrogen sulphide and sulphides in the presence of sufficient hydrochloric acid and an oxidizing agent (ferric chloride) react with *p*-aminodimethylaniline hydrochloride (*as*-dimethyl–*p*-phenylene diamine hydrochloride) to produce the dye methylene blue in accordance with the equation:

$$\underset{\substack{|\\ NH_2 \cdot HCl}}{\overset{\substack{N(CH_3)_2\\ |}}{2C_6H_4}} + 6FeCl_3 + H_2S \rightarrow N\underset{\substack{\diagdown\diagup\\ \underset{\substack{||\\ N(CH_3)_2}}{C_6H_3}}}{\overset{\substack{\overset{\displaystyle N(CH_3)_2}{|}\\ C_6H_3\\ \diagup\diagdown}}{\quad S}} + 6FeCl_2 + 6HCl + NH_4Cl$$

Cl

Details of the quantitative method as applied to sewage were first worked out by POMEROY [248, 249] and the method is now a standard one [1, 2]. It will determine sulphide in concentrations of 0·1– 20 p.p.m. of H_2S and, by the use of larger volumes, concentrations as low as 0·01 p.p.m. can be estimated. Dissolved sulphide as well as sulphide bound as insoluble iron, zinc, manganese, and lead sulphides, can be determined, but copper sulphide is too insoluble to react. It is possible to estimate sulphides in sludges and river muds by this method [248]. Concentrations of sulphite and thiosulphate above 10 p.p.m. cause some interference but, according to Pomeroy, by increasing the amount of ferric chloride and lengthening the reaction time, up to 50 p.p.m. of these compounds can be tolerated.

Another method for determining total sulphide is based upon the volatilization of hydrogen sulphide from an acidified solution of the sample by a stream of inert gas (nitrogen or carbon dioxide*), the evolved hydrogen sulphide being absorbed in a solution of zinc acetate. The zinc sulphide produced is then determined by an iodometric titration procedure [1, 2, 3, 434]. The method is accurate in the absence of sulphite and thiosulphate which may cause serious errors due to interaction of H_2S and SO_2 on acidification giving free sulphur. The method is, however, tedious and time-consuming, and is unsuitable for routine work since in view of the extensive

* These gases must be freed from oxygen.

apparatus required only one determination at a time can conveniently be carried out.

A simple routine iodometric method for determining total sulphide in certain trade effluents containing sulphite and thiosulphate has been described by POMEROY[250] and used for the estimation of sulphide in petroleum waste waters. The sulphide is precipitated by adding zinc acetate and sodium carbonate to the sample. After settling, the non-sulphide iodine demand is determined on one-half of the supernatant liquid (thus giving the non-sulphide iodine demand of half the sample) and the iodine demand (due to sulphide and one-half of the non-sulphide) is then determined on the remainder (thus giving the sulphide iodine demand plus the non-sulphide demand of half the sample). The method is suitable for sulphide in the range 0·2–100 p.p.m. It does not, however, give accurate results with sewage and other samples containing much colloidal and suspended organic matter since any organic matter associated with the zinc sulphide precipitate causes some interference by reacting with iodine.

A method for the estimation of sulphide in gas liquor is given by KEY[20]. The liquor is run into excess of cadmium acetate or ammoniacal zinc chloride. The precipitated sulphide is washed, added to excess of acidified standard iodine, and the unused iodine is titrated with standard thiosulphate using starch as indicator.

A useful routine method of estimating sulphides in river waters has been developed by HOULIHAN and FARINA[251], and is based upon the application of the Winkler technique used for the determination of dissolved oxygen. Manganese chloride reagent is added to the sample (500 ml.), followed by the alkaline iodide azide reagent, and after settling the precipitate, $N/80$ iodine* is added and the mixture is acidified and then titrated with $N/80$ sodium thiosulphate. Absorption of iodine is due to sulphides and any other substances which react with iodine. A correction for any non-sulphide iodine demand is made by carrying out a blank determination on a portion of the sample freed from sulphide by passing oxygen-free nitrogen through the acidified solution. Simple apparatus for performing the test is described in the original paper.

An approximate method used in the past for estimating sulphides in trade wastes involved determinations of the iodine consumption of the sample before and after expelling all the hydrogen sulphide by boiling[19]. Although rapid and suitable for routine work, the method is open to several objections. For instance, there may be loss of volatile iodine-consuming compounds other than hydrogen sulphide (e.g. phenols) which would cause high results. Again,

---

* $N/80$ potassium permanganate can also be used since it liberates an equivalent of iodine from the iodide when acid is afterwards added.

acidification would be necessary to expel all the sulphide from insoluble sulphides, but in the presence of thiosulphate (which is often associated with sulphide) there would be an error due to interaction of H_2S and SO_2.

The methods for sulphide so far outlined give *total* sulphide, i.e. dissolved sulphide plus insoluble sulphide. If dissolved sulphide only is required, the suspended matter is removed by filtration in a current of pure nitrogen and H_2S is liberated from the filtrate by acidification and absorption in zinc acetate solution; an apparatus for performing this determination is described by WHEATLAND and LOWDEN[252].

SULPHITE AND THIOSULPHATE

Sulphite is present in waste waters from paper works using bi-sulphites in the preparation of cellulose from wood, in certain wastes from the manufacture of transparent paper and in river waters receiving these wastes.

In the absence of thiosulphate, sulphite can be detected by heating the sample, acidified with sulphuric acid, when sulphur dioxide is evolved which is identified by the blue coloration produced when a piece of filter paper moistened with a mixture of potassium iodate solution and starch solution is held in the vapours:

$$2KIO_3 + 5SO_2 + 4H_2O = I_2 + 2KHSO_4 + 3H_2SO_4$$

$$\downarrow \text{ starch}$$

blue coloration

Another sensitive test for sulphites[136] is based upon the fact that in neutral solution they decolorize dilute solutions of triphenyl-methane dyestuffs. The sample, neutralized with sodium bicarbonate if necessary, is treated with an equal volume of a dilute solution of malachite green (2·5 mg per 100 ml.) when the green colour is immediately bleached if sulphite is present. Thiosulphates do not interfere.

Sulphite can be estimated by adding the sample to a known excess of iodine solution and determining the unused iodine by titration with standard sodium thiosulphate. This is only an approximate method since organic matter, thiosulphate and sulphide all cause interference.

The ABCM-SAC Joint Committee[274] suggest removing sulphides with zinc acetate, filtering and determining the sum of the sulphite and thiosulphate iodimetrically. A separate portion is then treated with formaldehyde to mask sulphite and the thiosulphate can then be determined iodimetrically.

KOHOUT [253] uses an iodimetric method for the determination of the 'iodine numbers' of river waters in order to detect the presence of wastes from sulphite cellulose factories. The river water (100 ml.) is placed in a graduated cylinder and distilled water (100 ml.) in a similar cylinder. Starch and potassium bicarbonate are added to each cylinder and 0·01N iodine solution is run in until the blue colours are identical in each cylinder. The results are expressed as iodine numbers in p.p.m. Uncontaminated river waters give iodine numbers of 2–8, whilst waters contaminated by sulphite cellulose wastes yield numbers varying from 19–202. Other substances present (e.g. phenols, urea) are usually not present in amounts sufficient to cause any appreciable interference with the test.

SULPHATE

The determination of sulphate is rarely called for except in connection with problems involving the corrosion of concrete.

The standard procedure for estimating sulphate involves the addition of barium chloride to the sample acidified with hydrochloric acid and the gravimetric determination of the precipitated barium sulphate [1, 2, 122, 123, 130, 254]. The method, which requires strict attention to detail, is fairly accurate but is tedious and unsuitable for very small amounts of sulphate.

The evaluation of the barium sulphate precipitate can also be carried out, according to BELCHER, GIBBONS and WEST [255], by dissolving it in excess of a boiling ammoniacal solution of 0·02M ethylene diamine tetra-acetic acid (EDTA) and back-titrating with standard magnesium chloride using Solochrome Black as indicator.

A volumetric method first described by SCHROEDER [2, 256] utilizes an internal indicator (tetrahydroxyquinone) to detect the endpoint in the reaction between sulphate and barium chloride; the first slight excess of barium chloride causes a colour change from yellow to red but although the method is rapid the end-point is not particularly good.

A popular volumetric method for the estimation of sulphate is based upon the precipitation of sparingly soluble benzidine sulphate* followed by the titration of the washed precipitate with standard sodium hydroxide using phenolphthalein as indicator [13, 16, 134A, 257]. The use of a modification of this method described by McCONNELL and INGOLS [258] permits the determination

---

* Benzidine is carcinogenic and should be handled with care.

of sulphate in the range 2–400 p.p.m. of SO_4. There is interference by phosphate but this can be prevented by adjusting to pH 2 before adding the benzidine reagent [135A]. The interference of phosphate can also be obviated by using a colorimetric procedure. The precipitated benzidine sulphate is washed with a mixture of alcohol and ether to remove any excess of benzidine, dissolved in 1 % sodium borate and the benzidine so liberated allowed to react with sodium 1 : 2-naphthoquinone-4-sulphonate to give a red colour which is measured photometrically at 490 mμ [259].

BELCHER and his co-workers [260] have found that 4-amino-4′-chloro-diphenyl hydrochloride is more sensitive towards the sulphate ion than any other reagent. The precipitated sulphate can be titrated with standard alkali as in the case of benzidine sulphate. This method is recommended by the Ministry [1] for the volumetric determination of sulphate but phosphate must first be removed by precipitation as magnesium ammonium phosphate.

A rapid method specially suitable for the estimation of low sulphate concentrations depends upon the turbidity produced when barium chloride is added to a sample containing traces of sulphate. The conditions for this determination must be rigidly standardized. In a recent modification in which the turbidity produced by barium sulphate is measured spectrophotometrically in 1 cm cells at a wavelength of 380 mμ [261], sulphate can be determined in 10 minutes over the range 2–80 p.p.m. of SO_4. Interference by phosphate or carbonate is prevented by carrying out the reaction in dilute hydrochloric acid solution.

CHAPTER 7

ALKALINITY, ACIDITY, FREE CARBON DIOXIDE, FREE CHLORINE, CHLORIDE, FLUORIDE AND HARDNESS

ALKALINITY AND ACIDITY [1, 3, 210]

ALKALIS are present in kier liquors from cotton mills and paper works, in wool scouring wastes and many chemical wastes.

Acids occur in iron and copper pickle liquors, in drainage from coal mines and coal tips, in some chemical wastes, and in waste waters from the manufacture of explosives.

Although the determination of pH value gives information about the intensity of the alkalinity or acidity, a titration method is required to estimate the actual amount of alkali or acid present.

If the pH value of the sample is greater than 8·3, carbonate alkalinity or caustic alkalinity is present, and this is determined by titration with N/10 hydrochloric or sulphuric acid using phenolphthalein or any of the alternative indicators shown in *Table 5*.

Table 5. Indicators suitable for determination of carbonate and/or caustic alkalinity

Indicator	Useful pH range	Colour change	
		Acid	Alkaline
Phenolphthalein	8·3–10·0	Colourless	Pink
o-cresolphthalein*	8·2–9·8	Colourless	Purple–red
Thymol blue	8·0–9·6	Yellow	Blue
Ethyl bis-2:4-dinitrophenyl acetate[262]†	7·5–9·2	Colourless	Blue
Tetrachlorophenolphthalein‡ . .	8·2–9·4	Colourless	Pink

* Somewhat more sensitive than phenolphthalein.
† Suitable for orange or red solutions.
‡ Useful if hypochlorite is present. The pink colour of phenolphthalein in alkaline solution is bleached by chlorine.

If the pH value of the sample lies between 4·0 and 8·3, bicarbonate alkalinity is present and may be determined by titration with N/10 hydrochloric or sulphuric acid, using methyl orange or one of the other indicators listed in *Table 6*.

A sample with a pH value of less than 4·0 contains, in general, mineral acid, the amount of acid present being determined by titration with N/10 sodium hydroxide, using methyl orange or one of the indicators listed in *Table 6*. If organic acids are present, the methyl orange end-point will be somewhat indefinite, and the acidity to phenolphthalein ('total acidity') should be determined. This may include mineral and organic acids, free carbon dioxide and acid produced from easily hydrolysable salts (such as ferric and aluminium salts).

Table 6. Indicators suitable for determination of mineral acidity, or of bicarbonate alkalinity

Indicator	Useful pH range	Colour change	
		Acid	Alkaline
Methyl orange	2·9–4·6	Orange–red	Yellow
Methyl orange–xylene cyanol*[263] .	2·9–4·6	Violet	Green
Bromophenol blue. . . .	2·8–4·6	Yellow	Blue
Tetrabromophenol-tetrabromosulphone phthalein†[264] ('tetrabromophenol blue')	3·0–4·6	Yellow	Blue

* Screening with the dyestuff makes the methyl orange end-point more distinct, especially in artificial light.
† Useful in presence of free chlorine or hypochlorite, which bleach the other indicators.

If non-volatile organic acids are present, the sample is evaporated to dryness, the residue is extracted with neutral alcohol and the extract titrated to the phenolphthalein end-point. Volatile organic acids are generally determined by distillation and titration of the distillate with standard alkali using phenolphthalein as indicator. The determination of volatile organic acids (the lower fatty acids of the acetic series) is often carried out for the routine control of the anaerobic digestion of sewage sludges and strong, organic wastes. An approximate method, described in the A.P.H.A. *Standard methods*[2], involves distillation of the sample acidified with sulphuric acid and titration of the distillate with N/10 caustic soda; as recovery of the volatile acids is not quantitative, an empirical factor of 0·7 is used in the calculation. Various modifications of this method have been proposed to secure greater accuracy[265, 266]. In a procedure giving 98% recovery of volatile acids, the sample is subjected to a preliminary flocculation with aluminium sulphate and lime at pH 7·5 and filtered, sulphuric acid is replaced by phosphoric acid (which does not decompose organic material) and silver sulphate is added to prevent decomposition of chlorides[267].

A chromatographic technique has been used for the separation and determination of organic acids in plant tissues[268] and the method has been applied by MUELLER, BUSWELL and LARSON[269] to the determination of volatile acids in digesting sludges and industrial wastes. The acids are adsorbed on a silica gel column, eluted with a mixture of butyl alcohol and chloroform, and the total acidity determined by titration with N/50 caustic soda to phenol red indicator. The individual acids may, if desired, be separated and identified by the use of different mixtures of solvents. MANGANELLI and BROFAZI [270] have used paper chromatography for the quantitative separation and determination of the C_2 to C_6 fatty acids in digesting sewage sludges.

FREE CARBON DIOXIDE [2, 4, 13, 14]

The carbon dioxide over and above that required to convert alkali or alkaline earth carbonates to bicarbonates is generally called 'free carbon dioxide'. It accelerates corrosion and is toxic towards fish.

A special sample of the water in a completely filled bottle should be taken for this estimation. The usual method of determination is only an approximate one and involves titration of the sample of water in a Nessler tube with standard sodium hydroxide or sodium carbonate in the presence of phenolphthalein until the indicator acquires a faint permanent tint. If the sample is acid towards methyl orange (pH below 4·0), the mineral acidity must be determined and a correction applied. Corrections should also be applied if iron and aluminium salts are present.

An accurate but rather lengthy method for determining free carbon dioxide is given by PARKHOUSE [271]. It involves the transference of the carbon dioxide by means of a current of carbon dioxide-free air to a solution of sodium hydroxide and the titration of the resulting mixture of sodium hydroxide and sodium carbonate with standard hydrochloric acid to phenolphthalein and to the B.D.H. '4·5' indicator. The method is capable of determining up to 10 p.p.m. of carbon dioxide with an accuracy of 0·1 p.p.m.

If the pH value and the methyl orange alkalinity of a sample are both known, it is possible, according to KOZMA [272], to calculate the free carbon dioxide approximately by means of the following equation:

$$\log CO_2 = \log \text{alkalinity} + 6 \cdot 3075 - pH$$

where CO_2 = free carbon dioxide in p.p.m.

and alkalinity = methyl orange alkalinity (expressed as p.p.m. of $CaCO_3$).

More accurate values can be estimated from determinations of pH, temperature, and bicarbonate alkalinity by the use of nomograms published by DYE [273].

FREE CHLORINE[2]

In problems connected with river pollution, 'free chlorine' is generally taken to mean chlorine present as molecular chlorine (Cl_2), hypochlorous acid ($HClO$), or hypochlorites (e.g. $NaClO$), chloramines (NH_2Cl, $NHCl_2$, NCl_3) or similar compounds capable of yielding available chlorine (e.g. organic chloramino compounds); all of these can liberate iodine from potassium iodide in acid solution and can give a yellow coloration when treated with an acid solution of o-tolidine. These reactions form the basis of methods for the quantitative determination of free chlorine.

In dealing with potable waters, however, it is customary to make a distinction between 'free available chlorine' (e.g. chlorine present as molecular chlorine, hypochlorous acid, or hypochlorite*) and 'combined available chlorine' (e.g. chlorine combined with ammonia in the form of chloramines or other nitrogenous compounds †) and methods are in use (e.g. the o-tolidine–arsenite test) for distinguishing between these various forms[2, 274–277]. The reason for this distinction lies in the fact that, in the case of drinking waters, we are more concerned with the destruction of bacteria, and the bactericidal action of chloramines is considerably slower than that of molecular chlorine or hypochlorites. Since there appears to be little difference in toxicity to fish between 'free available chlorine' and 'combined available chlorine', there is little point in differentiating between these forms of chlorine in river pollution work. However, part of the well-known o-tolidine–arsenite test[2] allows compensation for interfering substances (such as nitrites and the oxidized forms of iron and manganese) and it is, therefore, recommended that when these interfering substances are present, the use of sodium arsenite be adopted. If sodium arsenite be added *before* the o-tolidine, it prevents colour formation by chlorine and chloramines, but does not inhibit colours due to interfering substances. This reading can then be deducted from that given by the direct o-tolidine test.

Neither the potassium iodide test nor the o-tolidine test is specific for free chlorine. Nitrites, ferric salts, manganic compounds and many other oxidizing agents give a yellow coloration with o-tolidine in acid solution but, as already mentioned, their interference can be circumvented by the use of sodium arsenite. A large number of oxidizing agents, besides free chlorine (e.g. nitrites, ferric salts, chromates), liberate iodine from an acid solution of potassium iodide. The ABCM-SAC Joint Committee, however, have found

---

* The relative proportions of Cl_2, $HClO$, or hypochlorite depend on the pH value.

† The type of chloramine present depends on the $Cl:N$ ratio and on the pH value.

that there is little interference from nitrites, oxidized manganese, or ferric iron if the pH of the sample is first adjusted within the range 4·5–8·0 by means of acetic acid or sodium acetate; potassium iodide is then added and the liberated iodine titrated with thiosulphate[274].

MILTON[278] has described a test for free chlorine which is not only twice as sensitive as the o-tolidine test but is almost specific since only free bromine reacts similarly. The sample (5 ml.) is treated with 1 ml. of 1 per cent aqueous sodium cyanide and then with 5 ml. of a 25 per cent aqueous solution of pyridine containing 2 per cent of benzidine hydrochloride*. A reddish colour develops, reaching its maximum within 10 minutes. This test has been modified by MORRIS and GRANT[279] to permit the determination of total available chlorine in water.

BELCHER, NUTTEN and STEPHEN[280] have reported that 3:3′-dimethylnaphthidine (0·1 per cent solution in glacial acetic acid) is superior to o-tolidine as a reagent for chlorine in sensitivity and in the stability of the colour produced. It is about ten times as sensitive as o-tolidine and gives a stable red colour which is suitable for the photometric determination of free chlorine in the range 0·05–1·0 p.p.m. Other oxidizing agents interfere.

A new specific test for chlorine (not given by other oxidizing agents such as iodine, bromine, Mn^{iv}, Fe^{iii}, H_2O_2, and chloramines) is based on the indophenol reaction between aromatic amines (e.g. aniline) and phenol in alkaline solution in the presence of chlorine; the intensity of the blue colour is determined photometrically at 610 mμ[281].

An accurate amperometric method of titrating chlorine residuals in sewage and sewage effluents has been described[282–284] involving the use of the reagent phenylarsene oxide (C_6H_5AsO), one molecule of which interacts with two equivalents of chlorine. The reaction is independent of pH and there is no interference by colour, organic matter, iron, manganese, or nitrite.

CHLORIDE[1, 2, 3]

Chlorides are present in sewage, sewage effluents and farm drainage, and in large amounts in certain acid pickle liquors (as free hydrochloric acid), in brine from a salt works, in spent regenerant solution from water softening plants using the base-exchange process, in oil-well waters, and in tidal waters containing sea water. In estuarial waters, it is necessary to determine the chloride content not only to calculate the proportion of sea water present (see page 116) but also to compute the percentage saturation of dissolved oxygen.

---

* This is an example of the König reaction (see pp. 84, 85, 94).

The usual method of determining chloride in river waters is the volumetric procedure originally put forward by MOHR[285]. This depends upon the precipitation of silver chloride by addition of a dilute standard solution of silver nitrate (1 ml. = 1 mg of Cl) in the presence of potassium chromate indicator, which, just after the end-point is reached, forms a reddish precipitate of silver chromate with the slightest excess of silver nitrate, so that the colour changes from the yellow due to potassium chromate to a faint orange–red. Common interfering substances are acids, alkalis, sulphides, thio-cyanates, phosphates, cyanides, sulphites and any anions forming sparingly soluble silver salts. Acidity should be neutralized by addition of a little pure chloride-free sodium bicarbonate or calcium carbonate. If the sample is appreciably alkaline towards phenol-phthalein or contains sulphide, the addition of a few crystals of zinc sulphate will prevent interference. Volatile sulphur compounds, which may be present in waste waters from oil refineries and syn-thetic rubber manufacture, should be removed by evaporation[286]. Thiocyanate, if present, can be separately estimated and a correction made to the titration*; alternatively, thiocyanate can be destroyed by boiling with hydrogen peroxide. Sulphites can be rendered harm-less by addition of hydrogen peroxide. Coloured samples can often be decolorized by flocculation with zinc sulphate and sodium carbonate.

The Mohr titration method is suitable for river waters and effluents containing about 5–200 p.p.m. of Cl. With higher con-centrations of chloride, a suitable dilution should be used.

The 'chlorinity' of sea water is generally determined by the Mohr method. The chlorinity, in parts per 1000 (‰), was at one time defined as the weight of chlorine equivalent to the halogens† in 1000 grams of sea water, but owing to periodical alterations in the atomic weights of Cl, Ag, etc., chlorinity has now been re-defined for accurate work as follows[287, 288]:

$$Cl‰ = 0·3285234 \times Ag$$

(where Ag = weight of silver precipitated)

If 10 ml. of sea water is titrated by the Mohr method with a solution of 27·25 grams of silver nitrate per litre, the volume in ml. of silver nitrate required will equal approximately the 'salinity' of the sample[287]. The 'salinity' (expressed in parts per 1000) is defined as the weight in grams *in vacuo* of solids (dried to constant weight at 480° C to remove organic matter and to convert car-bonates to oxides) from 1000 grams (vacuum weight) of sea water,

---

* The chloride equivalent can be calculated from the relation
$$S \times 1·11 = Cl$$

† Silver nitrate precipitates chloride and bromide from sea water but only negligible amounts of iodide.

the amount of Cl and Br lost during drying being compensated for by adding a weight of Cl equivalent to this loss[287]. The direct determination of salinity is difficult but tables for the conversion of titration results to chlorinity, salinity and specific gravity at any temperature are given by KNUDSEN[289].

The relation between chlorinity and salinity is given by the equation[287]:

$$S = 0{\cdot}03 + 1{\cdot}805 \ Cl$$

where   S = salinity in parts per 1000
                 Cl = chlorinity in parts per 1000

There is an extensive literature on the Fajans adsorption indicator method for the titration of chloride with silver nitrate[124, 130] but this has not become popular. LANDINGHAM[290] has, however, proposed the use of phenosafranin as an adsorption indicator for the determination of the salinity of sea water.

If appreciable amounts of phosphates are present, the Mohr method is not accurate and Volhard's method[124, 210] should be used; this involves addition of excess of silver nitrate to the sample acidified with dilute nitric acid followed by coagulation of the silver chloride by shaking with a little nitrobenzene and finally back-titration with standard thiocyanate using ferric alum as indicator.

A simple colorimetric method for chloride has been described[291] based upon the reddish–brown colour obtained by adding to 100 ml. of the water sample 1 ml. of 10 per cent potassium chromate and 0·45 ml. of $N/35{\cdot}5$ silver nitrate. The colour is compared after 1 minute with standards within the range 0·4–2·0 p.p.m. of Cl. The method is accurate to about 2 per cent. Acid or alkaline waters should be neutralized and preliminary treatment is necessary in the presence of iron, sulphide, or much organic matter.

Although mercurimetric methods for the volumetric determination of chloride depending on the formation of slightly dissociated mercuric chloride are quite old[124], they have not until recently achieved much popularity[292, 293]. A tentative procedure, somewhat more sensitive than the Mohr method, is now given in the latest edition of the A.P.H.A. *Standard Methods*[2] and involves addition of standard mercuric nitrate to the sample adjusted to pH 3·1 and containing a mixed indicator (diphenylcarbazone + bromophenol blue) which turns violet at the end-point.

FLUORIDE[2, 3, 4, 134, 274]

Fluorides occur in certain chemical waste waters (e.g. effluents from the production of aluminium from bauxite and from the manufacture of phosphatic fertilizers), in some waters from oil wells, in effluents from atomic energy plants, and in waste waters from the scrubbing of flue gases and from the etching of glass.

Volumetric methods for the determination of fluoride are generally based upon the titration of the sample with standard thorium nitrate in a solution buffered at about 2·9–3·3, using sodium alizarin sulphonate as indicator; the colour at the end-point changes to pink due to the formation of a lake between the alizarin and the slightest excess of thorium ions[124, 130]. The method as applied to natural waters is described by BOND and MURRAY[294], the titration being carried out at pH 3·3 in the presence of acetic acid; a preliminary treatment with barium chloride eliminates interference of sulphate, phosphate and carbonate. Interference of aluminium occurs. MILTON[295, 296] has found that the use of the sodium salt of sulphodichlorohydroxydimethyl-fuchsin dicarboxylic acid (Solochrome Brilliant Blue BS or Chrome Azurol S) as indicator in place of sodium alizarin sulphonate gives a much sharper end-point in the titration.

The most popular method of estimating low concentrations of fluoride in waters is the colorimetric procedure based on the Scott modification of the Sanchis method[2, 297] and depends upon the bleaching action of fluorides on the reddish lake formed by zirconium oxychloride or nitrate and sodium alizarin sulphonate in hydrochloric acid and sulphuric acid solution. Any interference due to free chlorine can be prevented by adding to 100 ml. of the sample 1 drop of $N/10$ sodium thiosulphate[298] for each 1·8 p.p.m. of chlorine. If more than 500 p.p.m. of Cl', 200 p.p.m. of SO_4'', 200 p.p.m. (expressed as $CaCO_3$) of acidity or alkalinity, 2 p.p.m. of Fe, 0·5 p.p.m. of Al, or 1 p.p.m. of PO_4''' are present, interference occurs and it is preferable to separate the fluoride by a distillation procedure (e.g. steam distillation with perchloric acid or concentrated sulphuric acid in the presence of glass beads) to volatilize the fluoride as silicon tetrafluoride[2, 14]. Factors affecting this distillation are discussed by MEGREGIAN and SOLET[299]. The time-consuming distillation can be avoided, according to SHOUP[300], by precipitating interfering substances (aluminium, organic colour, iron, manganese, carbonates, phosphates, and sulphates) in the presence of a boric acid–caustic soda buffer (pH 8·0) with cadmium nitrate and mercuric nitrate; the fluoride can then be directly determined on an aliquot of the centrifugate or filtrate.

LAMAR[301] has shown that if the zirconium salt–alizarin reagent is made up with 2·1N sulphuric acid instead of with a mixture of hydrochloric and sulphuric acids, much more sulphate and chloride can be tolerated without any interference, namely up to about 500 p.p.m. of SO_4'' and about 1,000 p.p.m. of Cl'. MEGREGIAN and MAIER[302] have described an improved method suitable for the spectrophotometric and visual determination of fluoride in waters, using a reagent with zirconium: alizarin ratios different from those used in the other methods. The visual method, which uses a reagent prepared, as suggested by Lamar [301], with sulphuric acid instead of mixed hydrochloric and sulphuric acids, covers the range 0–2 p.p.m. of F and is sensitive to increments of 0·02 p.p.m. of F. This procedure appears to be more reliable than the other methods and gives better colours for matching. A B.D.H. Lovibond nesslerizer disc (range 0·4 – 1·1 p.p.m.) is available for use with this method for visual work and LONGWELL [303] has described an absorptiometric method.

A fluorometric method for traces of fluoride (as little as 0·2 gamma of F) has been described by WILLARD and HORTON [304] and is based on the decrease caused by fluoride in the fluorescence of an aluminium–morin complex in 50 per cent alcoholic solution at pH 4·9. Fluoride ions are adsorbed on light magnesium oxide in boiling solutions and this can be made the basis for determining traces of fluoride in large volumes of water [305].

HARDNESS [2, 3, 4, 15, 306]

The total hardness, or soap-consuming power, of a water is generally regarded as the sum of the concentrations of the calcium and magnesium ions but can also include all other metallic ions reacting with soap (e.g. Fe, Al, Zn, Mn, Sr) with the exception of the alkali metal ions. Although the most accurate method of arriving at a hardness figure is to add together the concentrations of calcium, magnesium, and other metals causing hardness, this is rather tedious and in practice quicker routine methods have been used. These include the Clark [15] and Wanklyn [12] soap titration tests (which depend upon the formation at the end-point of a permanent lather), the Blacher potassium palmitate procedure [15], and the Wartha–Pfeifer method [15] (involving boiling with caustic soda–sodium carbonate and titrating the clear filtrate or supernatant liquid with N/10 acid). All these methods have now been rendered virtually obsolete by the elegant and rapid 'versenate' titration method of SCHWARZENBACH and his co-workers [307]. According to this procedure, the calcium and magnesium ions are titrated in a buffered solution with a standard solution of disodium ethylene diamine tetra-acetate (EDTA or 'sodium versenate') in the presence of an alcoholic solution of a blue dye, Eriochrome Black T*; this indicator forms red slightly-ionized complexes with calcium and magnesium at a

---

* This is the sodium salt of 1-(1-hydroxy-2-naphthylazo)-6-nitro-2-naphthol-4-sulphonic acid (No. 203 in the colour index of the Society of Dyers and Colourists). It is also called Solochrome Black WDFA.

pH value of about 10, and as soon as these ions (first the calcium and then the magnesium) have been sequestered by the titrant (which yields more stable complexes than does the indicator) there is a colour change from red to blue which marks the end-point. If calcium alone is present in the sample, the calcium-dye is not stable enough to serve as indicator, hence it is usual to incorporate a little magnesium salt in the titrant before it is standardized against pure calcium carbonate. There is now a very extensive literature on this method [308-315]. DISKANT [316] claims that diethanolamine and triethanolamine are superior to ethyl alcohol for preparing stable indicator solutions. BETZ and NOLL [311, 312] state that if sodium sulphide is incorporated in the titrant, the following ions do not interfere: 10 p.p.m. of copper, zinc, lead, tin and aluminium; 20 p.p.m. of ferrous or ferric iron; 10,000 p.p.m. of SO_4'' or Cl'; 500 p.p.m. of SO_3'', CrO_4'', NO_2' or NO_3'; 1,000 p.p.m. of CO_3''; and 200 p.p.m. of SiO_2.

The ABCM-SAC Joint Committee recommend the EDTA method only when the cations present are calcium, magnesium and the alkali metals [306]. If other metals are present, this Committee has proposed an ingenious ion-exchange procedure; the cations are adsorbed on Zeo-Karb 225 ion-exchange resin, the liberated acid is titrated with standard caustic soda, and the sum of the cations so obtained is corrected by deducting the alkali metals (preferably determined by flame photometry). Schwarzenbach [307] also showed that calcium ions alone can be determined in the presence of magnesium if murexide (ammonium purpurate) is used as indicator (pH above 12, colour change red to violet). In a modification of this procedure proposed by KNIGHT [314], the colour change at the end-point is rendered more easily visible by incorporating Naphthol Green B with the murexide, the change of colour then being from olive-green through grey to blue [4].

Other indicators recommended for the direct titration of calcium with EDTA are:

(1) calcein*, or fluorescein complexone [319, 320], obtained by condensing iminodiacetic acid with fluorescein, and more sensitive than murexide. It is used at pH 12 (when Mg is completely precipitated as hydroxide) and gives a colour change from a fluorescent bright green to pinkish-orange†;
(2) metalphthalein [308], used at pH 10·5–11, and giving a colour change from red to grey.

The classical volumetric method of determining calcium

---

* About 20–30 times as much Mg as Ca may be present without interference.
† A better colour change (green to purple) is obtained if thymolphthalein is included with the indicator.

ions[119, 123] involves precipitation of calcium as the oxalate, solution of the washed precipitate in hot dilute sulphuric acid, and titration at 70–80° C with N/10 or N/100 potassium permanganate. If appreciable organic matter is present, it should first be destroyed by evaporation with nitric acid. The separation of calcium from many interfering ions (e.g. silicate, phosphate, iron, aluminium, manganese, titanium, and magnesium) can be achieved by precipitating the calcium as oxalate from a solution containing such organic acids as oxalic acid[119] or acetic acid[4, 317] at a pH value of about 4. In the procedure of LINGANE[318], the hydrochloric acid solution containing calcium and any interfering ions is heated almost to boiling, treated with hot ammonium oxalate solution, and the calcium oxalate is precipitated by adding ammonia drop by drop with stirring until the pH rises to $4 \cdot 0 \pm 0 \cdot 5$; it is convenient to use methyl orange as indicator and a potassium hydrogen phthalate buffer for comparison.

Hardness is usually expressed in this country in terms of calcium carbonate, the unit being 1 p.p.m. of $CaCO_3$. Conversion to and from other units can be carried out with the aid of *Table 38* in the Appendix

CHAPTER 8

METALLIC CONTAMINANTS

ONE of the outstanding advances made in analytical chemistry within recent years is the increasing use of organic reagents for the detection and estimation of traces of metals. Such compounds as dithizone, o-phenanthroline, sodium diethyldithiocarbamate, and diphenylcarbazide—at one time chemical curiosities—are now comparatively common reagents in most well-equipped laboratories. Many of these reagents are almost specific for a particular element, or at any rate highly selective, and some are sensitive enough to permit the determination of concentrations of metal as low as 0·01–0·1 p.p.m. Examples of some organic reagents suitable for the colorimetric determination of traces of the commoner metals are given in *Table 7.*

Table 7. Some organic reagents suitable for the colorimetric estimation of traces of the commoner metals

Metal	Organic reagent	Colour produced	Approximate pH	Maximum transmittance of filter for photometric determination: mμ	Useful range of visual determination: p.p.m. of metal	References
Cadmium	Dithizone	red	strongly alkaline solution	510	—	1, 3, 132, 133
Chromium	Diphenylcarbazide	reddish–violet	acid solution	540	0·05–0·5 (a)	1, 3, 131, 132, 133
Copper	Dithizone	violet	2·3	510	0·04–14*	132, 133, 338
Copper	Na diethyldithio-carbamate	yellow–brown	>9·0	420	0·1–0·8 (a)	131, 132, 133
Copper	Cuproine (2:2'-biquinoline)	purple	4·3–5·8	540	—	322, 344
Iron	o-Phenanthroline	orange–red	2·0–9·0	508	0·01–1·0 (b)	132, 133
Iron	Thioglycollic acid	purple	8–12	540	0·04–1·2(a)	1, 3, 131–133, 139 140
Iron	Tripyridyl	red–purple	9·6	555	0·01–2·0 (b)	2, 355
Lead	Dithizone	red	8–10	520	—	1, 2, 3, 131–133
Mercury	Dithizone	orange–yellow	strongly acid solution	500	—	132, 133
Nickel	Dimethylglyoxime (+ bromine)	reddish–brown	—	445	—	132, 133, 139, 140
Uranium	Dibenzoylmethane	yellow	7·0	395	—	382, 383
Zinc	Dithizone	purple–red	4·0–5·5	535	0·1–1·0†	1, 2, 3, 132, 133
Zinc	Zincon	blue	9·0	620	0·1–2·4 (a)	394

(a) = 50 ml. Nessler tubes.   (b) = 100 ml. Nessler tubes.
* Samples 25–250 ml. using photometric method.
† Using 5 ml. or 10 ml. of sample and extracting with 5 ml. of 0·001 per cent dithizone in CCl₄.

One of the most versatile and useful of these reagents is dithizone (or, diphenylthiocarbazone) [132, 133]

$$S=C\begin{cases} NH \cdot NH-C_6H_5 \\ N=N-C_6H_5 \end{cases}$$

which by replacement of one or both hydrogen atoms forms highly coloured dithizonates with no less than seventeen of the metals (manganese, iron, cobalt, nickel, copper, zinc, lead, silver, cadmium, indium, platinum, palladium, tin, mercury, thallium, bismuth and gold). The dithizone is used as a dilute (0·001 per cent) solution in chloroform or carbon tetrachloride (which is green) and the aqueous sample is extracted with this reagent when the colour of the organic solvent changes from green to that of the metal dithizonate (red, purple, yellow, etc., depending upon the particular metal). In order to make this reagent specific for a particular metal, various devices can be employed, such as adjustment of pH, or use of cyanide, thiosulphate and thiocyanate as complex-forming agents. Thus, in slightly alkaline solution containing cyanide, only lead, thallium, stannous tin and bismuth react to form dithizonates. Bismuth can be extracted from a slightly acid solution and so can be separated from lead. Tin does not react with dithizone if oxidized to the stannic form. In dilute mineral acid solution, only palladium, gold, silver, mercury and copper react with dithizone (also bismuth incompletely).

In view of the extreme toxicity of many metals towards fish and other animal life, vegetable life and bacteria, the importance of reliable methods for the determination of traces of these metals in river waters, sewage effluents, and trade effluents needs little justification. Practical details of the methods used are given in the invaluable reference books by ALLPORT [131], SANDELL [132] and SNELL and SNELL [133], in various handbooks of standard methods [1, 2, 3], in papers by RIEHL [321], Butts and his associates [322], and FOULKE [323] and in a valuable series of monographs published by Hopkin and Williams [324].

It is advisable, before proceeding to the quantitative determination of the metal or metals, to carry out a preliminary qualitative examination of the sample, for if certain interfering elements can be shown to be absent the quantitative procedure can often be much simplified and valuable time saved. Spot tests, using drops of sample and reagents on white porcelain spot plates or on filter paper, are particularly useful in this connection and are given in FEIGL's book [136], in a paper by Butts and his associates [322], and in a report of an international committee [138].

It is of the greatest importance that reagents and distilled water used for the detection and estimation of traces of metals should be as free as possible from metallic contamination. Distilled water should not be prepared in a copper still in order to avoid contamination with copper. Special reagents virtually free from arsenic and lead can be purchased. In all cases of doubt, it is essential that blank determinations should be carried through all the stages of the particular method, thus enabling the result of the sample analysis to be corrected, but naturally the accuracy of the sample determination is much reduced if the blank value obtained with the reagents and distilled water is unnecessarily large.

Arsenic[2, 3, 325]

Arsenic is found in many weed-killers, in some sheep-dipping liquors and in some tannery effluents.

A very sensitive qualitative test for arsenic in waters, based on the Reinsch reaction, is described by SACCHETTA and MACHADO[326]. The water (25 ml.) is evaporated to dryness, the residue taken up in water (1 ml.), concentrated hydrochloric acid (1 ml.) is added, and a copper wire is inserted. After heating on the water bath for 15 minutes, a grey coloration due to As_2Cu_3 appears on the wire if more than 0·2 p.p.m. of arsenic is present in the sample.

The most popular method of estimating traces of arsenic in waters is based upon the well-known Gutzeit test[133, 327]. The arsenic, obtained by wet digestion of the sample with sulphuric and nitric acids and reduced to the trivalent state by a suitable reducing agent (e.g. sodium sulphite), is volatilized as arsine (AsH_3) with arsenic-free zinc and hydrochloric acid in the presence of stannous chloride, and the evolved gas, after passing through glass wool containing lead acetate to absorb any H_2S, is allowed to react with paper impregnated with mercuric chloride or bromide. The yellowish–brown stain so produced is compared with a series of stains given by standards ranging from 0·001–0·05 mg of arsenic.

For somewhat larger amounts of arsenic (0·4–100 mg), the ABCM-SAC Joint Committee[325] recommend (after destruction of organic matter with nitric and sulphuric acids) reduction of the arsenic to the elementary state with sodium hypophosphite, dissolution of the precipitated and washed arsenic in an excess of standard iodine, followed by back-titration with standard sodium arsenite. Mercury, selenium, and tellurium interfere with this method.

Barium

Barium may occur in effluents from places where barytes ($BaSO_4$), witherite ($BaCO_3$) and other barium minerals are mined. Soluble barium compounds are poisonous.

There is a scarcity of good procedures for the determination of small amounts of barium and the only available chemical methods are the colorimetric estimation as barium chromate[132, 133] and the more sensitive turbidimetric estimation as barium sulphate[133]. The ABCM-SAC Joint Committee recommend that barium soluble in dilute hydrochloric acid should be determined turbidimetrically as $BaSO_4$, any lead or strontium present being masked with EDTA[328].

If barium is present as insoluble barium sulphate, it can be brought into solution by fusing with sodium carbonate, leaching the melt with water, and dissolving the well-washed residue of barium carbonate in dilute hydrochloric acid.

A sensitive method of detecting and determining barium is by spectrum analysis (page 19). According to WILSKA[329], the smallest concentration of barium that can be determined in this way is 0·05 p.p.m.

Cadmium[1, 2, 3, 328]

Cadmium occurs in cadmium plating effluents, and its compounds are poisonous.

It can easily be detected in small amounts (about 1 p.p.m.) by the intense red precipitate formed when a drop of the filtered ammoniacal sample is treated on filter paper with a saturated solution of ferrous–2:2'-dipyridyl complex containing excess of potassium iodide[136, 322].

Before the advent of dithizone, cadmium was determined colorimetrically in ammoniacal cyanide solution as the yellow colloidal sulphide[330]. Small amounts of zinc, nickel, cobalt and copper do not interfere, but iron and lead interference occurs and these metals must be removed.

SERFASS and his associates[331] determine cadmium colorimetrically with dithizone in effluents containing organic matter and most common ions. The organic matter is first destroyed by wet digestion of the sample with nitric and sulphuric acids. Any silver, mercury, and copper present are then removed by extraction with dithizone in mineral acid solution. Nickel and cobalt are complexed with dimethylglyoxime; the nickel complex is extracted with chloroform whilst the cobalt complex, though not extracted by chloroform, does not react with dithizone. Cadmium is then estimated colorimetrically by means of the red complex it forms with dithizone in strongly alkaline solution. Butts and his co-workers[322] adopt a different procedure for dealing with interfering elements before determining cadmium with dithizone.

The Ministry[1] as well as the ABCM-SAC Joint Committee[328] recommend a dithizone procedure for the determination of small amounts of cadmium. A similar dithizone method is given by MULLIN and RILEY[332] for the determination of cadmium in sea water.

Chromium [3, 18, 132, 133, 322]

Chromium may occur as hexavalent chromium (chromate or bichromate) in waste waters from the manufacture of chromates, in chromium plating wastes, in wastes from the anodizing of aluminium, and as trivalent chromium in chrome tanning liquors. Chromates are yellow, bichromates are orange and trivalent chromium salts are generally green. Chromates are poisonous and strongly bactericidal.

A very sensitive qualitative test for hexavalent chromium depends upon the intense violet coloration obtained on the addition of a solution of *s*-diphenylcarbazide,

$$CO\underset{\displaystyle NH \cdot NH \cdot C_6H_5}{\overset{\displaystyle NH \cdot NH \cdot C_6H_5}{<}}$$

in alcohol, acetone or acetic acid to an aqueous solution of a chromate acidified with sulphuric acid, hydrochloric acid or acetic acid. According to Sandell[132], the optimum acidity for this test is about $0 \cdot 2N$ and the best acid to use is sulphuric acid. The test is nearly specific, only mercury and molybdenum reacting in a similar way in acid solution. The yellow coloration given by ferric iron can be prevented by addition of phosphoric acid. Solutions of diphenylcarbazide are not very stable, but, according to EGE and SILVERMAN[333], a reagent stable for 5 months can be prepared by incorporating phthalic anhydride in the alcoholic solution. Trivalent chromium gives no colour with diphenylcarbazide and must, therefore, be first oxidized to the hexavalent form either with sodium peroxide or by boiling the acid solution (containing a little silver nitrate as catalyst) with potassium persulphate. Although the estimation of not too small amounts of hexavalent chromium can be carried out colorimetrically by taking advantage of the intense yellow colour of chromates in alkaline solution, a more sensitive and reliable method, which can be carried out directly on the centrifuged sample, is based on the use of diphenylcarbazide in acid solution. In the method given by STONES[334] for the estimation of total chromium (trivalent + hexavalent) in sewage, the sample is treated with sodium sulphite and concentrated sulphuric acid to reduce any chromate to the trivalent condition. This preliminary reduction is necessary to avoid any subsequent loss of chromium as volatile chromyl chloride. After digesting to destroy organic matter, potassium permanganate is added to oxidize trivalent chromium to hexavalent chromium, any excess of permanganate being subsequently destroyed by adding a few drops of concentrated hydrochloric acid. The chromate is then estimated with diphenylcarbazide. A similar method is recommended by the ABCM-SAC Joint Committee [372].

When chromates are present in fair quantity, one of the following volumetric methods can be used for the quantitative determination:

(a) Titration of the solution acidified with sulphuric and phosphoric acids with standard ferrous ammonium sulphate using diphenyl-amine or diphenylamine sulphonic acid as indicator. Addition of phosphoric acid is unnecessary if o-phenanthroline is used as indicator [122, 123, 125].

(b) The acidified sample is treated with potassium iodide and the liberated iodine estimated with standard sodium thiosulphate using starch as indicator. Nitrites, if present, interfere with this titration, but they can be destroyed by a preliminary treatment with sodium azide and phosphoric acid [16, 335].

Copper [1–4]

Copper occurs in copper pickling liquors, copper plating wastes, and cuprammonium rayon wastes. Copper compounds are very toxic to fish and other animal life in streams and are extremely toxic to algae and other vegetable life and to bacteria.

Traces of copper can be detected by shaking the sample, slightly acidified with mineral acid, with a very dilute (0·001 per cent) solution of dithizone in carbon tetrachloride. In the presence of copper, the green colour of the reagent changes to violet–red. The test is not affected by the presence of cyanide and the only common interfering elements are mercury and silver. Another very sensitive test for small amounts of copper is based on the yellow or brown coloration (or precipitate) given by ammoniacal solutions of cupric salts with sodium diethyldithiocarbamate [336], which is said to be sensitive to 1 part of copper in 50,000,000 parts of water [324]. Interference due to small amounts of iron can be prevented by carrying out the test in ammoniacal solution (pH greater than 9) in the presence of such complexing agents as citrate, tartrate, or better, pyrophosphate [324]. Large quantities of iron are best removed by precipitation in hot solution with ammonia [4]; in the presence of sufficient ammonia and ammonium salts there is no adsorption of copper on the precipitated ferric hydroxide [337]. The yellow colour given by copper can be extracted with certain organic solvents (amyl or isoamyl alcohol, carbon tetrachloride). Cyanide inhibits the formation of the colour.

These two qualitative tests can be adapted to the quantitative determination of traces of copper. SWOPE and her co-workers [338] give a procedure for determining copper in sewage and industrial wastes which involves a preliminary digestion of the sample with concentrated nitric and sulphuric acids, adjustment of a suitable aliquot (containing less than 7 μg of copper) to pH about 2·3 with ammonia, buffering with a malonic acid–sodium hydroxide buffer at pH 2·3 and final extraction with a very dilute solution of dithizone in carbon tetrachloride. Interference due to mercury, bismuth or silver is prevented by shaking the carbon tetrachloride layer with an acid solution of potassium iodide which converts these metals to non-interfering complexes. In this way, concentrations of copper from 0·04–14 p.p.m. can be determined using 25–250 ml. of sample. These authors also used the sodium diethyldithiocarbamate method, the yellow colour being extracted with carbon tetrachloride and determined photometrically. The ABCM-SAC Joint Committee recommend extraction of copper as its diethyldithiocarbamate with carbon tetrachloride from EDTA–citrate solution in the presence of ammonia [325]. CHOW and THOMPSON [339] used sodium diethyl-dithiocarbamate for the spectrophotometric determination of traces of copper (down to about 0·002 μg) in sea water, the coloured complex being extracted with xylene. The carbamate method can also be used visually without extracting with organic solvents, but although this is simpler in practice, the range is much less, being restricted to amounts of copper between 0·005 mg and 0·05 mg (in 50 ml. Nessler tubes), for, with larger amounts of copper, cloudy solutions tend to be obtained. JEWSBURY [340], who prefers this method to the extraction procedure, eliminates interference of nickel, cobalt, manganese, iron, lead and cadmium by adding ethylene diamine tetra-acetic acid, which forms complexes with these interfering metals, excess of EDTA being removed with magnesium sulphate.

A new reagent almost specific for copper, namely 2:2′-diquinolyl (2:2′-biquinoline, or 'cuproine') [341-344], gives promise of being more widely used when it becomes less expensive.

2 : 2′-diquinolyl

This reagent, which is several times as sensitive as sodium diethyl-dithiocarbamate, gives a purple coloration with traces of cuprous copper (obtained by reduction of cupric copper with hydroxylamine hydrochloride) in neutral or slightly acid solution. Moderate quantities of iron and nickel do not interfere. The determination can be carried out in aqueous solution or the copper complex can be extracted with amyl alcohol. The application of this method to the determination of copper in sewage and trade wastes is described by Butts and his associates [322]. A paper by ELWELL [343] suggests that sulphurous acid is a better reducing agent than hydroxylamine hydrochloride when certain interfering elements (e.g. chromium) are present.

RILEY and SINHASENI [344] have applied the diquinolyl method to the determination of copper in sea water. Extraction of the cuprous-diquinolyl complex three times with n-hexanol was carried out at pH 4·3–5·8 using hydroquinone to prevent fading of the colour; the optical density was measured at 540 mμ in 1 cm or 4 cm cells with a spectrophotometer.

Another almost specific reagent for copper, namely bis-cyclohexanone oxalyldihydrazone, has been proposed by NILSSON [345] and details of its use are given in a publication of Hopkin and Williams [324].

$$\text{CO—NH—N}{=}\text{C} \underset{\text{CH}_2\text{—CH}_2}{\overset{\text{CH}_2\text{—CH}_2}{\diagdown\diagup}} \text{CH}_2$$
$$\text{CO—NH—N}{=}\text{C} \underset{\text{CH}_2\text{—CH}_2}{\overset{\text{CH}_2\text{—CH}_2}{\diagdown\diagup}} \text{CH}_2$$

bis-cyclohexanone oxalyldihydrazone

This reagent, which can detect 1 part of copper in 25,000,000 parts of water, gives a blue complex with copper over the range pH 7·0–10·0. The reaction is carried out in ammoniacal solution in the presence of ammonium citrate to prevent precipitation of other metal hydroxides. The application of this reagent to the determination of small amounts of copper in pulp and paper has been described by WETLESEN and GRAN [346].

Other useful reagents proposed for the determination of copper are the following:

(a) *dithio-oxamide* [1, 324], recommended by the Ministry of Housing and Local Government,

(b) *bis-(2-hvdroxyethyl) dithio-carbamate* [2, 322, 348] and

(c) certain derivatives of 1:10-phenanthroline, which do not react with ferrous iron on account of steric hindrance due to substitution of the positions adjacent to the nitrogen atoms. The most important of these are *2:9-dimethyl-1:10-phenanthroline* (neocuproine) [347] and *2: 9-dimethyl-4:7-diphenyl-1: 10-phenanthroline* (*bathocuproine*) [348], which are specific reagents for cuprous copper.

Bathocuproine was used by BORCHARDT and BUTLER [348] for the determination of traces of copper (0·1–40 p.p.m.) in pulp and paper mill wastes. The copper is reduced to the cuprous state with hydroxylamine hydrochloride and the complex is extracted by hexanol over the pH range 4–10 and measured spectrophotometrically at 479 mμ. Bathocuproine is probably the best reagent yet discovered for copper but unfortunately is extremely expensive.

Iron [1–4]

Iron is found in the ferrous (divalent) and ferric (trivalent) states in iron pickling liquors, ochre waters from coal mines, drainage from coal tips, and galvanizing and wire-drawing wastes. If qualitative tests show that ferrous iron is present, it should be determined quantitatively in such a way as to avoid its prior oxidation to the ferric state (e.g. direct titration in acid solution with standard dichromate). A method for estimating ferrous iron in river muds and pollutional sediments is given by FAIR, MOORE and THOMAS [349].

Numerous reagents are available for the detection and colorimetric estimation of ferrous iron and ferric iron. Potassium ferrocyanide (deep blue colour or precipitate with ferric salts), potassium ferricyanide (deep blue colour or precipitate with ferrous salts), and potassium or ammonium thiocyanate (deep wine-red coloration with ferric salts) have long been used for these purposes but have many disadvantages which have to a considerable extent led to their replacement by some of the newer organic reagents, such as 2:2′-dipyridyl, 1:10-phenanthroline, 2:2′:2″-tripyridyl, sulphosalicylic acid, and thioglycollic acid:

2:2′-dipyridyl
(α:α′-dipyridyl)

1:10-phenanthroline
(*o*-phenanthroline)

2:2′:2″-tripyridyl

HO₃S COOH
OH

sulphosalicylic acid

HS·CH₂·COOH

thioglycollic acid

2: 2′-dipyridyl gives a red soluble complex with ferrous iron in slightly acid solution but not with ferric iron [136, 138]. The reaction is sensitive and virtually specific. The complex cation formed has the formula $[Fe(C_{10}H_8N_2)_3]^{+2}$.

Fluorides, phosphates, and aliphatic hydroxy-acids, which so markedly affect the detection and determination of ferric iron with thiocyanate, have no effect on the dipyridyl reaction. In order to detect or determine ferric iron with dipyridyl, a preliminary reduction with hydroxylamine hydrochloride to the ferrous state is necessary.

1: 10-phenanthroline is very similar to dipyridyl and gives a red soluble complex with ferrous iron in slightly acid solution but not with ferric iron[138, 324]. The complex cation formed has the formula $[Fe(C_{12}H_8N_2)_3]^{+2}$.

Sulphosalicylic acid[138] gives a purple coloration with slightly acid solutions of ferric salts. Several anions (fluorides, phosphates, aliphatic hydroxy-acids) interfere by masking the coloration but the only interfering cation is titanium.

The most popular reagents for the colorimetric determination of traces of iron are thiocyanate[18, 131–133], thioglycollic acid[16, 131–133, 134A], 2:2'-dipyridyl[18, 131–133], and o-phenanthroline[132, 133, 322]. Many waters can be directly examined for iron without any preliminary treatment other than acidification. If much organic matter is present, the sample should be evaporated to dryness, ignited gently, and extracted with concentrated hydrochloric acid to dissolve the iron. Alternatively, a wet oxidation procedure with concentrated nitric and sulphuric acids can be used to destroy organic matter.

Potassium (or ammonium) thiocyanate is still much used for the colorimetric determination of ferric iron and it has the advantages over other reagents of cheapness and of yielding the characteristic wine-red coloration even in quite strongly acid solutions (pH 0·1–2·0). It is necessary to use a large excess of thiocyanate and the colour is not very stable and fades rather easily especially in strong sunlight. Metals which form insoluble thiocyanates interfere with the test and mercuric salts, fluorides, phosphates and organic hydroxy-acids tend to bleach the coloration. Organic solvents stabilize and intensify the colour of the ferric thiocyanate and the determination has been carried out with success in solutions containing 60 per cent of acetone[350] and in methyl cellosolve (2-methoxyethanol) solution[351]. The red ferric thiocyanate can also be concentrated and extracted from aqueous solutions, using such immiscible solvents as diethyl ether, ethyl acetate, amyl acetate, etc. A disc for use with the Lovibond comparator is available for this procedure over the range 0·4–5·0 p.p.m. of iron, the ferric thiocyanate being extracted from a 5 ml. sample with a mixture of equal volumes of amyl acetate and amyl alcohol[139, 140].

Thioglycollic acid reacts with both ferrous and ferric iron in ammoniacal solution (pH greater than 8·0) to give a purple coloration, citrate being added to prevent precipitation of metallic hydroxides. The reagent is thus useful for the determination of total iron (i.e. ferrous + ferric). Most anions do not appreciably affect the determination but nickel, cobalt and uranyl salts cause interference and should be removed. Permanent glass colour standards for this method are available for use with (a) the B.D.H. Lovibond nesslerizer, thus permitting the determination of iron over the range 0·04–1·2 p.p.m. of iron (50 ml. samples), and (b) the Lovibond comparator, covering the range 2–20 p.p.m. of iron (5 ml. samples). The thioglycollic acid method is recommended for the determination of total iron by the Ministry[1] and by the ABCM-SAC Joint committee[352].

Dipyridyl and phenanthroline determine ferrous iron only and ferric salts must first be reduced to the ferrous state. The red colour is stable over the pH range 3–9 and is not subject to so many interferences as the thiocyanate colour. Amounts of iron as low as 0·05 p.p.m. can easily be determined visually. Butts and his co-workers[322] separate iron from interfering substances, prior to a determination with o-phenanthroline, by a preliminary extraction of ferric chloride from hydrochloric acid solution with di-isopropyl ether.

Several derivatives of o-phenanthroline have been prepared, the most sensitive being bathophenanthroline or 4:7-diphenyl-1:10-phenanthroline, which is specific for iron[353]. This reagent forms a stable red complex with ferrous iron at pH about 4·0. The colour can be extracted with isoamyl alcohol or n-hexyl alcohol and the colour intensity measured spectrophotometrically or visually. As little as 0·001–0·01 p.p.m. of iron can be accurately determined in this way.

Another very sensitive reagent for iron is 2:2′:2″-tripyridyl[354, 355]. This compound gives a reddish–purple stable complex with ferrous iron over the pH range 1·5–12·0. Interfering heavy metals are sequestered by buffering with ethylene diamine at pH about 9·6. The determination can be carried out photometrically or visually; in the latter case, using 100 ml. samples in Nessler tubes, iron can be estimated over the range 0·005–2·0 p.p.m. The reagent is unfortunately extremely expensive in this country. The method has been tentatively recommended for iron in the latest revision of the A.P.H.A. *Standard methods for the examination of water, sewage and industrial wastes*[2].

When the quantities of iron present are too large for colorimetric determinations, volumetric methods are satisfactory. Thus, ferrous iron can be accurately determined by titration with standard potassium dichromate (0·1, 0·01 or even 0·001 N) in hydrochloric acid or sulphuric acid solutions, using one of the following internal indicators:

(1) diphenylamine*,
(2) diphenylamine sulphonic acid*,
(3) N-methyl-diphenylamine sulphonic acid*,
(4) N-phenylanthranilic acid,
(5) 1:10-phenanthroline (as the ferrous sulphate complex, 'ferroin'), and
(6) 5:6-dimethylferroin (good, but expensive).

Of these, (2), (3) and (6) are the most satisfactory[125].

If ferric iron is to be determined in this way, it must first be reduced to the ferrous condition with stannous chloride.

The dichromate titration of ferrous iron may give inaccurate results in the presence of easily oxidizable organic matter. In such cases, to avoid interference by organic matter, use can be made of a modification due to Heisig[356] of the Andrews–Jamieson method in which standard potassium iodate is used as titrant in the presence of high concentrations of hydrochloric acid and an organic solvent (chloroform or carbon tetrachloride)[125, 357–359]. The acidity at the end of the titration must be about 3–4 N, otherwise the iodine monochloride formed is partially hydrolysed. Owing to the easy oxidation of ferrous salts by air in strong hydrochloric acid solutions, excess of iodine monochloride is added to oxidize the ferrous iron before addition of acid, then strong hydrochloric acid is added and the iodine formed is titrated with standard potassium iodate in a stoppered bottle with vigorous shaking in the presence of a layer of carbon tetrachloride. At the end-point, the organic solvent layer loses its purple colour:

$$2FeSO_4 + 2ICl + 4HCl = 2FeCl_3 + I_2 + 2H_2SO_4$$
$$2I_2 + KIO_3 + 6HCl = KCl + 5ICl + 3H_2O$$

Smith and Wilcox[360] have shown that amaranth can with advantage be used as internal indicator (best added towards the end of the titration) in place of the organic solvent, the colour change being from red to colourless.

Lead[1–4]

Lead is present in rivers whose watersheds contain lead mines, in effluents from the manufacture of accumulators, in lead paint wastes, and wastes from the manufacture of pewter ware. Lead compounds are toxic to all forms of life.

---

* Phosphoric acid must also be present if these indicators are used.

If present in not too small amounts (greater than 2 p.p.m.) lead can be detected by Feigl's test with sodium rhodizonate which forms a coloured inner complex salt with lead[136]:

To carry out the test, a drop of the sample is placed on filter paper and the spot touched with a drop of freshly prepared aqueous sodium rhodizonate. In the presence of lead a blue colour is formed which changes to scarlet on adding a drop of buffer solution, pH 2·8. Even very sparingly soluble compounds of lead (e.g. lead sulphate) respond to this test. If the lead is first separated by precipitation as lead sulphate, the test becomes quite specific for lead since any co-precipitated barium sulphate does not react. The detection of traces of lead (down to about 0·01 p.p.m.) is best done with dithizone. The sample containing Rochelle salt and potassium cyanide is shaken with a 0·002 per cent solution of dithizone in carbon tetrachloride when the green colour of the reagent changes to red in the presence of lead. Only bismuth and the rare element thallium interfere with this test.

Prior to the more widespread use of the dithizone procedure, a popular method used in this country for the determination of small amounts of lead was the sulphide method[361]. This method depends upon the formation of brownish colloidal lead sulphide when sodium sulphide is added to an ammoniacal lead solution in the presence of ammonium citrate (which prevents the disturbing effect of aluminium, calcium and magnesium salts on the coloration) and potassium cyanide (which prevents interference by copper and by small amounts of iron by converting these metals to complex cyanides). For accurate work, and when organic matter is present, the lead is isolated, after a wet digestion with nitric and sulphuric acids, by precipitation with hydrogen sulphide as lead sulphide. This precipitate, which may also contain copper and traces of iron, is dissolved in nitric acid, converted to insoluble lead sulphate by precipitation with sulphuric acid in an alcohol–water medium, the lead sulphate is then dissolved in ammonium acetate and the lead estimated colorimetrically as sulphide. The colour comparison is simplified by using the appropriate disc supplied for use with the B.D.H. Lovibond nesslerizer, which covers the range 0·4–4 p.p.m. of lead (if a 25 ml. aliquot is taken). GAD[362] has applied the sulphide method directly as a field test to potable waters without any preliminary treatment, and states that using 100 ml. samples in Hehner cylinders, as little as 0·2 p.p.m. of lead can be estimated. The determination of traces of lead (down to about 0·01 p.p.m.) is best carried out by extracting the slightly ammoniacal sample (pH about 8·5–10) with a carbon tetrachloride or chloroform solution of dithizone in the presence of sodium citrate and potassium cyanide[132, 322, 372]. Only bismuth and thallium, which are unlikely to be present, interfere. Any interference by ferric iron, which oxidizes dithizone, is prevented by addition of hydroxylamine hydrochloride.

Manganese[1–4]

Manganese compounds are not normally toxic to plants and animals, with the exception of the purple-coloured permanganates which have bactericidal properties.

Manganese can occur in drainage from coal and ash tips, and this drainage can be objectionable on account of the brown precipitate of manganic hydroxide which is produced when the drainage reacts in the presence of air with the natural alkalinity of the stream. Manganese compounds can also occur in chemical waste waters where they are often associated with lime sludges.

The following tests can be used for the detection of manganese:

(*a*) A drop of the sample containing Mn^{ii} is placed on filter paper, made alkaline with dilute caustic soda, and then after waiting a few seconds to permit oxidation of the manganous hydroxide to manganic hydroxide by air, a drop of a solution of benzidine in dilute acetic acid is added. In the presence of manganese, a blue or blue–green coloration is obtained. Interference due to iron is prevented by adding Rochelle salt[136]. Other oxidizing agents (e.g. chromates and permanganates) react similarly. Lime sludges containing manganese in the oxidized form respond to the test without adding any alkali.

(*b*) When samples containing manganese in any state of valency are evaporated to dryness and fused with sodium carbonate and a little potassium nitrate, a green mass is obtained due to the formation of sodium manganate:

$$MnO + O_2 + Na_2CO_3 = Na_2MnO_4 + CO_2$$

This is a very sensitive and specific test for any manganese compound[138].

(*c*) A drop of the neutral sample is treated with a drop of saturated potassium periodate, a drop of dilute acetic acid, and then 2 drops of a solution of tetramethyl-*p*-diaminodiphenylmethane in chloroform. Permanganate is formed by oxidation and reacts with the amine giving a blue colour[136]. This test will detect 0·001 µg of manganese, or 1 part of manganese in 50,000,000 parts of water.

The determination of manganese is generally carried out by boiling the sample with excess of potassium periodate in the presence of sulphuric acid, or if iron is present, a mixture of sulphuric and phosphoric acids[2, 3, 7, 210, 322]. Unless the sample is low in chlorides and organic matter, a preliminary digestion with nitric and sulphuric acids is necessary to destroy organic matter and remove chlorides. Small amounts of silver nitrate catalyse the oxidation of manganese with periodate and are specially desirable if only traces of manganese are present. The intensity of the colour of the permanganate produced is measured photometrically or by comparison with standards. As little as 0·01 p.p.m. of manganese can be estimated in this way.

An alternative method of oxidizing manganese to permanganate is by means of ammonium persulphate[363] in acid solution using silver nitrate as a catalyst[1, 2]. According to Sandell[132], the reaction should be carried out in the presence of nitric and phosphoric acids and reasonable amounts of organic matter do not interfere if extra persulphate is used and the period of heating is longer. Mercuric sulphate can be added to prevent interference of chlorides[132]. According to NYDAHL[363] persulphate is superior to periodate as an oxidizing agent for traces of manganese.

Mercury[3, 132, 352]

Mercury compounds, which are extremely toxic to all forms of life, including bacteria, may be present in waste waters from the manufacture of insecticides and fungicides, and in 'white water' from paper mills using mercury compounds (such as phenyl mercuric acetate) to prevent slime formation.

In dilute nitric acid solution, monovalent and divalent mercury salts give a purple–blue coloration with diphenylcarbazide[138]. Interference due to molybdates is avoided by complexing with oxalic acid, while if chromates are present they can be reduced to the un-reactive trivalent state by sulphur dioxide. Dithizone affords a much more sensitive test for mercury. When mercurous or mercuric salts in dilute mineral acid solution (preferably sulphuric acid about normal in strength) are shaken with a chloroform or carbon tetrachloride solution of dithizone, the green colour of the reagent changes to yellow or orange. Among the commoner metals, only silver and copper interfere, while among the anions chlorides should not be present in appreciable amounts since they form complexes with mercury.

Dithizone was used by JOHANSSON[364] for the colorimetric determination of mercury in 'white water' from paper mills. The water was treated with hydrogen sulphide and the precipitated mercury sulphide was digested with a mixture of nitric and sulphuric acids and the solution, after adjustment to pH 1·0, was extracted with a solution of dithizone in chloroform. In the dithizone method recommended by the ABCM-SAC Joint Committee[352], organic matter is first destroyed by a special nitric acid–potassium permanganate digestion under slight pressure, hydroxylamine is added to suppress the effect of iron and the mercury is then extracted as the dithizonate with toluene from the solution acidified with sulphuric acid.

Nickel[1–3]

Nickel occurs in many electroplating wastes. It is toxic to fish and other river life, and has an adverse effect on biological sewage treatment and on sludge digestion.

The classical test for nickel, namely the red precipitate or colour formed with an alcoholic solution of dimethylglyoxime[324]

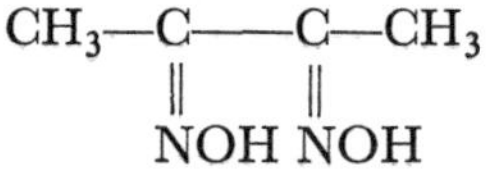

$$CH_3-C\text{-----}C-CH_3$$
$$\|\qquad\|$$
$$NOH\ NOH$$

in ammoniacal solutions (or with the water soluble sodium salt of dimethylglyoxime), is one of the oldest examples of the use of an organic reagent for the detection of a metal, and will detect 1 part of nickel[365] in 2,000,000 parts of water. The red compound produced has the following co-ordination formula:

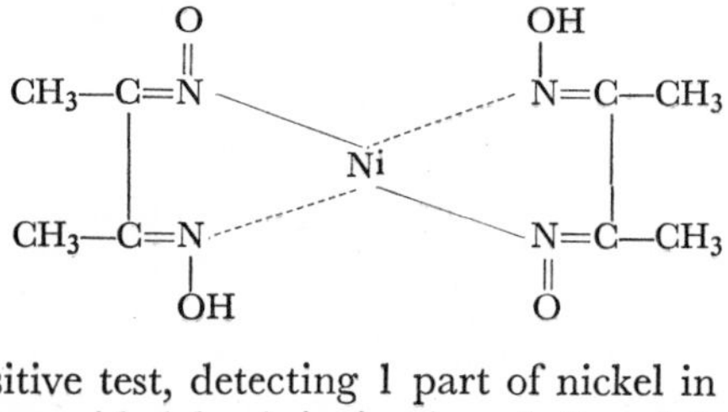

A more sensitive test, detecting 1 part of nickel in 5,000,000 parts of water, is provided by 'nioxime' or 1:2-cyclohexanedione dioxime[324, 366]:

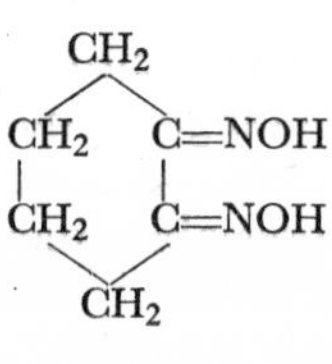

This is used as a 0·8 per cent aqueous solution and reacts with nickel in slightly acid (pH 3·0), neutral or ammoniacal solutions to give a purple–red colour or precipitate. If iron is present, the reaction with either dimethylglyoxime or with nioxime should be carried out in ammoniacal tartrate solution.

These tests for nickel fail in the presence of cyanide. A sensitive test for nickel in the presence of cyanide has been described by Feigl[136]. The sample is mixed with bromine water, rendered alkaline with ammonia, and then treated with an alcoholic solution of dimethylglyoxime when a reddish–brown coloration appears due to the formation of a complex compound of tetravalent nickel. This test can be made the basis of a quantitative method for the determination of nickel in amounts covering the range 0·1–1·0 p.p.m.[367, 368]. The presence of ammonium tartrate prevents interference of iron. The separation of nickel from many elements interfering with this method can be achieved by making use of the solubility of the nickelous compound of dimethylglyoxime in chloroform[132, 369]. By extracting a faintly ammoniacal solution containing citrate or tartrate in this way, nickel can be separated from ferric iron, aluminium, cobalt and a number of other elements. Although some copper is also removed by the chloroform extraction, washing the extract with dilute ammonia dissolves the copper leaving the nickel in the chloroform layer. The chloroform extract containing the nickel dimethylglyoxime is then shaken with dilute hydrochloric acid whereby the nickel passes to the aqueous phase and can then be determined colorimetrically by the bromine–dimethylglyoxime procedure. This method has been used (after destruction of organic matter) by Riehl[321] for the determination of nickel in sewage and sewage sludges: by GARDNER, SERFASS and MURACA[370] for the determination of nickel in plating waste waters; by the Ministry[1] and by the ABCM-SAC Joint Committee[352].

Selenium[2, 3]

Selenium may occur in waters draining selenium-containing soils or rocks (e.g. in parts of the U.S.A.). It is used commercially in the manufacture of some photo-electric cells. Selenates and selenites are toxic to living organisms. Selenium compounds emit a peculiar odour reminiscent of decaying radishes when heated with sodium carbonate upon charcoal.

A sensitive test for selenites, detecting 1 p.p.m. of selenium or even less, is described by Feigl[136]. The sample acidified with hydrochloric acid is treated with excess of a freshly prepared 1 per cent solution of *as*-diphenylhydrazine in glacial acetic acid when a red–violet coloration soon appears. Selenates should first be reduced to selenites by boiling with concentrated hydrochloric acid. Any interference by ferric iron and cupric copper is prevented by adding oxalic acid.

The A.P.H.A.[2] give a tentative method for the estimation of selenium in the range 0·01–0·5 p.p.m. using 1 l. of sample. The sample (after treatment with sodium peroxide and evaporation) is distilled with hydrobromic acid, bromine, and sulphuric acid, when volatile selenium tetrabromide passes over and is hydrolysed in aqueous solution to selenious acid. After removing excess of bromine with sulphur dioxide, the selenious acid is reduced by means of hydroxylamine hydrochloride to pink colloidal selenium which is matched visually against standards:

$$H_2SeO_3 + 2NH_2OH \cdot HCl = Se + N_2O + 4H_2O + 2HCl$$

FOGG and WILKINSON[371] regard this procedure as unsatisfactory since they found that the test sample and the standards gave different tints; these workers[371, 372] give a modified method in which the sample, after wet oxidation with a mixture of nitric, perchloric and sulphuric acids, is distilled as selenium tetrabromide and the selenious acid in the distillate is then reduced with ascorbic acid to yield pink colloidal selenium which can be accurately matched against standards.

Another method suitable for traces of selenium (0·1–5·0 p.p.m.) in water has been described by LAMBERT and his associates[373]. The selenium is converted to selenious acid by means of sulphuric acid, potassium bromide and sodium hypochlorite, and, after removal of the excess of bromine, the selenious acid is allowed to react with cadmium iodide and the liberated iodine determined colorimetrically.

Silver [132, 133]

Silver occurs in waste waters from the manufacture of photographic chemicals, often as insoluble silver chloride or bromide. It is very toxic to fish and other river life, including bacteria.

A sensitive qualitative test for traces of silver utilizes the purple–red colour given by silver ions in approximately N/10 nitric acid solution with a dilute acetone solution of p-dimethylamino–benzal-rhodanine[324].

Reliable methods for the determination of traces of silver are few. If present in solution, probably the best method is based upon the yellow keto dithizonate formed when the silver solution is shaken with a chloroform or carbon tetrachloride solution of dithizone in the presence of 0·5–1 N sulphuric acid, but mercury interferes. Interference due to copper is avoided, according to Sandell[132], by employing cupric dithizonate as reagent instead of dithizone and a 'mixed colour' method of colour comparison is then used, the colours ranging from violet to yellow.

If silver is present as insoluble bromide or chloride, the precipitate is dissolved in ammonia, and the dilute ammoniacal solution is reduced with sodium hydrosulphite (sodium dithionite, $Na_2S_2O_4$), when yellow colloidal silver is formed which can be estimated colorimetrically[374]. According to GAD and NAUMANN[375], the method is suitable for concentrations of silver ranging from 0·1–0·5 p.p.m.; with higher silver concentrations the colloidal silver tends to precipitate but addition of gum arabic as protective colloid enables the method to be used up to concentrations of silver of 2 p.p.m.

Titanium[119, 121, 132, 133]

Titanium occurs in waste waters from the manufacture of titanium dioxide and titanium pigments and also as white insoluble titanium dioxide in effluents from paper mills using titanium dioxide as a 'filler'.

Titanium compounds are not, so far as is known, toxic to fish and other river life and are objectionable chiefly when present as suspended matter.

The detection of titanium is generally carried out by evaporating the sample to dryness, igniting to destroy organic matter, fusing the ash with potassium bisulphate to convert titanium dioxide to titanic sulphate, dissolving the product in dilute sulphuric acid and adding hydrogen peroxide when a stable yellow or orange coloration is obtained[136, 138]. Addition of phosphoric acid in this test prevents interference by iron. By adding fluoride the colour is bleached, owing to the formation of stable $[TiF_6]$ ions.

Another sensitive qualitative test for titanium, described by Feigl[136], involves treatment of the sample, or residue obtained on evaporation, with excess of a 0·1 per cent solution of chromotropic acid in concentrated sulphuric acid when a violet coloration is obtained.

The determination of titanium is usually carried out by the hydrogen peroxide method[131–133] on the solution obtained by leaching the potassium bisulphate melt with dilute sulphuric acid. As little as 1 p.p.m. of titanium can be determined visually by this colorimetric method in 50 ml. Nessler tubes. Vanadium, chromium and molybdenum interfere. If these elements are present, the sample is evaporated to dryness, fused with sodium carbonate and a little sodium nitrate, and the melt on cooling is leached with hydrogen peroxide to remove vanadate, chromate and molybdate[126]. The titanium remains as insoluble titanium dioxide, which can be fused with potassium bisulphate and estimated by the hydrogen peroxide method.

For the determination of still smaller quantities of titanium (in the range 0·01–0·8 p.p.m.) use can be made of disodium 1:2-dihydroxybenzine–3:5-disulphonate('tiron' or 'tiferron') which gives an intense yellow colour with tetravalent titanium over the pH range 4·3–9·6 [376, 377]. Interference due to iron is prevented by carrying out the reaction in an acetic acid–sodium acetate buffer at pH 4·7 and reducing the iron to the unreactive ferrous condition with sodium hydrosulphite (sodium dithionite, $Na_2S_2O_4$). Fluorides interfere, and molybdates and uranyl salts must be absent since they give yellow colours with the reagent.

Uranium [132, 133]

Uranium compounds are highly toxic and may be present in waste waters from the processing of uranium minerals and ores and in discharges from atomic energy plants. A publication of the Department of Scientific and Industrial Research [378] gives an account of chemical methods available for the determination of macro and micro quantities of uranium, and Sandell [132] describes colorimetric methods suitable for trace amounts of uranium such as are likely to occur in waste waters. When using colorimetric methods it is usually advisable to separate uranium from interfering elements by making use of the fact that uranyl nitrate $[UO_2(NO_3)_2]$ can be extracted quantitatively by ether from an aqueous solution containing nitric acid and ammonium nitrate [132, 378].

The thiocyanate method of CURRAH and BEAMISH [379] depends upon the yellow coloration produced when ammonium thiocyanate is added to an acid solution of a uranyl salt; interference due to iron is obviated by adding stannous chloride, or better, ascorbic acid [380], to reduce ferric iron to ferrous iron. Molybdenum must be absent as even traces interfere by giving a yellow–orange colour. CLINCH and GUY [381] modify the method by extracting the uranium as thiocyanate from a solution containing EDTA at pH 3·5–3·9 by a mixture of tributyl phosphate and carbon tetrachloride. The optical density of the extract is determined spectrophotometrically at 350 mμ. The presence of EDTA prevents the extraction of any ferric thiocyanate.

A reagent about five to six times as sensitive as thiocyanate for the determination of uranium is dibenzoyl–methane ($C_6H_5CO \cdot CH_2 \cdot CO \cdot C_6H_5$) which according to YOE and his co-workers [382] gives a bright yellow stable coloration with uranyl salts over the pH range 6·5–8·5. By using 50 ml. Nessler tubes (tall form) as little as 0·05 p.p.m. of uranium can be estimated. If interfering ions (e.g. iron, molybdenum and vanadium) are present, the ether extraction procedure should be used for the separation of the uranium. A spectrophotometric method is described by BLANQUET [383]; the complex is formed in aqueous pyridine in the presence of EDTA and tartaric acid and the extinction is determined at 415 mμ.

A sensitive method for uranium has recently been described by CHENG [383A]. In the presence of EDTA and cyanide, uranyl ions react with the dye 1-(2-pyridylazo)-2-naphthol in ammoniacal solution (pH 10) to give a deep red complex. This can be extracted by o-dichlorobenzene and the absorbance measured at 570mμ. In this way traces of uranium can be determined in the presence of many metals (e.g. copper, nickel, zinc, iron, mercury and silver). Among the anions, only phosphate interferes due to precipitation of uranyl phosphate.

Very small amounts of uranium (down to about 3 μg) can be determined polarographically [378]. The most sensitive method for traces of uranium is based upon the intense yellow–green fluorescence given by uranium compounds when fused with sodium fluoride. This fluorophotometric method will determine as little as 0·001–10 μg of uranium [384], but many elements interfere and must be removed. The procedure has been applied to the routine determination of uranium in the residue from the evaporation of small quantities (10 ml.) of water [385].

The fluorescence test is also the most sensitive qualitative test for traces of uranium and is best carried out by examination in ultraviolet light [136].

Vanadium

Vanadium occurs frequently in certain Argentine waters. Its compounds are toxic and find some uses in industry but are not commonly present in trade wastes.

The common vanadium compounds are the blue vanadyl salts in which vanadium is tetravalent (e.g. vanadyl sulphate, $VOSO_4$, containing the divalent VO^{++} ion) and the vanadates (e.g. sodium vanadate, $NaVO_3$) in which the element is pentavalent. Vanadyl salts are converted by oxidizing agents (such as bromine water, acid permanganate) to vanadates, and the latter can be reduced back again to vanadyl compounds by reducing agents (e.g. passage of sulphur dioxide through hot dilute sulphuric acid solutions, or evaporation with concentrated hydrochloric acid).

BELCHER and his co-workers [386] have described a test for vanadates based upon the red–violet colour given by vanadates in N sulphuric acid solution with a 1 per cent solution of 3:3′-dimethylnaphthidine in glacial acetic acid. When carried out as a spot test, as little as 2 p.p.m. of vanadium can be detected. Other oxidizing agents (e.g. chromates, permanganates) must be absent since they react in a similar way. The most sensitive qualitative test for vanadium (detecting 0·1 p.p.m. or even less) is that described by BACH[387] and depends upon the reaction between vanadates and 8-hydroxy–quinoline in dilute acetic acid solution to give a violet–black complex $(C_9H_6ON)_4V_2O_3$, which can be extracted by *iso*-amyl alcohol giving a red solution. This test can be adapted to the quantitative determination of vanadium[388, 389]. A Lovibond comparator disc is available for the visual determination by this method, enabling as little as 0·2 p.p.m. of vanadium to be determined in a 50 ml. sample[134A, 139]. Interference due to limited amounts of iron (up to 100 μg) can be prevented by adding sodium pyrophosphate and interference from titanium by adding sodium fluoride. Copper interferes and must be removed.

A volumetric method for determining vanadium in quantities ranging from 10–1000 p.p.m. has been described by SWOPE, HATTMAN and PELLKOFER[390]; it involves oxidation of the vanadium to vanadate by means of permanganate, addition of a known excess of ferrous sulphate, and back-titration with 0·006N ceric sulphate.

Zinc[1–3]

Zinc is found in zinc-mine wastes and in rivers in the vicinity of such mines, in wastes from factories making zinc compounds, in zinc plating wastes, galvanizing wastes, viscose rayon wastes, and wastes from the manufacture of rubber. Zinc compounds are very toxic to fish.

Although numerous satisfactory reagents, which are almost specific or at any rate highly selective, are available for most of the common metals found in trade wastes and river water, there is a scarcity of good tests for small amounts of zinc.

One of the oldest tests for zinc depends on the white turbidity obtained when the acidified sample is treated with a solution of potassium ferrocyanide[4]. The turbidity is caused by the formation of insoluble potassium zinc ferrocyanide and as little as 0·4 p.p.m. of zinc can be detected in a colourless water. More than traces of iron and copper as well as metals forming sparingly soluble ferrocyanides cause interference.

The most satisfactory test for traces of zinc is based upon the use of dithizone. On shaking a sample with a 0·001 per cent solution of dithizone in carbon tetrachloride for about 2 minutes, the green colour of the reagent changes to violet or red if zinc is present. According to FISCHER and LEOPOLDI[391] interference by other heavy metals (e.g. copper, cadmium, lead, silver and mercury) is prevented by carrying out the test at pH 4·5–5·0 in the presence of sodium thiosulphate. This procedure[132, 133] is now generally used for the estimation of zinc in amounts down to about 0·01 p.p.m. Modifications of the method have been recommended by the ABCM-SAC Joint Committee[392] and have been applied by Butts and his associates[322] to the colorimetric determination of zinc in sewage and trade wastes and by MURACA and his co-workers[393] to the colorimetric determination of zinc in plating waste waters.

The ferrocyanide method has been much employed in the past for the turbidimetric estimation of zinc in potable waters; the procedure is only satisfactory in the case of clear colourless waters of low organic content and containing less than 1 p.p.m. of iron and less than 0·5 p.p.m. of copper[4].

RUSH and YOE[394] have discovered a sensitive new reagent for zinc with the rather formidable names o-{2-[α-(2-hydroxy–5-sulphophenylazo)-benzylidene] hydrazino} benzoic acid, or, 2-carboxy-2'-hydroxy-5'-sulphoformazylbenzene. It has the following structure,

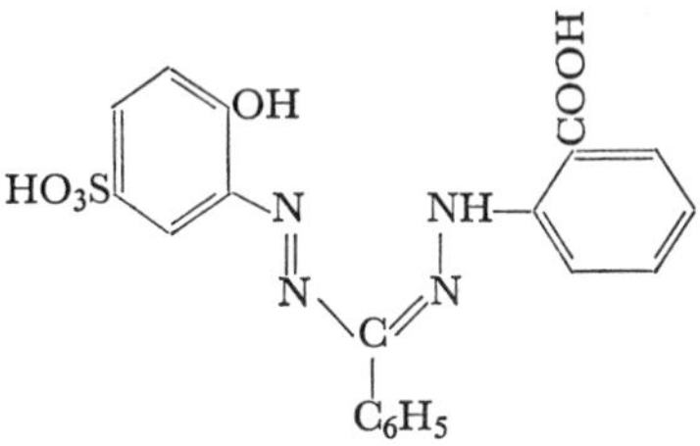

and the authors wisely propose to call it 'zincon' for short. Zinc in alkaline solution (pH 8·5–9·5) and copper at pH 5·0–9·5 both give a blue colour with the reagent but owing to the difference in the effect of pH on the colour formation it is possible to estimate zinc and copper in the presence of each other since only copper reacts in slightly acid solution. In the determination of zinc in a solution buffered at pH 9·0, Beer's law is followed over the range 0·1–2·4 p.p.m. of zinc. Although the reagent is not quite so sensitive as dithizone, it has the advantage of avoiding tedious extraction. If appreciable amounts of interfering metals are present (e.g. iron, chromium, manganese and nickel), it is advisable to separate the zinc with an ion-exchange resin.

A newer method for the estimation of traces of zinc in waters has been described by HOUGHTON[395]. In sulphuric acid solution (pH 1·7)* containing thiocyanate, the dye Brilliant Green,

$$N(C_2H_5)_2 \cdot C_6H_4 \cdot C(C_6H_5):C_6H_4:N(C_2H_5)_2HSO_4,$$

produces over the range 0–20 μg of zinc a colour change from slight greenish-yellow to blue-green†. Fluoride is used to inhibit the influence of ferric iron and gum acacia is added to prevent turbidity.

---

* The amount of acid required is critical.
† For visual work, it has been found in the Mersey River Board laboratory better to use $\frac{1}{10}$ of the amount of dye recommended by Houghton.

The effect of 1 μg of zinc in 50 ml. (0·02 p.p.m.) is clearly visible in Nessler tubes. Small amounts of ferrous iron do not interfere and up to 10 p.p.m. of aluminium and lead have no effect. The influence of copper (up to 3 p.p.m.) is slight and is obviated by adding sodium diethyldithiocarbamate.

CHAPTER 9

VARIOUS CARBON COMPOUNDS: CYANIDE, THIOCYANATE, CYANATE, FORMALDEHYDE, PHENOLS, TAR BASES, HYDROCARBONS, SYNTHETIC INSECTICIDES, SYNTHETIC DETERGENTS, FATS AND GREASE

CYANIDE[1, 2, 3, 133, 274]

CYANIDES are likely to occur in dangerous concentrations in waste waters from electroplating, gold-mining and gilding, in waste waters from the case-hardening of steel, in effluents from gas works and coke ovens, in wastes from the surface cleaning of various metals with cyanides, and in effluents from the scrubbing of gases produced from blast furnaces.

In view of the extremely toxic effects of cyanides on fish (as little as 0·03 p.p.m., expressed as HCN, can be fatal) the importance of using very sensitive as well as specific methods for the detection and estimation of cyanides needs little emphasis.

Cyanide can be present as 'free cyanide', for instance as HCN and the simple metallic cyanides like KCN or NaCN. Less frequently, it is present in the form of stable complex cyanides, such as $K_4Fe(CN)_6$ and $K_3Co(CN)_6$, which do not exhibit the reactions of the simple cyanides, but some complex cyanides (e.g. potassium zinc cyanide) are relatively unstable and do show the reactions of the simple cyanides. If so-called 'total cyanide' (i.e. 'free cyanide' plus cyanide present as complex salts) is required, the complex cyanide must first be broken down to a simple cyanide by distillation with one of the following reagents:

(i) a hydrochloric acid solution of cuprous chloride[1, 274],
(ii) tartaric acid[2],
(iii) Mercuric chloride, magnesium chloride and sulphuric acid[2, 396] (Serfass method),
(iv) lead acetate[274], or lead nitrate[20] (this treatment does not decompose ferrocyanide, and complex nickel and copper cyanides only distil slowly),
(v) phosphoric acid in the presence of citric acid and ethylene diamine tetra-acetic acid[397] (probably the best procedure).

The presence of free cyanide generally betrays itself by a

characteristic bitter almond odour but unfortunately many persons are relatively insensitive to this smell. A modification of the Prussian blue test suggested by RATHENASINKAM [398] will detect as little as 0·4 p.p.m. of HCN; a strip of filter paper is treated with a drop of 10 per cent ferrous sulphate and a drop of 10 per cent caustic soda, and is suspended for about 10 minutes over the acidified sample in a glass-stoppered flask when the liberated HCN diffuses and reacts to form ferrocyanide on the paper so that when the paper is immersed in hot dilute hydrochloric acid a blue or blue–green stain of Prussian blue appears.

Smaller quantities of cyanide can be detected by the benzidine–pyridine method of ALDRIDGE [399], which, according to KRAWCZYK [400], gives a perceptible orange coloration with as little as 0·1 p.p.m. of HCN using a 100 ml. sample.

The Aldridge method [399] is one of the best methods for the estimation of traces of cyanide; it is an example of the KÖNIG synthesis [401] in which cyanogen bromide (or chloride) gives a dye by reaction with pyridine and an aromatic amine (cf. under Tar Bases, page 94). The cyanide is first converted to cyanogen bromide by means of bromine water in dilute acetic acid solution:

$$HCN + Br_2 = CNBr + HBr$$

After removing the excess of bromine with sodium arsenite, the cyanogen bromide is allowed to react with pyridine and benzidine in dilute hydrochloric acid solution; a quaternary compound of cyanogen bromide and pyridine is formed which condenses with benzidine* to give a di-anil derivative having an intense orange to red colour which can be determined photometrically or by comparison with standards [1, 3, 18]. Discs designed for use with both the Lovibond comparator and the B.D.H. Lovibond nesslerizer can be applied to the visual determination within the range 0·01–1·0 p.p.m. of HCN [140]. The method can usually be applied without any preliminary distillation procedure since the complex cyanides of zinc, cadmium and copper react easily [1]. Thiocyanate reacts in the same way as cyanide (since it is also converted to CNBr by bromine). Hence if both cyanide and thiocyanate are present, the determination should be repeated after the sample has been aerated to remove cyanide as volatile HCN. Cyanide can also be separated from thiocyanate (as well as from complex cyanides) by extraction from acid solution as HCN with isopropyl ether and can then be recovered from the ether extract by shaking with aqueous sodium hydroxide [397].

If the sample is coloured and turbid, or contains interfering substances, or has a very low content of cyanide, the modification of

* See footnote on p. 46.

Aldridge's method suggested by Nusbaum and Skupeko[402] can be used with advantage; this involves the extraction of the orange colour with *n*-butyl alcohol and permits the determination of cyanide in polluted waters containing only 0·02–0·5 p.p.m. of HCN.

Another very sensitive method for cyanide based upon the König synthesis is due to Epstein[397, 403, 404]. The cyanide is converted by chloramine-T to cyanogen chloride which is allowed to react with pyridine containing 1-phenyl-3-methyl-5-pyrazolone and a small proportion of *bis*-(1-phenyl-3-methyl-5-pyrazolone) to give a blue colour*. The procedure is recommended in the latest revision of the A.P.H.A. *Standard Methods*[2].

Other colorimetric methods for determining cyanide are based on the formation of red ferric thiocyanate[405] and on the production of Prussian blue[406] but these procedures are rather time-consuming and not very sensitive. Methods involving the oxidation in alkaline solution (pH 10–11) of phenolphthalin or cresolphthalin to the corresponding red phthalein by cupric ions in the presence of cyanide[1, 407–409] were popular at one time but unfortunately are not specific for cyanide. The method was, however, applied by the Water Pollution Research Laboratory in a special investigation involving the determination of concentrations of cyanide as low as 0·05 p.p.m., the pink colour being measured in 20 cm cells in a Spekker absorptiometer[410].

Schilt[410A] has recently described a new colorimetric method for cyanide which is stated to be accurate, highly sensitive to traces of cyanide and subject to fewer interferences than the other methods. Ferroin (prepared from ferrous ammonium sulphate and 1:10-phenanthroline) is allowed to react with cyanide at pH 9·2–9·7 to give a violet complex, dicyano-*bis*-(1:10-phenanthroline)-iron (II), which can be extracted with chloroform and determined spectro-photometrically at 597 mμ.

One of the oldest volumetric methods for determining cyanides is that of Liebig in which the cyanide solution is titrated with silver nitrate to form a soluble complex alkali argentocyanide[122–124]:

$$2 \, KCN + AgNO_3 = KAg(CN)_2 + KNO_3$$
or,
$$2CN^- + Ag^+ = [Ag(CN)_2]^-$$

When all the cyanide has reacted, the slightest excess of silver nitrate produces a turbidity due to precipitation of silver cyanide:

$$KAg(CN)_2 + AgNO_3 = 2AgCN + KNO_3$$

The completion of the first stage (i.e. the formation of the alkali argentocyanide) is thus indicated by the first appearance of a turbidity. This end-point is not always easy to see especially if

---

* The presence of a small amount of the *bis*-pyrazolone is necessary to stabilise the colour.

the sample is not clear. To overcome this difficulty, a simple modification first proposed by RYAN and CULSHAW [411] can be used; the titration of the cyanide, adjusted to pH 10–11 with sodium hydroxide, is carried out in the presence of a few drops of a dilute solution of *p*-dimethylaminobenzylidene-rhodanine in acetone, when at the end-point the slightest excess of silver nitrate causes a colour change from yellow to salmon-pink [2]. As little as 1 p.p.m. of HCN can be determined by this method (using a micro-burette and a dilute standard silver nitrate), whilst high concentrations are determined by using stronger silver nitrate. Chlorides do not interfere with the method. Dithizone has also been proposed as an indicator for this titration [411A].

THIOCYANATE AND CYANATE

Thiocyanates may be present in gas liquor from a gas works but the amounts are nowadays usually small. They also occur in some plating wastes.

Thiocyanates can be detected by the wine-red coloration they give with ferric chloride in hydrochloric acid solution. This test can be made the basis of an approximate colorimetric determination; cyanides do not interfere but mercury salts, fluorides and organic hydroxy-acids should be absent [1, 3, 18, 19, 274].

As already indicated (page 84), Aldridge's method can be used for the determination of traces of thiocyanate; if cyanide is present, it can be removed by aerating the sample acidified with acetic acid [1].

A colorimetric method for thiocyanate sensitive to 0·5 p.p.m. of CNS′ or even less has been described by KRUSE and MELLON [404] and is based upon the formation of a complex copper pyridine thiocyanate, $Cu(C_5H_5N)_2(CNS)_2$, which can be extracted by chloroform to yield a yellow solution. Cyanide interferes and must be removed.

If thiocyanate is present in fair quantity, it can be estimated by precipitation as cuprous thiocyanate which is either titrated with standard potassium iodate in fairly concentrated hydrochloric acid solution in the presence of chloroform [19] (an adaptation of the Andrews–Jamieson method), or, is decomposed with caustic soda, acidified with nitric acid and titrated with silver nitrate using iron alum as indicator [20].

Cyanates, which can occur in certain plating wastes, have been determined by a modification of Epstein's cyanide method [404]. A simpler method, suggested by GARDNER *et al.* [412], involves removal of ammonia by boiling with excess of caustic soda and sodium sulphide, hydrolysis of the cyanate to ammonia by boiling with acid, and estimation of the ammonia so formed by means of Nessler's reagent.

FORMALDEHYDE

Formaldehyde occurs in wastes from the manufacture of synthetic resins and plastics, in some tannery wastes and in penicillin wastes. It is a reducing agent and strongly bactericidal, and is, therefore, an undesirable constituent of river waters.

Formaldehyde gives a blue to greenish–blue colour with a 0·5 per cent solution of carbazole in pure concentrated sulphuric acid[413]. This test, which can detect as little as 0·01 mg of formaldehyde, can be carried out either as a spot test, or better, in a test-tube as a 'ring' test in such a way that the carbazole–sulphuric acid reagent forms a layer underneath the sample.

A specific test for formaldehyde not given by other aldehydes is described by Feigl[136]. It depends on the violet colour produced when formaldehyde is heated at 60° C, for about 10 minutes with a fairly concentrated sulphuric acid solution of chromotropic acid (1:8-dihydroxynaphthalene–3:6-disulphonic acid).

Methods for the colorimetric determination of small amounts of formaldehyde are reviewed by REYNOLDS and IRWIN[414]. The method using chromotropic acid appears to be the most specific and involves heating the sample with chromotropic acid in 72 per cent sulphuric acid at 60° C for 10 minutes, or in a boiling water bath for 30 minutes, and comparing the violet colour with that of a series of standards, or measuring it absorptiometrically[415]. Most other aldehydes, with the exception of acrolein, do not interfere unless present in large proportion. As little as 1 p.p.m. of formaldehyde can be estimated by this method.

SCHRYVER's method for determining formaldehyde[131, 416, 417], though not so specific as the chromotropic acid procedure, is easier to carry out and is more sensitive. It is based upon the intensity of the magenta colour obtained when very dilute solutions of formaldehyde are treated with phenylhydrazine hydrochloride and potassium ferricyanide and then acidified with hydrochloric acid. The colour can be compared with that of a series of standards, or measured absorptiometrically[418]. In another modification of the method[419], the colour is extracted with n-butyl alcohol, and determined photometrically at 520 mμ, thus enabling formaldehyde to be estimated in the range 0·1–0·7 p.p.m. even in the presence of iron which normally interferes. The method is said to be improved by using 15N sulphuric acid for acidification instead of hydrochloric acid[420].

NASH[421] has shown that when traces of formaldehyde are added to solutions of acetylacetone ($CH_3CO \cdot CH_2CO \cdot CH_3$) in the presence of excess of ammonium salts at pH about 5·5–6·5 (ammonium acetate–acetic acid buffer), a yellow coloration develops due to the formation of a pyridine derivative, diacetyldihydrolutidine (Hantzsch pyridine synthesis):

$$
\begin{array}{ll}
\underset{\displaystyle CH_3\!-\!CO\!-\!CH_2}{\overset{\displaystyle \underset{|}{\overset{CH_2}{\underset{O}{|}}}}{}} & \text{(formaldehyde)} \\[1em]
CH_3\!-\!\overset{|}{CO} & \\[1em]
CH_2\!-\!CO\!-\!CH_3 & \text{(2 molecules of} \\
\overset{|}{CO\!-\!CH_3} & \quad \text{acetylacetone)} \\[1em]
NH_3 & \text{(ammonia)}
\end{array}
$$

$$\downarrow\ -3H_2O$$

Diacetyldihydrolutidine

A method based on this reaction, suitable for the photometric determination of traces of formaldehyde up to 8 p.p.m., is recommended by the ABCM-SAC Joint Committee[3, 274].

Volumetric methods[15, 124] are preferable when large amounts of formaldehyde are present. Reactions suitable for this purpose are:

(a) oxidation of formaldehyde by H_2O_2 in presence of caustic soda to sodium formate,

(b) formation of hexamethylene tetramine by the action of ammonium chloride and caustic soda on formaldehyde.

In both cases, the unused caustic soda is estimated by titration with hydrochloric acid.

PHENOLS ('Tar acids')[1-3, 6]

Phenols are derivatives of benzene and other aromatic hydrocarbons in which one or more hydroxyl groups replace hydrogen atoms and so are directly attached to the aromatic ring. Phenols thus contain one or more of the $\geqslant$C—OH groups; if one hydroxyl group is present, the phenol is said to be 'monohydric', if more than one hydroxyl group is present, the phenol may be dihydric, trihydric, etc., or more generally 'polyhydric'. Monohydric and polyhydric phenols are often designated as 'tar acids' and 'higher tar acids' respectively in gasworks practice. A few typical examples of phenols are given in *Table 8*.

Table 8. Typical examples of phenols

Monohydric phenols	Dihydric phenols	Trihydric phenols

Phenol, C_6H_5OH or

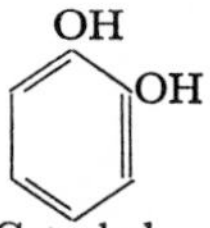

Catechol

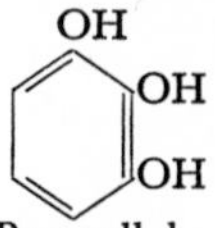

Pyrogallol

Cresols, $CH_3C_6H_4OH$ (3 isomers)

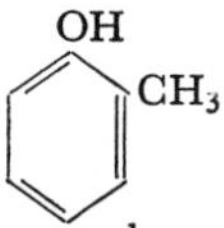

o-cresol

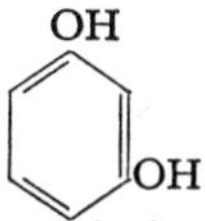

Resorcinol

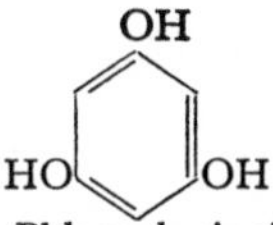

Phloroglucinol

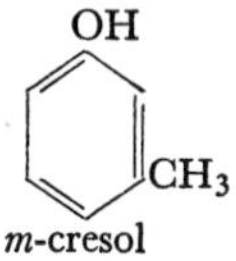

m-cresol

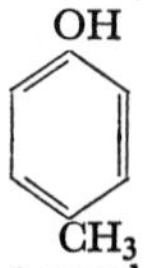

p-cresol

Quinol

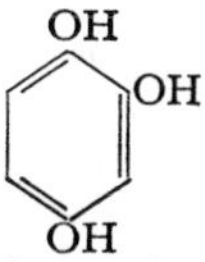

Hydroxyquinol

Xylenols, $(CH_3)_2C_6H_3OH$ (6 isomers)

Pentachlorophenol

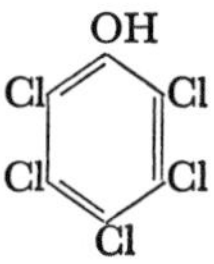

α-naphthol (1-hydroxy-naphthalene)

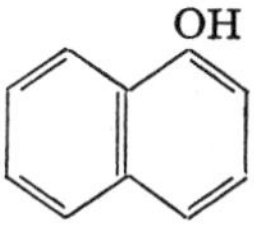

β-naphthol (2-hydroxy-naphthalene)

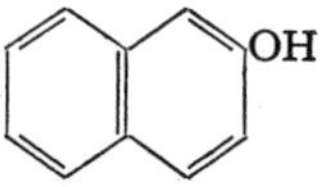

Ordinary phenol, the three cresols, the xylenols, as well as many polyhydric phenols are present in coal-tar and gas liquor. Phenols are also found in synthetic resin and plastics wastes, rubber-proofing wastes, cutting-oil wastes, drainage from tarred roads, commercial disinfectants, many chemical wastes, dye manufacturing wastes, and certain wastes from the dyeing and finishing of rayon (where phenols are used as delustreing agents).

The presence of phenols in a stream is objectionable because of their strong bactericidal action, their toxicity to fish and the unpleasant tastes and odours produced when water containing phenols is chlorinated.

Phenols generally impart to a sample a characteristic 'disinfectant' odour. One of the oldest tests for phenols is the Millon reaction[422] in which the sample is heated with a freshly prepared solution of mercury in nitric acid when, in the presence of phenols, * a red colour develops. In place of Millon's reagent, which does not keep well, NASSE[423] recommends the employment of an aqueous solution of mercuric acetate, to which a few drops of dilute sodium nitrite and of dilute acetic acid are added when the test is to be performed. Another sensitive test for phenols, first applied to proteins containing tyrosine, is due to FOLIN and CIOCALTEU[424] who use a reagent containing a mixture of phosphotungstic and phosphomolybdic acids which is reduced by phenols in the presence of sodium carbonate to blue products of lower valency. The method can be adapted to quantitative work[131] but unfortunately is not specific for phenols as many other reducing compounds behave in a similar way.

A useful review of methods for the quantitative determination of phenols is given in the *Chemical Age*.[425] For many years, the standard method used in this country for the estimation of phenols (monohydric as well as polyhydric)† has been that of Fox and GAUGE[426]. This involves the coupling of the phenol in caustic soda solution with freshly diazotized sulphanilic acid, obtained by the action of sodium nitrite on a cooled solution of sulphanilic acid in dilute sulphuric acid. A yellow or orange azo dyestuff is thus produced; in the case of phenol itself the reactions taking place can be represented by the following equations:

Diazotization: $2SO_3H \cdot C_6H_4 \cdot NH_2 + 2HNO_2 + H_2SO_4$
$$= 4H_2O + (SO_3H \cdot C_6H_4N_2)_2SO_4$$
sulphanilic acid diazonium sulphate

* The test was originally applied to proteins which give the reaction on account of the presence of tyrosine (a phenol) in the molecule.

† A preliminary distillation carried out at pH 8 enables the volatile monohydric phenols to be estimated.

Coupling: $(SO_3H \cdot C_6H_4 \cdot N_2)_2SO_4 + 2C_6H_5OH$
$$= H_2SO_4 + 2SO_3H \cdot C_6H_4 \cdot N : N \cdot C_6H_4OH$$
azo dye

The method is simple and rapid and makes use of cheap, easily available reagents which are stable and can be purchased in a high state of purity. The shade of colour produced, however, does depend upon the particular phenol present. For example, phenol itself gives a yellow dye, the mixed cresols a yellow–orange dye, the xylenols a rather deeper orange colour, and the naphthols a reddish colour. As a rule, the phenols in polluted waters, road drainage and gas liquor give a yellow–orange colour in the test and it is therefore customary in practice to use a mixture of the three cresols containing 35 per cent of the *ortho* compound, 40 per cent of the *meta* compound and 25 per cent of the *para* compound in the preparation of standards for the colour comparison[131, 426]. A B.D.H. nesslerizer disc is standardized on this mixture and covers the range $0 \cdot 1 - 0 \cdot 9$ p.p.m. of cresols if a 50 ml. sample is used[139, 140]. A disadvantage of the method is that when some of the higher phenols are present, orange, orange–red or reddish colours may be produced and matching may be difficult unless special standards are prepared by trial from xylenols, naphthols or mixtures of these[19, 131] yielding a colour similar in tint to that given by the sample. The Fox–Gauge test can often be applied directly without any pre-treatment. Some samples containing interfering vegetable tannins (which contain phenolic groupings) should be pre-treated by extraction of the acidified sample with chloroform which dissolves the phenols but not the tannins; the phenols can then be recovered from the chloroform extract by shaking with aqueous sodium hydroxide. The Fox–Gauge method has been criticized on account of lack of reproducibility but satisfactory results are generally obtained if due attention is paid to certain details, namely:

(*1*) the diazotization must be carried out in well cooled solution, preferably using ice;

(*2*) the diazonium compound when once prepared should be used within 5–10 minutes of preparation;

(*3*) the amount of sodium hydroxide specified in the test should be strictly adhered to, consequently samples which are acid or alkaline should be first neutralized.

The Fox-Gauge method is recommended by the Ministry[1] for the determination of total phenols (monohydric + polyhydric).

A rapid photometric method of similar type to the Fox-Gauge method, but more sensitive to low concentrations of phenols, and substituting *p*-nitraniline for sulphanilic acid (i.e. the electrophilic NO_2 group replacing the electrophilic HSO_3 group) is described and strongly recommended by BEIER [427] who applies it to the determination of phenols in waste waters from coke and gas works.

In the U.S.A., the GIBBS method[2, 428] for the determination of phenols has achieved much popularity. The phenol is allowed to react with 2:6-dibromoquinone chloroimide in a solution buffered at pH about 9·4, when an indophenol dye is produced having in the alkaline solution a blue, green or purple colour depending on the nature of the phenol. The reaction in the case of ordinary phenol can be expressed by the equation:

$$O:C_6H_2Br_2:NCl + C_6H_5OH = O:C_6H_2Br_2:N \cdot C_6H_4OH + HCl$$
$$\text{2:6-dibromoquinone} \qquad \text{indophenol dye}$$
$$\text{chloroimide}$$

ETTINGER and RUCHHOFT [429] claim to have improved the sensitivity of the method and increased the stability of the colour by extracting the coloured product with n-butyl alcohol but RIEHL and WILL [430] have not reported favourably on this modification. The Gibbs method, although very sensitive, has several disadvantages. Thus, the full development of the colour takes place only when the samples have been standing at least one hour. Again, the shade of colour obtained varies with different phenols; phenol and m-cresol give a blue colour, o-cresol a purple colour, while p-cresol gives no colour at all.* Moreover, the pH must be fairly closely controlled in the region of pH 9·4 by buffering with borax, and any marked variation may lead to an alteration in shade. It is also essential to use a *freshly prepared* alcoholic solution of the reagent. Riehl and Will [430] even state that the solid reagent deteriorates on keeping and that it is therefore advisable to purchase the compound only in small quantities at a time. Amines interfere with the method and sulphides prevent colour development.

Another method of obtaining the same indophenol dyes was worked out by HOUGHTON and PELLY [431] and further studied by HILL and HERNDON [432]; they produced these dyes by mixing dimethyl-p-phenylene diamine (p-aminodimethylaniline), prepared as required by reduction of p-nitrosodimethylaniline with zinc dust, with the sample buffered with sodium bicarbonate, and then oxidizing to the indophenol with sodium hypochlorite. This procedure has many of the disadvantages of the Gibbs method, and in addition suffers from other defects, such as the trouble involved in the preparation of the unstable amine, and the careful control necessary to prevent bleaching of the dye by any excess of hypochlorite. NUSBAUM [433], however, has recently much improved and simplified this method. The troublesome preparation of the amine

---

* The method therefore gives low results with gas liquors and other samples containing p-cresol.

is avoided by using p-amino-dimethylaniline oxalate, which is now available commercially and unlike the other salts of p-amino-dimethylaniline is stable and does not oxidize or discolour on keeping. Sodium hypochlorite as an oxidizing agent is replaced by potassium ferricyanide which does not interfere when present in excess and also serves to oxidize any interfering sulphides. The final pH is kept at about 8·3–8·7 with a borax buffer, and the colour, after 15 minutes, is extracted with isoamyl alcohol or, better, chloroform. Although amines interfere, they can be removed by shaking the sample with a strongly acidic ion-exchange resin and filtering. A similar method is recommended for monohydric phenols by the ABCM-SAC Joint Committee[434], carbon tetrachloride being used to extract the colour.

Another colorimetric method for estimating phenols depends upon the interaction of phenols in alkaline solution (pH 9·6–10·0) with 4-amino-antipyrine (4-aminophenazone) in the presence of an oxidizing agent (potassium ferricyanide) to give an intense red coloration[435–437]. In the case of phenol itself, the reaction is believed to take place as follows[438, 324]:

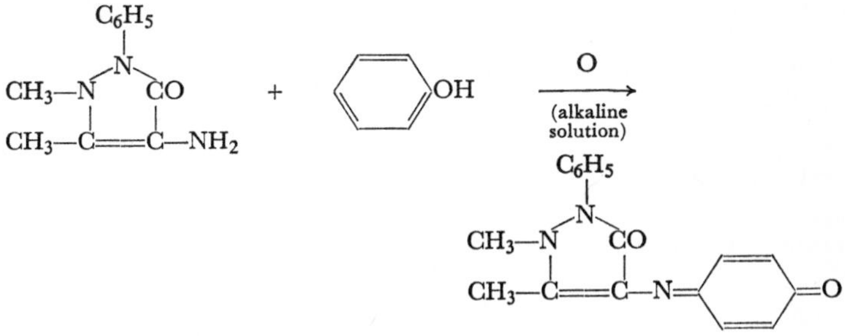

The method has some disadvantages, e.g. aromatic amines react, phenols containing alkyl, aryl, nitro, and many other groups in the $para$ position do not react, oxidizing and reducing agents as well as substances reacting with ferricyanide must be absent and the intensity of the coloration depends upon the nature of the phenol. Despite these defects the method has been recommended as one of the standard procedures in the A.P.H.A. $Standard\ Methods$[2] and some workers[439] regard it as the quickest, most precise and most accurate method for phenols. It is stated to be sensitive to as little as 0·02 p.p.m. of phenol[440].

When relatively large amounts of phenols are present, (e.g. more than 20 p.p.m.), a volumetric method of estimation by bromination may be used[1, 3, 15, 17, 19]:

$$C_6H_5OH + 3Br_2 = C_6H_2Br_3OH + 3HBr$$
$$s\text{-tribromophenol}$$

The phenol is treated with excess of $n/10$ bromine ($n/10$ $KBrO_3$ + KBr + hydrochloric acid) and the unused bromine is determined by adding potassium iodide and titrating the liberated iodine with sodium thiosulphate. The results can be expressed in terms of phenol, or in terms of bromine absorbed. The method is not specific and may yield high results since many organic compounds besides phenols react with bromine.

In concluding this section on phenols, it must be emphasized that only some of the methods reviewed give a reasonable proportion of the total phenols (monohydric + polyhydric), for instance the Fox-Gauge method (without a preliminary distillation) and the bromination method. Most of the other methods determine only the monohydric phenols. If it is desired to assess the extent to which phenols are removed from phenolic wastes receiving aerobic biological treatment, it is essential to select a sensitive method giving *total* phenols since polyhydric phenols, being more resistant to biological oxidation than are monohydric phenols, may appear in the final effluent.

Tar bases (e.g. pyridine, quinoline, *iso*-quinoline and acridine) are present in coal-tar, in effluents from gas works and coke ovens, in oil refinery waste waters, and in rivers polluted by these various wastes. Tar bases are toxic to fish and tend to impart unpleasant tastes and odours to surface waters.

In the picrate method of determining moderate quantities of these bases, proposed by Fox and Gauge[6, 426,] the sample is rendered alkaline with sodium hydroxide and the tar bases are extracted with chloroform. The chloroform layer is then shaken with dilute sulphuric acid when the bases pass to the upper acid layer and are isolated by making the acid slightly alkaline with sodium hydroxide and extracting with chloroform. The chloroform extract containing the tar bases is then dried with anhydrous sodium sulphate, filtered into a beaker containing a known amount of dry picric acid, evaporated slowly, dried at 70° C and the picrates weighed.

The determination of *traces* of pyridine (0·005–1·0 p.p.m.) and other tar bases in polluted rivers is best carried out by the method proposed by KRONER, ETTINGER and MOORE[441]. This method is based upon the König synthesis[401] already mentioned in connection with the Aldridge method of estimating cyanide (page 84) i.e. addition of cyanogen bromide to the pyridine or pyridine base, followed by condensation with an aromatic amine ($R \cdot NH_2$) in accordance with the scheme:

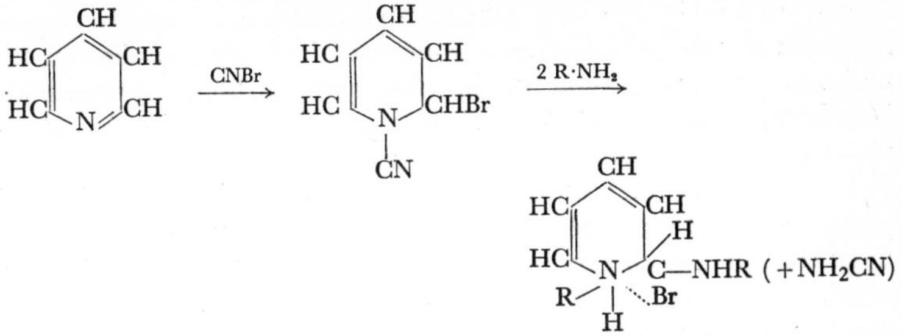

The aromatic amine used is benzidine, or 4:4′-diamino-diphenyl $(NH_2 \cdot C_6H_4 \cdot C_6H_4 \cdot NH_2)$. The pyridine is first isolated from the sample by distillation and is buffered with sodium acetate to pH 6–8 and then allowed to react with cyanogen bromide and benzidine hydrochloride. The red dye so produced is extracted with butyl alcohol and estimated colorimetrically.

HYDROCARBONS

Many polynuclear hydrocarbons (e.g. naphthalene, anthracene, pyrene, 3:4-benzpyrene, etc.) occur in coal tar, in small quantities in gas works effluents, and in sewage effluents derived from sewage containing gas liquor:

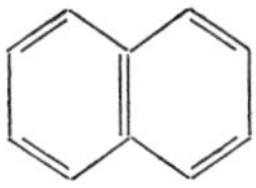

naphthalene, $C_{10}H_8$

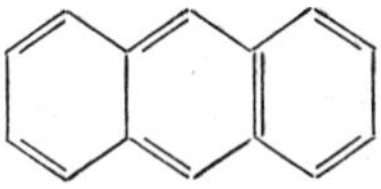

anthracene, $C_{14}H_{10}$

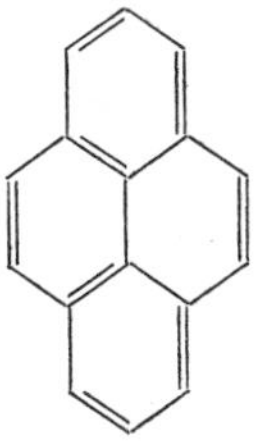

pyrene, $C_{16}H_{10}$

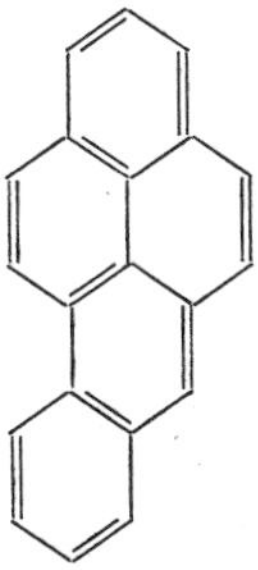

3:4-benzpyrene, $C_{20}H_{12}$

WEDGWOOD [442] [443], and WEDGWOOD and COOPER [444-447], by a combination of chromatographic and spectroscopic techniques, have developed a method of separating, identifying and estimating traces of polynuclear hydrocarbons in various effluents. The absorption spectra are measured by means of a Unicam spectrophotometer and compared with those of the pure hydrocarbons. Pyrene, for instance, has a very characteristic absorption peak in the ultra-violet region at a wavelength of 335 mμ.

A colorimetric method of determining naphthalene in industrial wastes has been described by MEDIN and HERNDON[448] and depends upon the blue colour produced when anhydrous aluminium chloride is added to a chloroform solution of naphthalene. The method can be used over the range 0·2–200 p.p.m. of naphthalene. Water interferes, consequently all apparatus must be carefully dried and the chloroform solution dried over anhydrous alumina. Phenols and anthracene do not interfere but sulphides must be removed with silver nitrate and sodium hydroxide.

SYNTHETIC INSECTICIDES

Numerous synthetic insecticides are now known and are toxic in very small concentrations not only to insects but also to fish. Sensitive methods for the estimation of traces of these compounds are therefore much needed. The most widely known of the newer insecticides are DDT and the γ-isomer of benzene hexachloride. These two insecticides have been used at sewage filter installations for controlling and destroying certain flies (especially the species *Psychoda* and *Anisopus*) which are such a nuisance during the warmer months of the year.

BERCK[449] has described a colorimetric method suitable for the determination of concentrations of DDT as low as 0·003 p.p.m. in river water and suspended solids. It is based upon the Schechter–Haller method[450] in which the DDT, after preliminary isolation by extraction with a mixture of ether and *n*-hexane, is nitrated to a polynitro derivative, a benzene solution of which gives an intense blue colour with sodium methoxide dissolved in methyl alcohol. It is to be noted that solids suspended in streams, such as clay, silt, and very fine sand, can easily adsorb DDT[449].

A method for the estimation of traces of the γ-isomer of benzene hexachloride ('gammexane') has been described by SCHECHTER and HORNSTEIN[451]. The water or effluent is first extracted with carbon tetrachloride to dissolve the insecticide and the extract is evaporated at as low a temperature as possible to remove the solvent. The benzene hexachloride is then dechlorinated to benzene by treatment with zinc and acetic acid and the benzene is absorbed in a mixture of nitric and sulphuric acids. The *m*-dinitrobenzene so formed is allowed to react with methyl ethyl ketone and alkali to give a reddish–violet coloration, the intensity of which is measured photometrically. The various chemical reactions must be performed in a special all-glass apparatus. As little as 0·005 mg of the insecticide can be estimated by this method. HANCOCK and LAWS[452] isolate benzene hexachloride from large volumes of effluents by adsorption on purified activated charcoal; the insecticide is then determined by a modified Schechter–Hornstein procedure using a simplified dechlorination and nitration apparatus. Other common chlorinated insecticides cause no interference with the method but aromatic hydrocarbons (e.g. benzene, toluene and xylene) interfere. In the presence of these hydrocarbons, the determinations are carried out with and without addition of zinc to enable a correction to be applied.

SYNTHETIC DETERGENTS ('SYNDETS')

The widespread use of synthetic detergents for domestic and industrial purposes, the consequent presence of small amounts of synthetic detergents in sewage effluents, trade wastes and river waters, the objectionable tendency of these detergents to cause persistent foam on streams and at sewage plants, and the toxicity of these detergents towards fish and aquatic flora, make it very important to find suitable methods for their estimation.

Many hundreds of syndets are now known. They are generally classified into three main groups based upon their behaviour on ionization in aqueous solution:

(1) *Anionic detergents*

These ionize in aqueous solution giving a negatively charged group (anion), e.g. $R \cdot O\overline{S}O_3$ (where R = a long hydrocarbon chain such as $CH_3(CH_2)_n$), and a positively charged ion (usually sodium).
Examples: (a) Primary and secondary sodium alkyl sulphates (Dreft, Teepol), $R{-}\overset{-}{O}SO_3 \ldots \overset{+}{N}a$
(b) Sodium alkylbenzene sulphonates (Tide, Daz), $R{-}C_6H_4{-}\overset{-}{S}O_3 \ldots \overset{+}{N}a$

(2) *Non-ionic detergents*

These do not ionize at all in aqueous solution.
Examples: Polyglycol ethers of alkylated phenols (Lissapol N, Stergene), $R{-}C_6H_4{-}(C_2H_4O)_n{-}OH$

(3) *Cationic detergents*

These are salts of strong quaternary organic bases and ionize giving a positively charged quaternary ammonium or pyridinium group (cation) and a negatively charged group.

Examples:—(a) $\dfrac{R_1}{R_2}\!\!\big\rangle(CH_3)_2\overset{+}{N}\ldots\overset{-}{Cl}$

(R$_1$ and R$_2$ are long hydrocarbon chains)

(b) $C_{16}H_{33}\!-\!\overset{+}{N}\ldots\overset{-}{Br}$

cetylpyridinium bromide

These have strong bactericidal properties and are used to some extent for washing utensils and equipment in hotels, restaurants and food factories. They are too expensive for general use.

The commercial detergents sold for household and industrial use are usually mixed with other substances ('builders') in order to improve their detergent action, e.g. sodium tripolyphosphate and other phosphates, sodium sulphate, sodium carbonate, sodium perborate, sodium silicate, and sodium carboxymethyl cellulose.

According to a Report of the Committee on Synthetic Detergents[453], the most popular detergents are the anionic types which comprise about 95% of the total usage, the remaining 5% being chiefly the non-ionic types. Of the anionic types made at present, the alkylbenzenesulphonates are the most widely used for domestic purposes. Unfortunately, these are the most difficult to break down during sewage purification and so about 50% or more of the amount present in the crude sewage passes through the treatment plant and is found in the final effluent. Recently a new series of non-ionic detergents have been developed in the U.S.A. by the Sugar Research Foundation. They are esters of sucrose with higher fatty acids (palmitic, stearic, etc.) and have good detergent and scouring properties. They should, theoretically, be easily decomposed during sewage treatment and so should not give rise to the problems generally associated with synthetic detergents. Large scale tests of these new products are being carried out and will be awaited with great interest.

The most widely used methods in this country for determining small amounts of anionic synthetic detergents are based upon the formation of a chloroform-soluble blue complex of methylene blue and the detergent (see references 454–461). The committee on synthetic detergents has now suggested that determinations of anionic synthetic detergents in sewage and river waters should be carried out by a standard procedure recommended by the Government Chemist's department[453, 460, 461]. This method, whilst utilizing the formation of the blue complex of methylene blue and the detergent, differs from previously published methods in carrying out the extraction of the complex with chloroform in an alkaline solution (phosphate–sodium hydroxide buffer at pH 10) instead of an acid medium. The chloroform extracts are eventually washed with an acid solution of methylene blue. By using this double extraction procedure, interference due to chloride, nitrate, thiocyanate and proteins, to which previous methods were subject in varying degree, is reduced to negligible amounts. The colour intensity of the chloroform extract is measured absorptiometrically using an orange filter at 650 mμ. The anionic detergent sodium dioctylsulphosuccinate ('Manoxol O.T.'), which can be purchased in a high state of purity and is stable both in the solid state and in aqueous solution, is recommended as a reference standard for the preparation of the calibration curve. Sulphides interfere with the method by reducing the methylene blue but they can be removed by a preliminary oxidation with hydrogen peroxide. If a distinction between sulphate detergents (e.g. Teepol) and sulphonate detergents (e.g. Tide) is desired, the procedure described by DEGENS and his associates [459] can be adopted. The combined anionic detergents (sulphate + sulphonate) are first determined; the concentration of sulphonate detergents is then determined on another portion of the sample after the sulphate detergents have been hydrolysed by boiling with sulphuric acid. The difference between the two determinations gives the concentration of sulphate detergents.

FAIRING and SHORT [462] have described an accurate method of determining anionic detergents of the alkyl benzenesulphonate class (as little as 0·05 p.p.m.) by solvent extraction of the 1-methylheptylamine salt followed by spectrophotometric measurement of the methylene blue complex at 650 mμ. Interference from substances normally present in surface waters and sewage is eliminated by using a double extraction procedure involving (1) extraction at pH 7·5 with a chloroform solution of 1-methylheptylamine, and, after acid hydrolysis, (2) extraction at pH 4·8 with a hexane solution of 1-methylheptylamine.

To avoid many of the shortcomings of methylene blue methods (e.g. interferences from substances which form extractable methylene blue complexes and from substances which react with the detergent and so prevent the formation of a methylene blue complex), a referee method for determining traces of alkylbenzenesulphonate detergents (a few parts per 1000 million) has been put forward [463]. The method, which is lengthy and unsuitable for routine work, involves the following stages:

(*i*) adsorption of the detergent on activated carbon,
(*ii*) resorption with alkaline benzene-methanol,

(*iii*) acid hydrolysis to destroy interfering organic sulphates, phosphates, etc.,

(*iv*) treatment with light petroleum to remove hydrocarbons, alcohols and sterols,

(*v*) extraction of the detergent in chloroform as a complex 1-methylheptylamine salt and, finally,

(*vi*) infra-red determination in carbon tetrachloride solution at 9·6–9·9 μ.

Anionic synthetic detergents can also be determined by titration methods[464]. EDWARDS and GINN[465] have described a modified titration method for determining anionic detergents in sewage based upon the original two-phase titration procedure of BARR, OLIVER and STUBBINGS[466]. The titration is carried out with a standard solution of the cationic detergent, cetyl trimethylammonium bromide, in the presence of hexane, a solution of bromophenol blue or azophloxine being used as indicator. The dyestuff forms a coloured salt with the slightest excess of cationic detergent, thus indicating the end-point by the colour imparted to the hexane layer. Interference by proteins and soaps is prevented by buffering between pH 7·0 and 7·5, and interference due to hardness by adding the di-sodium salt of ethylene diamine tetra-acetic acid (EDTA). The results are unaffected by thiocyanates, nitrates, or urine, and there is no interference by sodium chloride or sodium sulphate in concentrations up to about 1000 p.p.m.

On the basis of the experiments of SCHAFFER and CRITCHFIELD[467] and HEATLEY and PAGE[468], Imperial Chemical Industries, Ltd., have developed a routine method for estimating non-ionic detergents of the polyethanoxy type (e.g. Lissapol N) present in concentrations of about 2–20 p.p.m. of active agent. Practical details are described by the ABCM-SAC Joint Committee[461] who stress that the procedure should be regarded merely as tentative. The method depends upon the extraction of the non-ionic detergent with ether in the presence of salt and the formation of an insoluble complex compound of the detergent with barium phosphomolybdate in hydrochloric acid–ethanol solution. This complex is digested with a mixture of sulphuric and perchloric acids and the phosphate so formed, which is a measure of the amount of detergent present, is estimated colorimetrically by reduction to molybdenum blue according to the TSCHOPP procedure[469], i.e. using sodium metabisulphite in the presence of sodium sulphite and metol. The results are reproducible to within ±2 p.p.m. The method is suitable for satisfactory sewage effluents and probably also for reasonably clean river waters, but for polluted samples (e.g. sewage) a preliminary deproteinization with zinc sulphate and barium hydroxide is necessary as a rule. The method, although rather lengthy, is the only routine one at present available.

FATS AND GREASE[2]

The estimation of fatty and greasy matter in sludges, effluents and polluted river waters is usually carried out by extraction of the sample with an organic solvent followed by the evaporation of the extract and the weighing of the dried residue. Numerous organic solvents have been recommended in the past for this estimation, especially light petroleum, hexane, diethyl ether, benzene, and chloroform. Since the amount of lipoidal matter extracted depends upon the particular solvent selected, it is important that the name of the solvent used should always be specified.

KNECHTGES, PETERSON and STRONG[470] investigated petroleum, ethyl ether, isopropyl ether and chloroform as solvents for the extraction of greasy material from samples of sludge from six different sewage plants and found that chloroform extracts the largest quantity of fatty matter and light petroleum the smallest amount; chloroform extracting about twice as much lipoidal material as did petroleum. Metallic soaps are more easily soluble in chloroform than in petroleum but even when the sludge was acidified to hydrolyse these soaps to fatty acids, petroleum still extracted less material than did chloroform without acidification. Similar results have been reported by other workers[471, 472]. HOLROYD[473], however, has found that when samples of sewage sludge are digested with acid, filtered, washed with water and dried, the amounts of greasy matter extracted from the dried residue by light petroleum, carbon disulphide, ethyl ether, and chloroform are not significantly different. GEHM and TRUBNICK[474] have given several reasons for preferring, in general, petroleum as a grease solvent for sewage sludges. POMEROY and WAKEMAN[475] in a comprehensive study of numerous grease solvents concluded that petroleum or hexane tended to dissolve material which more nearly resembled the grease contained in sewage, sludge, and trade wastes. In the U.S.A., light petroleum has been recommended as the standard grease solvent and acidification is always adopted as a pre-treatment procedure in order to hydrolyse metallic soaps to fatty acids. In the A.P.H.A. *Standard Methods*[2] grease is officially defined as 'that material which is extracted from an acidified sample [of sewage or sludge] by petroleum ether (boiling range 35–54° C)' when using the standard method.

STEPHENSON[476] has reported that the drying of acidified sewage sludges by heat leads to low grease results, and has suggested a shorter more accurate procedure for grease determination than that recommended in the U.S.A. It involves dehydrating the liquid sludge (which has been previously acidified with hydrochloric acid) by stirring with magnesium sulphate monohydrate for about 15–30 minutes and extracting the ground product with light petroleum for five hours in a Soxhlet apparatus.

It is sometimes desirable to ascertain the nature of the fatty material extracted from a sample. For example, it is often important to know the proportion of unsaponifiable matter present, i.e. sterols, hydrocarbons and mineral oils (e.g. motor oils) not volatile at 100° C. This determination is generally carried out by saponifying the vegetable and animal fats with boiling alcoholic potash and then extracting the unsaponifiable material with light petroleum or ethyl ether [477]. Gehm and Trubnick [474] have found that boiling *aqueous* 10 per cent sodium hydroxide is just as satisfactory as the alcoholic alkali for this saponification, and much more convenient to use.

A general procedure for identifying qualitatively grease derived from sewage is described by GRIBKOFF and NAKADA [478].

Chapter 10

OTHER CHEMICAL METHODS

IN THE preceding chapters, methods for the determination of the more important substances found in sewage, trade wastes and river waters have been reviewed. In the present chapter a tabular outline is given (*Table 9*) for the estimation of some less important substances which may sometimes be encountered in pollution problems.

Table 9. Methods for the determination of some additional substances occasionally found in sewage, trade wastes and river waters

Substance, element or material	Occurrence	Method of determination	Useful range of method	References
Acrylonitrile	Chemical waste waters	Concentration by distillation with $H_2SO_4 + CH_3OH$ to give an azeotrope boiling at 61.4^0 containing 38.7% of acrylonitrile which is then determined polarographically	—	479
Acetylene .	Lime wastes from acetylene generators	Reaction with ammoniacal $0.01N$ silver nitrate to give insoluble silver acetylide and titration of acidified filtrate with $0.01N$ ammonium thiocyanate	—	7
Aluminium .	—	(a) Colorimetric, with Haematoxylin (b) Colorimetric, with Aluminon	$0.1–0.5$ p.p.m. Up to 20 µg	4, 140 3, 392
Antimony .	Dye wastes	Titration of reduced solution (after preliminary treatment) with $0.01N$ $KBrO_3$	Up to 50 mg	3, 328
Boron . .	—	(a) Titrimetric, pH adjusted to 7.6, mannitol (3 g per 100 ml.) is added, and the liquid is titrated back to pH 7.6 with standard caustic soda (b) Photometric, using turmeric (curcumin)	20 µg and more	130, 480 481

Table 9—cont.

Substance, element, or material	Occurrence	Method of determination	Useful range of method	References
Bromide .	Sea-water (about 65–70 p.p.m. of Br) Estuary water	Oxidation by chlorine water to bromate. After removing excess of chlorine with sodium formate, the bromate is determined iodometrically by adding a few drops of ammonium molybdate solution (catalyst), potassium iodide, and hydrochloric acid and titrating the liberated iodine with 0·001N thiosulphate. Organic matter should be destroyed by evaporation of the sample and gentle ignition	0·05–2·5 p.p.m. (25–1,000 ml. sample)	482
Glucose .	—	Sample heated with alkaline potassium ferricyanide. The ferrocyanide so formed is estimated by acidification and titration with 0·01 N ceric sulphate using Setopaline C as indicator	—	483
Hydrogen peroxide	Peroxide kier and bleach liquors, waste waters from testing of rocket motors	Colorimetric, as yellow pertitanic acid, by reaction with H_2SO_4 solution of titanic sulphate	—	130, 133
Lactose .	Dairy wastes	After removal of proteins with sulphuric acid and sodium tungstate, alkaline copper tartrate and sodium bisulphite are added, and the cuprous copper so formed is allowed to reduce phosphomolybdic acid to molybdenum blue, which is determined absorptiometrically	0–5,000 p.p.m.	484

Table 9—cont.

Substance, element, or material	Occurrence	Method of determination	Useful range of method	References
Magnesium .	Sea-water (about 1,400 p.p.m.) Estuary water	(a) Gravimetric, as $Mg_2P_2O_7$ (b) Colorimetric, with Titan yellow (c) Titrimetric, with EDTA	— 0·1–4·0 p.p.m. —	4 2, 140, 324 See page 56
Phosphate .	Sewage Rivers Commercial syndets	Colorimetric determination as 'molybdenum blue', after reduction of phospho-molybdate by one of the following: (a) Stannous chloride (Deniges' method) (b) Metol-sulphite (Tschopp's reagent) (c) Ascorbic acid	 0·02–0·5 p.p.m. of P_2O_5* 0·1–2·4 p.p.m. of P_2O_5* 1–600 μg of P_2O_5	 1, 140 3, 140, 254, 469 485
Silica . .	—	Colorimetric, as yellow silico-molybdate, oxalic acid being added to destroy colour due to phosphate	1–20 p.p.m.	2, 4, 14, 140
Sugars .	Citrus wastes Sulphite Cellulose wastes Beet sugar wastes	Converted to reducing sugars by acid hydrolysis, then heated with alkaline potassium ferricyanide. The excess of ferricyanide is determined iodometrically	—	486
Trichloro-ethylene†	—	Sample + pyridine + caustic soda→orange colour when heated for 5 minutes in boiling water bath	1–20 p.p.m.	487
Tin . .	Plating wastes	After destruction of organic matter with $H_2SO_4 + H_2O_2$, the tin is volatilised by distillation with $H_2SO_4 + HCl + HBr$, and determined photometrically with toluene—3:4— dithiol at 530 mμ	0·01– 0·18 mg (5 cm. cell, 100 ml. sample)	488

* Using B.D.H. Lovibond nesslerizer discs. Larger amounts can be estimated by taking small amounts of sample, or by using a dilution.
† Carbon tetrachloride and chloroform give a similar colour reaction.

CHAPTER 11

SIGNIFICANCE AND INTERPRETATION OF CHEMICAL AND PHYSICAL TESTS

THE significance of some of the more important chemical and physical tests used at sewage disposal works, at trade effluent purification plants, and in river survey work is shown in condensed form in *Table 10*.

Table 11 supplements this by listing some of the more important substances present in many common waste waters.

In this chapter an attempt will be made to discuss in greater detail the significance of chemical and physical tests and the interpretation of the results of an analysis. In general, each test should be considered not in isolation but in relation to the analysis as a whole. Moreover, it is often difficult to interpret chemical analyses fairly unless they are supplemented by bacteriological and biological surveys, by observations on stream flows and rainfall, by data on the volume and frequency of the discharges to the stream and by other relevant information on the local conditions prevailing.

Table 10. Some important chemical and physical tests used in river pollution work and their significance

Test or determination	Type of pollution measured or significance
Transparency	Turbidity due to organic and/or inorganic colloids
Immiscible liquids . . .	Oil
pH value	Intensity of acidity or alkalinity; may effect corrosion of river structures
Acidity, alkalinity . . .	Amount of acid or alkali; may affect corrosion of river structures
B.O.D. . . . . Permanganate value, 4h. Dichromate value . . Organic carbon . .	Organic pollution
Permanganate value , 3 min. .	Easily oxidized inorganic and/or organic pollution
Dissolved oxygen . . .	Roughly indicates extent of easily oxidized pollution; suitability of water for fish
Suspended solids . . .	Insoluble matter likely to deposit on stream bed and interfere with fish spawning grounds, or cause silting

Test or determination	Type of pollution measured or significance
Dissolved solids . . .	Soluble mineral salts; may affect type of vegetation and fish
Stability	Liability of water to undergo change; may determine freedom from odour nuisance due to H_2S
Combined nitrogen (ammoniacal, albuminoid or organic, nitrous and nitric) .	Degree of stabilization of nitrogenous matter
Metallic contaminants . .	Toxic pollution*
Cyanides	Toxic pollution*
Phenols	Toxic pollution*; odour; taste
Sulphide	Toxic pollution*, odour
Free chlorine	Toxic pollution*; odour; taste
Chloride	Salinity; can affect stream life, and solubility of dissolved oxygen
Sulphate	May effect corrosion of concrete; possible biochemical reduction to malodorous H_2S
Calcium and magnesium . .	Hardness (soap-consuming power)
Synthetic detergents . .	Froth; toxic pollution*
Iron and aluminium . .	Potential suspended matter †
Free carbon dioxide . .	Toxic pollution*; may cause corrosion of river structures

* Substances poisonous or injurious to aquatic life.
 † Iron and aluminium can react with natural river bicarbonate alkalinity to give insoluble precipitates of metal hydroxides.

Table 11. Substances present in some common waste waters

Waste water	Substances commonly present
Gas liquor . . . Coke-oven effluents . .	Phenols, ammonia, cyanides, thiocyanates, sulphides
Electroplating . . .	Cyanides, chromate, copper, nickel, cadmium, zinc, tin, silver
Chemical manufacture . .	Acids, alkalis, phenols, amines and other organic chemicals
Chrome tanning . . .	Lime, sulphide, chromium, nitrogenous organic matter
Viscose rayon manufacture .	Sulphuric acid, sodium sulphide, zinc
Iron pickle liquor . . Mine water . . .	Ferrous sulphate, sulphuric acid
Paper mill	Cellulose fibres, free chlorine, resins, starch and other sizing materials, titanium dioxide, clay, and other fillers
Kier liquor (kiering of cotton, straw, etc.) . . .	Caustic soda, sodium carbonate, lime, organic matter
Dairy, meat and food industry; farm drainage, sewage .	Easily fermentable nitrogenous organic matter
Cotton textile	Starch, gums, dyes, acids, alkalis, free chlorine, sulphides, soaps, detergents
Wool scouring . . .	Fats and grease, alkalis
Synthetic resin . . .	Phenols, formaldehyde
Engineering works . . .	Oils
Petroleum refinery . . .	Phenols, hydrocarbons, oils, acids, sulphides and other sulphur compounds

DISSOLVED OXYGEN

The concentration of dissolved oxygen is one of the most important indices of the purity of a stream. Among the more significant factors affecting the dissolved oxygen concentration are the amount and nature of the organic matter present, the temperature, bacterial activity, dilution, photosynthesis, and reaeration from the atmosphere. Reaeration is much influenced by a number of factors, e.g. the dissolved oxygen deficiency, the character of the stream bed, the depth, volume and velocity of flow of the water, the turbulence, the presence of weirs, and the concentration of dissolved solids and surface-active agents. A very important factor is the turbulence since it has been shown that a shallow turbulent beck has an oxygen exchange coefficient about 150–400 times as great as that of a stagnant water[489].

One of the first indications of the presence of organic pollution is a fall in the dissolved oxygen content of the stream below the source of the pollution. Since the deoxygenation of water by sewage and trade wastes is a comparatively slow process, the point of maximum deoxygenation may be anything up to several miles downstream of the point of pollution. Owing to the many complicating factors involved, it is not yet possible to predict precisely the effect of a discharge on the oxygen level of a stream.

The amount of oxygen taken up by water from the atmosphere is dependent on the temperature, the barometric pressure, and the amount of chloride in the water. Solubility of oxygen falls markedly with rise in temperature and increases with a rise in pressure, and is rather less in water containing chloride than in fresh water; thus, the amount of oxygen dissolved by sea water (containing 20,000 p.p.m. of chloride, expressed as Cl) in equilibrium with air is only about 80 per cent of that taken up by fresh water.

The figures generally used for the solubility of oxygen in fresh and salt water are those given by the American Public Health Association[2] and were calculated by WHIPPLE and WHIPPLE[490] from gasometric determinations carried out by Fox[491] as early as 1909. Investigations at the Water Pollution Research Laboratory by TRUESDALE, DOWNING and LOWDEN[152, 492], however, have shown that the correct values determined by a modification of the standard Winkler method are lower than the generally accepted values, the error in some cases being as much as 3–4 per cent. According to these workers, the solubility of oxygen can be represented by the empirical equation:

$$C = 14{\cdot}161 - 0{\cdot}3943T + 0{\cdot}007714T^2 - 0{\cdot}0000646T^3$$

where C_s = saturation concentration of oxygen in p.p.m.
and T = temperature in degrees centigrade.

Data based on this recent work for the solubility of oxygen in water, in equilibrium with air, at various temperatures and salinities under a pressure of 760 mm, are given in *Table 34* in the Appendix.

As an example, it will be seen from the table that if the river temperature is 13° C the amount of dissolved oxygen present is 10·2. p.p.m. and this would represent 100 per cent of saturation. A lower figure than this (e.g. 5·1 p.p.m. = 50 per cent of saturation at 13° C) would probably indicate the presence of organic pollution whilst a figure greater than 100 per cent would indicate that active photosynthesis was taking place.

MORTIMER [493] has given a useful nomogram for calculating the percentage saturation of dissolved oxygen using the new solubility data of Truesdale, Downing and Lowden.

A simpler equation than the above, fitting the experimental data with reasonable precision has been given by GAMESON and ROBERTSON [494]:

$$C_s = \frac{475}{33 \cdot 5 + T} \text{ (for pure water between 0 and 30° C).}$$

For sea water of salinity 34‰ the corresponding expression is as follows:

$$C_s = \frac{385}{33 \cdot 5 + T} \text{ (for sea water between 0 and 30° C).}$$

TRUESDALE and GAMESON [495] have published a convenient table showing the solubility of oxygen in sea water in equilibrium with air at various temperatures and this is reproduced by kind permission of the Secretary General of the Bureau du Conseil International pour l'Exploration de la Mer in *Table 35* in the Appendix.

The values given in the tables do not represent the solubility of pure oxygen in water which is very much higher. Air contains only 20·9 per cent of oxygen, the rest being mainly nitrogen. When air is dissolved in water, the amounts of oxygen and nitrogen dissolved depend upon the partial pressure (Henry's law) and solubility of each gas (oxygen is about twice as soluble in water as nitrogen). At 14° C water saturated with air contains about 10 p.p.m. of oxygen but the solubility of pure oxygen at that temperature is about 48 p.p.m. or nearly five times as much. It is, therefore not surprising that figures exceeding 100 per cent of saturation are sometimes obtained in river waters particularly when photosynthesis is proceeding.

The Royal Commission on Sewage Disposal [496] considered that the dissolved oxygen content of a river should not fall below about 60 per cent of saturation in the summer if nuisance was to be avoided, but it is generally considered nowadays that this gives a fairly wide margin of safety.

The dissolved oxygen content of a stream as determined by the usual sampling technique does not necessarily indicate the state of the water near the stream bed. Where the stream is deep and sluggish and complete mixing may not occur it is possible that, as pointed out by COKER [497], insect and other life such as mayfly nymphs, living on the bottom may find the oxygen supply there inadequate for their needs. Moreover, organic sludge deposits on the bed may undergo anaerobic decomposition and cause depletion or exhaustion of dissolved oxygen in the lower layers of water.

In relatively unpolluted streams, the water is often supersaturated with dissolved oxygen, i.e. values exceeding 100 per cent of saturation are obtained. This is due to photosynthesis whereby plant life (especially the green and blue-green algae) under the influence of sunlight convert carbon dioxide into oxygen. The production of oxygen by photosynthesis can be represented by the equation:

$$6CO_2 + 6H_2O(+ 675\ Kg - cal) = C_6H_{12}O_6 + 6O_2$$

a hexose sugar

Sunlight is necessary to supply the energy for this endothermic reaction. At night, the reverse reaction takes place. PRICE [498] quotes the case of a river in which, owing to intense photosynthesis, the dissolved oxygen reached the very high level of 243 per cent of saturation and this was accompanied, as would be expected, by alkaline conditions, i.e. a pH value of 9·83 (see also under Alkalinity, p. 139).

Owing to photosynthesis the dissolved oxygen content of a clean stream may vary considerably during the day and will generally be higher than at night, higher on a sunny day than on a relatively dull day and much higher on bright summer days than on dull winter days. The effect of sunshine on the hourly variation of dissolved oxygen in a river is well illustrated by data obtained by MOHLMAN and his co-workers [499] for the Illinois river and quoted by SCHROEPFER [500]. These are shown in *Table 12*.

The data in the table show that

(a) The maximum concentration of dissolved oxygen was 139 per cent of the average on the very sunny day but only 111 per cent of the average on the duller day. In actual amounts of dissolved oxygen, this would be 12·0 p.p.m. on the sunny day but only 7·7 p.p.m. on the dull day.

(b) The average dissolved oxygen content was considerably higher on the sunny day than on the preceding dull day.

(c) The highest concentration of dissolved oxygen occurs during the afternoon (2–6 p.m.) on each day.

Table 12.   *Effect of sunshine on hourly variation of dissolved oxygen on two consecutive days in August 1927, in Illinois river at Averyville, Illinois* [499, 500]

Time	Dissolved oxygen : per cent of average	
	23 August 1927 40% possible sunshine	24 August 1927 99% possible sunshine
12 midnight	100	87
2 a.m.	87	77
4 a.m.	87	77
6 a.m.	88	75
8 a.m.	98	83
10 a.m.	96	78
12 noon.	98	92
2 p.m.	107	119
4 p.m.	111	139
6 p.m.	111	133
8 p.m.	108	122
10 p.m.	101	114
Average dissolved oxygen: p.p.m.	6·92	8·65

Schroepfer[500] has presented data showing that rivers having a low average concentration of dissolved oxygen show more hourly variation than those having a higher concentration of dissolved oxygen. Consequently, owing to the variations in dissolved oxygen from hour to hour, the taking of 'snap' samples can give misleading results. Obviously a sample for dissolved oxygen determination should be taken at a time when the oxygen content is as near the average as possible. Analysis of data on the Mississippi river showed that samples collected between sunset and midnight generally gave dissolved oxygen values nearer the average for the day, but, in practice, sampling would be inconvenient so late in the day and so Schroepfer suggests a time between 7 a.m. and 12 noon. Alternatively, the use of automatic recording apparatus based on the principle of the dropping mercury electrode would provide a continuous record of the dissolved oxygen throughout the day. BRIGGS, KNOWLES and SCRAGG [501] have given a preliminary account of an apparatus for the continuous determination and recording of dissolved oxygen based on the well-known Winkler method, the optical density of the liberated iodine being measured by a photoelectric cell and recorded on a chart. Continuous records obtained in this way should prove useful in assessing any fluctuations in dissolved oxygen content due to variations in the organic pollution load, the effects of photosynthesis, and weather conditions such as sunshine, wind action and rainfall.

When the amount of dissolved oxygen in a fishing stream falls below about 5 p.p.m. (or about 57 per cent of saturation at 20° C), fish, especially game fish, are liable to be adversely affected. A desirable figure for fish is at least 75 per cent of saturation but many coarse fish can live in water with a dissolved oxygen content as low as 30 per cent of saturation or even less. Experiments at the Water Pollution Research Laboratory [502] have shown that under laboratory conditions in test aquaria, fish can live for limited periods (up to one week) in much lower concentrations of dissolved oxygen than have hitherto been considered necessary. For example, tench (the most resistant to low concentrations of dissolved oxygen of the species studied) lived for a week at 3·1 per cent dissolved oxygen saturation (10° C) whereas rainbow trout lived for only 3½ hours at 15·3 per cent dissolved oxygen saturation (10° C). It does not, of course, follow that such low concentrations would be suitable under natural conditions. It was also shown that the higher the temperature, the greater is the concentration of dissolved oxygen required to support fish life.

The concentration of dissolved oxygen seems to be of particular importance to fish when poisonous substances are present in the stream. Experiments carried out by the Water Pollution Research Laboratory [503] indicate that the effect of toxic substances on fish is enhanced when the concentration of dissolved oxygen is low, and consequently it could happen that sub-lethal amounts of toxic substances might prove relatively innocuous during the day, when sufficient dissolved oxygen is present, but lethal at night when the dissolved oxygen concentration falls.

From what has been said, it is clear that it should be possible to assess very roughly the organic quality of a river water by its content of dissolved oxygen. Indeed, a classification of river quality based on dissolved oxygen content has been given by KEY[503A] and is shown in *Table 13*.

Table 13. Classification of river quality based on dissolved oxygen content

Type of river water	Dissolved oxygen % of saturation
Good . . .	90 or more
Fair . . .	75–90
Doubtful . .	50–75
Badly polluted .	Below 50

Since the concentration of dissolved oxygen depends upon a combination of factors, it must be emphasized that many other tests are necessary to obtain a complete picture of the state of a stream, e.g. B.O.D., ammoniacal nitrogen, toxic substances, pH, etc.

LASSLEBEN [504] has shown that very high concentrations of dissolved oxygen in water may prove dangerous to fish. He found that carp remained healthy in ponds containing dissolved oxygen between 125 per cent and 150 per cent of saturation but when the dissolved oxygen was greater than 150 per cent of saturation the fish developed maxillary diseases (e.g. diseases of the fins) and dropsy.

AMMONIACAL NITROGEN

Ammonia arises as a rule from the aerobic or anaerobic decomposition of nitrogenous organic matter and if present in a stream in appreciable amounts (say >0.2 p.p.m.) provides strong presumptive evidence of the presence of sewage or sewage effluent, especially if there is also a rise in the chloride content. In fact, the Royal Commission on Sewage Disposal[505] stated in their 8th Report that 'the most delicate chemical index of recent sewage pollution in a river water is the increase in the figure for ammoniacal nitrogen yielded by the water shortly below the outfall as compared with the water above'. The Commission, however, added that the ammoniacal nitrogen figure does not provide so good an index of the actually observed condition of the stream or of the polluting power of an effluent as does the B.O.D. test. It must also be remembered that a large number of trade wastes containing either ammonia or nitrogenous organic matter, for instance gas liquor, tannery effluents, dairy wastes, piggery wastes, and many chemical wastes, can cause an increase in the ammoniacal nitrogen content of a river.

Rivers known to be unpolluted generally contain extremely small amounts of ammoniacal nitrogen. Thus, in a survey of the unpolluted River Wharfe, the old West Riding of Yorkshire Rivers Board[506] found that the ammoniacal nitrogen content of the river varied only between 0 and 0.17 p.p.m.

It is well known that ammonia and ammonium compounds even in relatively small amounts are toxic to fish and that the toxicity is affected by the pH value of the water and by the concentration of dissolved oxygen. It is therefore desirable that a sewage effluent discharging to a small fishing stream should be well nitrified. SPICER[507] from observations in the Trent River Board area states that where the ammoniacal nitrogen figure of a river exceeds 5 p.p.m. few, if any, coarse fish are likely to be found and that even when the figure is over 1 p.p.m. the river is not very attractive to fish. It has been shown[503, 508, 509] however, that it is the proportion of ammonia in the form of *un-ionized* ammonia (which increases with rise in pH value) rather than the total ammonia or the ammonium ion that is responsible for the toxic effects on fish. For instance, ALABASTER and HERBERT[509] showed that although Watford tap water (dissolved oxygen content 4.41 p.p.m.), to which was added 30 p.p.m. of ammoniacal nitrogen, was rapidly toxic to trout, yet if carbon dioxide (30 p.p.m.) was also present it lowered the pH value, and therefore the concentration of un-ionized ammonia, to such an extent that trout were not affected by the water after a 12-hour exposure period. DOWNING and MERKENS[510], following up earlier work by Wuhrmann, have shown that the toxicity of solutions of un-ionized ammonia to rainbow trout is affected by the dissolved oxygen concentration of the water; the periods of survival of the fish in the range 0·86–1·96 p.p.m. of ammoniacal N increasing as the dissolved oxygen content rose from 1·5 to 8·5 p.p.m.

The presence of more than traces of ammoniacal nitrogen in river waters used as sources of drinking-water is not as a rule regarded with favour by water undertakings using chlorine for germicidal purposes. Waters high in ammonia have a high chlorine demand and require much longer contact periods for satisfactory sterilization. This difficulty can be circumvented by using nitrifying filters to oxidize ammoniacal nitrogen to nitrate; according to CAREY [511] this was done during World War II by Coventry in connection with the treatment of River Avon water.

ORGANIC NITROGEN AND ALBUMINOID NITROGEN

Organic nitrogen is the organically bound nitrogen in nitrogenous organic matter and includes the nitrogen in proteins and their decomposition products such as amino-acids, organic bases and urea. Albuminoid nitrogen is that fraction of the organic nitrogen which is easily decomposed when the sample, previously freed from ammonia, is distilled with alkaline potassium permanganate according to a standard procedure. In raw sewages, the albuminoid nitrogen is usually about half of the total organic nitrogen but this relation does not necessarily hold in the cases of effluents and river waters. Although the estimation of albuminoid nitrogen still finds favour in most laboratories in this country, the determination of organic nitrogen is claiming many adherents who regard it as more accurate and reliable. Nevertheless, the albuminoid nitrogen estimation is easier and quicker to carry out—an important consideration in busy laboratories doing large numbers of routine samples—and it gives all the information needed, namely a rough measure of the amount of nitrogenous organic matter present, animal or vegetable. Moreover, albuminoid nitrogen gives a measure of the relatively easily decomposable organic matter which from the standpoint of pollution is of greater significance than the total organic nitrogen. Organic nitrogen and albuminoid nitrogen are of particular value for estimating the strength of nitrogenous organic wastes (e.g. meat industry wastes) and for assessing the degree of purification attained by the treatment of these wastes, but in general they are less valuable indices of pollution than the B.O.D. test. Albuminoid nitrogen values much above 0·2 p.p.m. in a stream should generally be regarded with some suspicion but it must be emphasized that algae and decaying vegetation can give fairly high albuminoid nitrogen values at certain times of the year.

THE RATIO OF AMMONIACAL NITROGEN TO ALBUMINOID NITROGEN

In the majority of sewages and sewage effluents the amount of ammoniacal nitrogen greatly exceeds the amount of albuminoid nitrogen. Consequently, a high ammoniacal nitrogen: albuminoid nitrogen ratio in a river water is usually a good indication of the presence of sewage or sewage effluent. On the other hand in the case of vegetable pollution (e.g. peaty waters), the ammoniacal nitrogen is generally low and the albuminoid nitrogen relatively high and hence a low ammoniacal nitrogen: albuminoid nitrogen ratio is obtained. A much more reliable indication of vegetable pollution, however, is obtained by using a method proposed by Gibson[177], described below.

DIFFERENTIATION BETWEEN ANIMAL POLLUTION AND VEGETABLE POLLUTION

The differentiation between organic matter of animal origin and organic matter of vegetable origin is sometimes of great importance in helping to identify a discharge to a river and to locate the source of the pollution. Gibson[177], following up earlier work of Buydens, and Dixon and Jenkins, has shown that the ratio

$$\frac{\text{oxygen absorbed from } N/80 \text{ sodium hypochlorite in 4 hours at } 80° F}{\text{oxygen absorbed from acid } N/80 \text{ potassium permanganate in 4 hours at } 80° F}$$

is   less than 1·0 for vegetable organic matter
and   more than 1·0 for animal organic matter

This is illustrated by *Table 14* which is based partly on the work of Gibson and partly on unpublished experiments carried out in the laboratories of the Mersey River Board.

Table 14.   The $NaOCl:KMnO_4$ *ratio for various wastes and polluted waters*

Wastes, etc., of vegetable origin ($NaOCl:KMnO_4$ ratio <1·0)	Wastes, etc., of animal origin ($NaOCl:KMnO_4$ ratio >1·0)
Paper making wastes .	Sewage and Sewage effluents
Calico printing wastes	Farm drainage
Cotton bleaching wastes	Piggery wastes
Brewery wastes	Dairy wastes
Vegetable canning wastes	Tannery wastes
Vegetable pickling wastes	Rivers polluted by any of the above
Pea vining wastes	wastes
Coal washing effluents*	—
River waters polluted by any of the above wastes	—
Peaty river waters	—

* Coal-dust can be regarded as well-decomposed vegetable matter.

Quick results can often be obtained in Gibson's procedure if the hypo-chlorite and permanganate estimations are carried out in 3 minutes instead of 4 hours, but the conclusions reached are then less reliable.

Certain sewage sludges (e.g. Imhoff tank sludge, digested sludge and activated sludge) appear to be exceptions to Gibson's generalization for they behave as if they were of 'vegetable' origin and give a ratio of less than 1·0.

CHLORIDE

Chloride is present as sodium chloride in urine to the extent of about 1 per cent. Hence sewage always contains chloride, the amount present depending upon the strength of the sewage, the presence of trade wastes containing chlorides, and the chloride content of the water supply. Chloride remains unaltered during the purification of sewage and consequently approximately the same value should be obtained at each stage of the purification process, otherwise the samples are not truly comparable.

Waters containing chloride have been classified by KRUL and LIEFRINCK[512] as 'fresh' if the Cl content does not exceed 100 p.p.m., as 'brackish' if the Cl content is between 100 and 1000 p.p.m., and as 'salt' if the Cl content is over 1000 p.p.m. 'Salt' water may cause the death of freshwater fish and of freshwater weeds.

The chloride content of various waters is shown in *Table 15*.

Table 15. Average chloride content of various waters

	p.p.m. *of chlorion,* Cl'
Rain water . . .	2
Upland surface water .	12
Unpolluted river water.	up to 15
Spring water . .	25
Deep well water . .	50
Drinking water . .	10–20, but variable
Weak sewage . .	70
Medium sewage . .	100
Strong sewage . .	up to 500
Urine. . . .	4,500–5,000
Sea water . . .	20,000

It will be observed from the table that sea water contains about 20,000 p.p.m. of Cl. Hence, in tidal waters the Cl content may vary from a few p.p.m. up to about 20,000 p.p.m. depending upon the proportion of sea water present. The chloride figure at a particular point in an estuary may thus be used to calculate approximately the proportion of sea water at that point[513] since

$$\text{percentage of sea water present} = \frac{\text{Cl' content in p.p.m.} \times 100}{20,000}$$

It must be pointed out, however, that the chloride figure can be fairly high in streams passing through salt-bearing strata or where there is pollution by trade discharges with a high salt content (e.g. discharges of brine from a salt works or from water-softening plants using the base-exchange process). Sea water contains bromide to the extent of about 65 p.p.m. (expressed as Br) and a determination of the Cl:Br ratio, which is approximately 300:1 in sea water [287, 482], can also be used as an index of contamination by tidal waters.

When the possibility of trade effluent pollution or contamination by sea water is ruled out, a sudden rise in the chloride content of a stream usually indicates the presence of sewage, sewage effluent, farm drainage or piggery waste.

NITRITES AND NITRATES

Nitrate represents the final oxidation product of ammonia, and therefore completely treated sewage contains a high proportion of nitrate. Thus, nitrate in a river water is generally an indication of the presence of well treated sewage effluents. When percolating filters at a sewage disposal works are operating efficiently and are not overloaded, the final effluent should contain nitrate but little or no nitrite. Nitrification is much more intense at the higher temperatures of the summer months, when bacterial activity is greater, than during the colder winter months. In a badly worked or overloaded filter, where there is likely to be an oxygen deficiency or where faulty distribution of sewage takes place, nitrites tend to increase and nitrates to fall, probably due to reduction of NO_3' to NO_2' or to incomplete oxidation of ammonia; 'ponding' or choking of the filter is the probable result with production of unsatisfactory or bad effluents containing much nitrite (occasionally up to 20 p.p.m., as N). Thus, even a trace of nitrite in a river water may indicate pollution by imperfectly treated sewage, especially if the river water also shows increases in ammoniacal nitrogen and chloride (see page 136). Norwegian workers [514] have suggested that the concentration of nitrite would be a useful criterion for assessing sewage pollution in Oslo harbour.

In most activated sludge plants it is generally considered uneconomic to carry the purification of sewage beyond the clarification stage; little or no nitrate may be produced and yet the effluent may be well clarified with a low B.O.D. and a low content of suspended solids. However, at two activated sludge plants in this country (Mogden [515] and Colne Valley [516]), gas from the anaerobic digestion of the sewage sludges provides cheap power and this makes it an economic proposition to achieve a considerable degree of nitrification comparable to that obtained in percolating filters.

In highly polluted industrial rivers, such as the River Irwell in

Lancashire, the presence of nitrates derived from sewage effluents is regarded by the river board as a great advantage because when the dissolved oxygen content of the river falls to zero, which happens frequently in warm weather during the summer months, nitrates supply combined oxygen and so tend to delay or prevent the onset of anaerobic conditions and the production of foul odours.

In fishing streams, the presence of nitrates may appear to be of lesser importance. But it must be remembered that a highly nitrified sewage effluent will contribute less ammoniacal nitrogen to a stream than a poorly nitrified effluent. Fish thrive better in a stream when the ammoniacal nitrogen content is low (cf. page 113). Moreover, many fishing streams during summer drought conditions may be depleted of dissolved oxygen to a dangerously low level and nitrates may stimulate the growth of algae and other green plants which by photosynthetic action (page 110) help to supply extra dissolved oxygen.

METHYLENE BLUE STABILITY TEST

Methylene blue is an intense blue organic dyestuff which in the presence of reducing agents is converted into a colourless compound known as leuco-methylene blue. This change of colour occurs at an oxidation–reduction potential which is not far removed from zero, as *Table 16*, compiled from a British Drug Houses publication [517], shows.

Table 16. *Oxidation–reduction potential and colour of methylene blue at different degrees of oxidation* (pH 7·0 and 30° C)

Percentage oxidation	Oxidation–reduction potential V	Colour
2	− 0·040	Almost colourless
10	− 0·018	—
50	+ 0·011	Half coloured
95	+ 0·049	—
98	+ 0·062	Almost fully blue

Thus, methylene blue serves as an indicator of approximately zero oxidation–reduction potential and it is this property that makes it of value in determining the stability of a sample. A stable effluent or river water is one which is not liable to undergo significant change, and which remains aerobic for a reasonable period of time (usually five days); in the stability test what we really determine is the time taken for the sample when incubated out of contact with air to use up, by bacterial action, all its available oxygen (dissolved oxygen as well as combined oxygen in the form of nitrite and nitrate). The work of HEUKELEKIAN [518] and others [519] has shown that when organic matter undergoes oxidation by bacterial action, the order in which the various sources of oxygen are utilized by bacteria is as follows: (i) dissolved oxygen; (ii) nitrates and nitrites; and (iii) sulphates. No nitrate reduction occurs until all the dissolved oxygen has disappeared, and methylene blue is not reduced until all the nitrates are used up. When all the oxygen in the form of dissolved oxygen and nitrate is exhausted, aerobic conditions give place to anaerobic conditions, sulphate is reduced to hydrogen sulphide, other evil-smelling products of anaerobic action are formed, and methylene blue is reduced to the colourless leucocompound. Recent work by the Water Pollution Research Laboratory[520] on the oxygen balance in the Thames estuary, however, suggests that nitrate can be reduced not only under anaerobic conditions but also when there is still a small amount of dissolved oxygen present (up to 10 per cent of saturation).

Table 17. Analysis of activated sludge plant effluent passing the Royal Commission standards for B.O.D. and suspended solids, but failing the stability test

pH value	7·8
Oxygen absorbed from permanganate in 3 mins. (27° C)	7·4 p.p.m.
Oxygen absorbed from permanganate in 4 hours (27° C)	22·0 p.p.m.
Oxidized nitrogen (nitrite + nitrate)	nil
B.O.D. (5 days, 20° C)	11·6 p.p.m.
Suspended solids.	18 p.p.m.
Methylene blue stability test	Failed in 18 hours (giving H_2S)

In the case of river waters, the methylene blue stability test gives some idea of the length of time aerobic conditions would be maintained assuming that no re-aeration takes place. A water failing the test in a short time (say, 18 hours or less) is usually grossly polluted by organic matter and liable to become septic and give rise to complaints from river users and others of smells. It is, therefore, particularly important that sewage effluents discharging to streams which are already polluted, or to streams which afford little dilution, should pass a stability test, otherwise there is a possibility of odour nuisance from the river.

The stability test is especially valuable in showing pollution in samples which have undergone anaerobic fermentation since in these cases the B.O.D. test is apt to give unreliable results (cf. pp. 133–4). This point can be illustrated by the analysis of an activated sludge plant effluent shown in *Table 17*.

It is to be noted that this effluent would have been passed as satisfactory if judged solely on the basis of the Royal Commission tests for B.O.D. and suspended solids. Its failure to pass the stability test showed that it was by no means satisfactory. In fact, it contained a considerable proportion of the polluting supernatant liquor from a sludge digestion plant which, as explained on pp. 133–34, has an abnormally low B.O.D. Subsequent investigation showed that a workman in charge had in error permitted this liquor to go to the activated sludge final settlement tanks instead of to the raw sewage inlet for treatment.

OXYGEN ABSORBED FROM ACID PERMANGANATE

('permanganate value')

In this country, this test is usually carried out in 3 minutes and in 4 hours.

The 3 minutes test measures the immediate oxygen demand of the sample due to oxidizable inorganic matter as well as to *very* easily oxidizable organic matter. Thus, a high 3 minutes permanganate figure is obtained in the presence of considerable amounts of ferrous salts, nitrites, sulphides, sulphites, thiosulphates, thiocyanates and phenols. Trade wastes containing these substances (e.g. iron pickle liquor, mine waters, and gas liquor) will therefore give high 3 minutes permanganate values.

The 4 hours permanganate test is a simple and quick method of measuring approximately the oxidizable matter (organic and inorganic) in sewages, sewage effluents, trade effluents and river waters; a high value indicating as a rule organic pollution.* In the case of a sewage effluent discharging to an inland stream providing a dilution of at least 8 vol., the 4 hours permanganate value of the effluent should not be greater than 15–20 p.p.m. Treated effluents from sewage works dealing with sewage containing gas liquor and certain other trade wastes sometimes exceed this limit though they may still satisfy the Royal Commission B.O.D. standard of 20 p.p.m. With stream waters, the 4 hours permanganate figure should not as a rule be greater than about 3–5 p.p.m. though a higher figure is permissible if peaty matter is present. Observations on rivers within the Trent River Board area [521] suggest that there is a rough correlation between the 4 hours permanganate value and the prominent animal populations present in the water. Choice fish (trout and grayling) and caddis and may-flies were found in clean streams having an approximate 4 hours permanganate value ranging from 0–3 p.p.m.; chub, dace, water shrimps and snails were present when the permanganate value was about 3–6 p.p.m., whilst only coarse fish (roach and gudgeon) as well as hog-lice (*Asellus*) and leeches inhabited streams having a permanganate value of about 6–10 p.p.m. No fish were observed when the permanganate value of a stream exceeded 10 p.p.m.

* Provided that inorganic pollution is absent, as indicated by a relatively low 3 minutes figure.

The 4 hours:3 minutes permanganate value ratio in a river water is of considerable significance and in many cases may provide an important clue to the cause of the pollution. Effluents from domestic sewage and river waters containing untreated or treated domestic sewage generally yield a ratio of about 3·0 but this ratio can be disturbed by the presence of certain trade wastes. For instance, gas liquor in a sewage or river water tends to lower this ratio considerably, often to a value around 2·0. These facts are illustrated by the data given in *Tables 18–22* for various effluents and river waters in Lancashire.

Vegetable waste waters and streams polluted by such wastes usually have a high 4 hours:3 minutes ratio. This is illustrated by the figures shown in *Table 22*, from which it will be seen that the ratio lies between 4 and 10.

Table 18.   Ratio 4 h: 3 min permanganate value for a final effluent from domestic sewage (Bolton, Longworth)

| Date | Permanganate value p.p.m. | | Ratio 4 h:3 min |
	3 min	4 h	
2.2.49	2·8	8·6	3·1
11.1.50	3·6	10·2	2·8
3.12.50	1·4	4·2	3·0
30.5.51	2·6	7·6	2·9
10.10.51	4·0	10·8	2·7
5.2.52	1·6	5·6	3·5
24.6.52	2·0	6·8	3·4
3.2.53	2·4	7·2	3·0
13.5.53	3·2	9·6	3·0
3.9.53	2·4	7·2	3·0
		Average =	3·0

Table 19.   Ratio 4 h : 3 min permanganate value for a final effluent from sewage containing about 2 per cent by volume of gas liquor

| Date | Permanganate value p.p.m. | | Ratio 4 h:3 min |
	3 min	4 h	
6.8.47	20·8	42·2	2·0
16.12.47	25·4	54·0	2·1
11.2.48	20·4	44·4	2·1
24.6.48	12·4	27·6	2·2
28.4.49	25·2	51·4	2·0
13.10.49	15·6	31·8	2·0
18.5.50	30·8	62·8	2·0
19.10.50	14·0	30·8	2·2
18.4.51	19·0	42·6	2·2
9.1.52	13·2	29·6	2·2
		Average =	2·1

Table 20. *Ratio 4 h:3 min permanganate value for a river water polluted by gas liquor (Sankey Brook, at Penkford Bridge Newton)*

Date	Permanganate value p.p.m.		Ratio 4 h:3 min
	3 min	4 h	
1.4.52	46·8	89·6	1·9
6.5.52	64·4	140·0	2·2
15.7.52	58·0	116·0	2·0
11.12.52	51·2	92·0	1·8
15.4.53	47·0	92·0	2·0
16.7.53	71·0	132·0	1·9
14.10.53	34·4	77·0	2·2
14.4.54	56·8	102·0	1·8
14.7.54	26·8	53·0	2·0
12.10.54	36·8	68·0	1·9
		Average =	2·0

Table 21. *Ratio 4 h:3 min permanganate value for rivers above and below gasworks discharges of gas liquor*

River		Date	Permanganate value p.p.m.		Ratio 4 h:3 min
			3 min	4 h	
R. Douglas	above gasworks discharge .	3.7.53	6·0	18·0	3·0
	below gasworks discharge .	3.7.53	59·8	93·0	1·6
R. Irwell	above gasworks discharge .	6.5.53	3·6	12·0	3·3
	below gasworks discharge .	6.5.53	19·0	40·0	2·1
R. Medlock	above gasworks discharge .	15.4.53	1·6	5·2	3·3
	below gasworks discharge .	15.4.53	320	530	1·7

Table 22. *Ratio 4 h:3 min permanganate value for vegetable wastes and streams polluted by vegetable wastes*

Sample	Permanganate value p.p.m.		Ratio 4 h:3 min
	3 min	4 h	
Pea washing wastes.	688	3,000	4·4
Stream below discharge of pea vining wastes	66·0	282·0	4·3
Potato washing wastes	400	2,300	5·8
Carrot canning wastes	151	1,450	9·7
Vegetable pickle factory discharge . .	17·6	73·0	4·3
Dehydrated vegetable wastes . . .	146	742	5·1
Brewery wastes	320	2,080	6·5

BIOCHEMICAL OXYGEN DEMAND (B.O.D.)

This determination was first recommended as a standard test of purity for sewage effluents and river waters by the Royal Commission on Sewage Disposal under the rather cumbersome title 'dissolved oxygen taken up in 5 days at 65° F'. Later, Lederer with the American genius for inventing concise and pithy expressions happily re-named it 'Biochemical Oxygen Demand' which was subsequently abbreviated to 'B.O.D.' by which it eventually came to be known. It is questionable whether the test would ever have become so popular without the backing of so distinguished a body as the Royal Commission. It could scarcely have been realized at the time that the test was destined to become the subject of considerable controversy and of a much more voluminous literature than any other comparable determination.

The B.O.D. determination, being a biochemical test dependent upon the activities of bacteria, is subject to a number of errors. Indeed, WESTON[522] has drawn attention to the fact that at least eighteen variables may have an important influence on the test. Even a short, and by no means exhaustive, list would have to include the following factors:

Variation in temperature

The temperature recommended by the Royal Commission on Sewage Disposal for the determination of B.O.D. was 65° F (= 18·3° C). The Ministry of Housing and Local Government[1] has now suggested that in order to bring British practice into line with American and Continental procedure, the standard temperature for the test should be 20° C. It is very important that this temperature should be correct and that it should be kept reasonably constant over the period of 5 days. An increase or a decrease of only 1° C means an increase or decrease respectively in B.O.D. of 4·7 per cent.

Composition of dilution water

As a result of the recommendations of the Royal Commission on Sewage Disposal, it has hitherto been the practice in Great Britain to use aerated tap water as dilution water for the determination of B.O.D. The variation in the composition of tap water in different localities has been suggested as a reason for many of the discrepancies in B.O.D. results obtained in different laboratories examining the same sample. Moreover, the tendency nowadays to sterilize domestic water supplies introduces an additional hazard in the shape of free chlorine which has a marked adverse effect on bacterial activity. Hence the Ministry of Housing and Local Government[1] has, following American practice, now recommended the use of a standard synthetic dilution water instead of tap water. Experiments by WHEATLAND and SMITH[523], of the Water Pollution Research Laboratory, have indicated that this standard dilution water used for the determination of the B.O.D. of sewage should be *freshly* prepared, or, if this is not practicable, stored for not more than one week in thoroughly cleaned containers. If water stored for longer periods is used, much higher B.O.D. results are obtained since the ammonium compounds originally present in the synthetic water undergo nitrification and the active growths of nitrifying bacteria then tend to cause nitrification of ammonia in the sewage sample.

According to SAWYER and his co-workers[197], the basic requirements of a suitable B.O.D. dilution water are: correct pH limits, proper salinity, reasonable buffer capacity, the presence of necessary nutrients, the absence of toxic substances (e.g. chlorine, metallic contaminants, etc.) and finally the presence of a balanced and viable seeding material. It is not always easy to know whether all these requirements are satisfied and these authors have therefore proposed the use of two primary standards, i.e. solutions containing 300 p.p.m. of pure glucose (5-day B.O.D. at 20° C = 224 p.p.m.) and 300 p.p.m. of pure glutamic acid (5-day B.O.D. at 20° C = 217 p.p.m.) for use in checking and standardizing B.O.D. results and techniques.

The use of river water as dilution water in the B.O.D. test is not to be recommended since it has been shown by LAMB and JENKINS[524] that the results obtained on different days showed considerable variation.

Dilution used

The B.O.D. of a sample may depend to a considerable extent on the particular dilution used. It is therefore advisable to put on several dilutions and to base the value on the dilution showing about 50 per cent depletion of the dissolved oxygen. In the case of certain trade wastes (e.g. gas liquor) the B.O.D. is so largely dependent on the dilution that the test becomes quite unreliable as a measure of the strength of the waste, and it is better to adopt the 4 hours permanganate test.

Presence of bacteriostatic and bactericidal substances

The presence in sewage or trade wastes, or in the dilution water, of substances inhibiting or preventing altogether the growth of bacteria can cause huge errors in a B.O.D. determination and may render the test useless in some cases unless certain precautions are adopted.

Acids and alkalis have a marked effect upon bacterial activity and samples which are acid or alkaline should be neutralized to bring them within the pH range 6·5–8·3 and then seeded with sewage.

Toxic metals (e.g. copper, lead, mercury) are particularly undesirable in the sample or dilution water (cf. page 131) on account of their inhibiting effect even in small quantities on bacterial activity. Copper is especially notorious in this respect and the dilution water used should contain less than 0·01 p.p.m. of copper otherwise a marked depressing effect on the B.O.D. will be obtained.

River waters and trade wastes containing both organic pollution and metallic contaminants are likely to give misleadingly low B.O.D. results and the use of the 4 hours permanganate test is advised in order to assess the amount of organic matter present.

The B.O.D. of tidal waters and estuaries consisting of mixtures of fresh and sea water is affected by the salinity of the water, being generally reduced by the presence of much salt. GOTAAS [525] states that the rate of biochemical oxidation of sewage is greatest for low concentrations of sea water (up to 25 per cent). GRINDLEY and WHEATLAND [526] explain B.O.D. changes with salinity by variations in the numbers and activity of nitrifying organisms in the sample. The extent of nitrogenous organic pollution in an estuary is, therefore, better assessed by determinations of the carbon and nitrogen compounds present.

Nitrification

It has been reported by many workers [527–529] that sewage effluents which are in a state of incipient nitrification can show misleadingly high values in the standard 5-day B.O.D. test and yet be quite satisfactory. This is due to the fact that such effluents not only have an oxygen demand caused by oxidation of carbonaceous matter but also an oxygen demand due to nitrification (i.e. oxidation of ammoniacal nitrogen and nitrite nitrogen to nitrate nitrogen). The same phenomenon has been observed by ABBOTT [530] with some river waters. In one example given by LOCKETT [528] the 5-day B.O.D. of a sewage effluent was 31·4 p.p.m. of which only 9 p.p.m. was due to the actual carbonaceous pollution whilst the remaining 22·4 p.p.m. was accounted for by the conversion of ammoniacal nitrogen to oxidized nitrogen (i.e. nitrite + nitrate) by nitrifying organisms. Methods of preventing the onset of nitrification during the 5-day B.O.D. test include the following:

(i) Flash pasteurization of the sample at 60–80° C, thus destroying the organisms responsible for nitrification [531].

(*ii*) Chlorination of the sample, excess of chlorine being afterwards removed with sodium sulphite [531].

(*iii*) Acidification to pH 2–3 to sterilize the sample, followed by neutralization [532].

In these three cases, the usual B.O.D. procedure is then followed using dilution water seeded with settled domestic sewage. It is important that the sewage used for seeding should be free from nitrifying organisms [533].

(*iv*) ABBOTT[530, 534, 535] has found that methylene blue suppresses nitrification but does not influence the rate of oxidation of carbonaceous matter. Hence, errors due to the occurrence of nitrification were eliminated by adding a small proportion of methylene blue (6 ml. of a 0·05 per cent aqueous solution) to each litre of the dilution water used in the B.O.D. test and determining dissolved oxygen before and after incubation by the Rideal–Stewart method.

The effect of nitrification is of considerable significance when effluents from an activated sludge plant (containing much ammonia but little or no nitrate) and from a biological filtration plant (rich in nitrifying organisms) are mixed or discharged to a comparatively small stream in close proximity. In this connection STONES[536] has made the interesting observation that mixtures of these two types of sewage effluent can have biochemical oxygen demands greater than what would be expected from the values obtained for the individual effluents. The results of an experiment of this kind, taken from his paper, are shown in *Table 23*.

Table 23. B.O.D. of mixtures of activated sludge effluents and filter effluents from plants treating the same sewage[536]

Activated sludge (Sheffield bio-aeration) effluent % by volume	Filtration plant effluent % by volume	B.O.D. of mixture p.p.m.
0	100	12·6
10	90	16·0
20	80	18·8
30	70	20·2
40	60	19·6
50	50	18·4
60	40	17·0
70	30	14·4
80	20	12·0
90	10	7·8
100	0	6·0

It will be seen from this table that as the proportion of activated sludge effluent in the mixture increases the B.O.D. rises steeply from 12·6 p.p.m., when no activated sludge effluent is present, to a maximum of 20·2 p.p.m. (i.e. very slightly above the Royal Commission standard for sewage effluents), when 30 per cent by volume of activated sludge effluent is present thereafter falling rapidly until the B.O.D. of the 100 per cent activated sludge effluent is 6·0 p.p.m. These results are explained by Stones on the assumption that the increase in B.O.D. from 12·6 to 20·2 p.p.m. is due to the occurrence of nitrification, i.e. oxidation of ammonia in the activated sludge effluent by nitrifying bacteria present in the filter effluent at the expense of the dissolved oxygen. It is, therefore, quite conceivable that two satisfactory effluents having B.O.D. values well within the Royal Commission standard of 20 p.p.m. might on admixture give an unsatisfactory effluent with a B.O.D. considerably above the Royal Commission standard. Moreover, the discharge of such a mixed effluent to a small stream might lead to marked deoxygenation of the water to the detriment of any fish life present.

Presence of nutrient materials

Bacteria require for their growth and activities the presence of an adequate supply of mineral nutrients. Carbon, nitrogen, phosphorus, and sulphur are the most important elements needed but traces of potassium, calcium, magnesium, iron, manganese, zinc, cobalt, copper and molybdenum also appear to be necessary for most bacteria[537]. Many years ago, LEA and NICHOLS[538, 539] concluded from experiments on B.O.D. determinations of sewage and industrial wastes, using plain and supplemented bicarbonate dilution waters, that unless sufficient mineral nutrients (especially nitrogen and phosphorus) were present to satisfy the nutritional requirements of the bacteria, low B.O.D. results were obtained with certain trade wastes. They found that various types of paper-mill waste did in fact give greatly increased B.O.D. values (often two to five times as great) when instead of using a plain bicarbonate dilution water use was made of a supplemented dilution water containing magnesium sulphate, calcium phosphate, potassium dihydrogen phosphate and ammonium sulphate. On the other hand, with sewage and with pea canning wastes, which contain adequate amounts of nitrogen and phosphorus, there was no appreciable difference between B.O.D. determinations using plain and supplemented dilution waters. The results of Lea and Nichols appeared to indicate that an adequate supply of nitrogen and phosphorus would be afforded if the B.O.D. dilutions contained about 0·2–0·5 p.p.m. of nitrogen and about 0·02 p.p.m. of phosphorus.

SAWYER and his associates [540-542] have shown that certain industrial wastes are deficient in nitrogen or phosphorus or both. For instance, cotton kier liquor contains insufficient nitrogen; brewery waste is deficient in both nitrogen and phosphorus; and chrome tannery waste, although rich in nitrogen, contains inadequate amounts of phosphorus. Low B.O.D. values are therefore likely to be obtained with these and other mineral-deficient wastes unless the deficiencies are supplied in the dilution waters. Most stream waters probably contain sufficient mineral salts to give satisfactory B.O.D. results but difficulties may arise when a stream consists largely of trade effluents.

Seeding with bacteria

When determining the B.O.D. of sewages, sewage effluents, a few trade wastes (e.g. dairy wastes and piggery wastes) and most river waters, inoculation is rarely necessary since the essential bacterial flora will be present. In the case of certain trade wastes and with samples which are acid or alkaline and therefore require neutralization, seeding with bacteria may be essential and for this purpose it has been the practice to add fresh settled sewage or sewage effluent to the dilution water. It has, however, been shown by SAWYER and his co-workers[197] that this type of seed is not uniform in character and viability and gives results which differ according to the source of the sewage when tests are carried out on certain pure organic compounds of known B.O.D. ZEHNPFENNIG and NICHOLS [543] explain these variations in the character of the inoculum on the basis of changes in the relative proportions of protozoa and bacteria in the sewage and showed that if an inoculum is prepared by filtration through a suitable sintered glass filter so as to remove protozoa, satisfactory and reproducible B.O.D. results are obtained. TYLER and GUNTER [544] found that the standard method of seeding was unsatisfactory in the case of sulphite waste liquor (a waste of very high B.O.D. obtained in the manufacture of pulp for paper making by digesting wood chips with calcium bisulphite solution) and they recommend the use of a filtered soil extract as inoculum. The Ministry of Housing and Local Government[1] recommend for inoculating sterile trade wastes the use of dilution water containing per litre 5 ml. of fresh settled final effluent of good quality from an aerobic biological process. The Joint ABCM-SAC Committee[190], however, point out that sewage effluents might not always be suitable as an inoculum for trade wastes and it may be necessary in certain instances (e.g. when the B.O.D. is much less than two-thirds of the dichromate value) to use a specially conditioned seed.

Presence of anaerobic organisms

In samples where anaerobic organisms predominate (e.g. septic sewage, digested sludges, septic river muds, supernatant liquor from sludge digestion tanks), a lag period takes place during the first 2 or 3 days resulting in an abnormally low B.O.D. figure (see *Figure 1*, page 134).

Miscellaneous sources of error

There are many other possible sources of error in the B.O.D. test in addition to those already discussed. For instance, the presence of certain interfering chemical compounds (e.g. ferrous salts, ferric salts, nitrites, sulphites) can cause inaccuracies; methods for overcoming these interferences have been given in Chapter 4. Again, variations in the size of bottle used resulting in a different ratio of internal surface to volume may have some influence on bacterial activity. A discussion of various minor errors in the B.O.D. test is given by LEWIN [545].

COMPARISON OF B.O.D. AND PERMANGANATE TESTS

Both these tests, whilst quite distinct and showing in general little correlation, occupy an important place in analysis in the assessment of organic pollution for they estimate the amount of oxygen utilized in the oxidation of the organic matter in a sample and therefore give an approximate measure of the amount of organic material present. But whilst the B.O.D. is a biochemical test measuring the amount of organic matter oxidized as a result of the activities of aerobic bacteria under prescribed conditions (5 days, 20° C), the 4 hours permanganate test is a purely chemical test measuring the amount of organic matter oxidized chemically by an acid solution of $N/80$ potassium permanganate under another set of arbitrary conditions (4 hours, 27° C). It is not, therefore, to be expected that these two tests will give parallel results. The 4 hours permanganate test has the merits of simplicity and of giving a quick result. The B.O.D. test takes considerably longer and is more complicated but nevertheless reproduces more closely the conditions of oxidation taking place naturally in a river.

Generally speaking, the B.O.D. determination is the most useful and sensitive test for the detection and measurement of organic pollution, especially nitrogenous organic matter such as sewage, farm drainage, dairy wastes, gelatine wastes, food processing wastes and cannery wastes. This is illustrated by the analytical data given in *Table 24*.

Table 24. Analyses of nitrogenous organic waste waters

	Farm drainage	River polluted by dairy wastes	River polluted by sewage *	Unsatisfactory sewage effluents			Unsatis-factory dairy effluent
pH value	7·2	7·0	6·8	7·4	7·1	6·8	7·2
3 min permanganate test p.p.m.	3·0	1·0	1·0	6·8	4·4	5·0	4·5
4 h permanganate test p.p.m. .	10·0	4·6	3·8	18·0	14·2	10·0	10·9
Suspended solids ⎰ mineral p.p.m. .	3	—	6	4	2	8	11
⎱ volatile p.p.m. .	13	—	6	26	21	12	23
⎱ total p.p.m.	16	11	12	30	23	20	34
Nitrite nitrogen p.p.m. .	nil	nil	nil	nil	trace	nil	nil
Nitrate nitrogen p.p.m. .	nil	nil	nil	nil	1·5	nil	nil
Methylene blue stability test .	Failed 4 h (H_2S)	Failed 18 h (H_2S)	Failed 18 h (H_2S)	Failed 4 h (H_2S)	Failed 18 h (H_2S)	Failed 18 h (H_2S)	Failed 4 h (H_2S)
B.O.D. (5 days, 20° C) p.p.m..	39·0	60·0	12·9	39·6	40·9	32·5	76·0
Ammoniacal nitrogen p.p.m. .	—	0·10	0·92	—	—	—	—
Albuminoid nitrogen p.p.m. .	—	0·86	0·24	—	—	—	—
Dissolved oxygen, % of satura-tion	—	37	9	—	—	—	—

* Stream bed showed signs of sewage pollution (e.g. sewage fungus).

It will be observed from *Table 24* that in all cases the B.O.D. figure shows unmistakably the presence of organic pollution whereas the 4 hours permanganate test gives low values and shows itself to be unreliable as a test for organic matter. Most striking of all these analyses is that of the river polluted by dairy wastes where the B.O.D. is about thirteen times the permanganate value and the latter scarcely shows the polluting character of the sample. It is also noteworthy that the methylene blue stability test proves its value in all these cases in indicating pollution.

The Royal Commission on Sewage Disposal [546] recommended the B.O.D. test for sewage effluents and for stream waters in preference to the 4 hours permanganate test because the B.O.D. was found to be a more sensitive test for organic pollution and, moreover, imitated as far as is possible in a laboratory test the actual process of deoxygenation that takes place in a stream. They also showed that while the permanganate test often gave approximately the same figure for a stream polluted either by tank effluent or by a filter effluent, the B.O.D. was much higher when the river was polluted by tank effluent. As a result of extensive investigations by the Royal Commission [546], the 5-day B.O.D. value was adopted as 'the most trustworthy chemical index of the actual state of a stream', and they found that if this figure did not exceed 4 p.p.m. the river was normally free from signs of pollution. This limiting figure of 4 p.p.m. was the foundation upon which they based the well-known classification of rivers according to their B.O.D. which is given in *Table 25*.

Table 25. Royal Commission classification of rivers

Approximate 5-day B.O.D.* (p.p.m.)	Classification
1	Very clean
2	Clean
3	Fairly clean
5	Doubtful
10	Bad

* The Royal Commission used an incubator temperature of 18·3° C (65° F). The standard temperature now used is 20° C.

The normal Royal Commission B.O.D. standard for sewage effluents discharging to a river providing at least an 8-fold dilution by clean water of B.O.D. 2 p.p.m. was derived as follows [546], taking the limiting figure or maximum safe B.O.D. of the mixture of effluent and river water to be 4 p.p.m.:

Let $x = $ 5-day B.O.D. of sewage effluent (p.p.m.)

$y = $ 5-day B.O.D. of river (p.p.m.) just above effluent outfall (taken to be 2 p.p.m.)

$z = $ dilution factor (taken to be 8), i.e. proportion of river water to effluent.

Then, by the law of mixtures,

$$4(z + 1) = (x \times 1) + (y \times z)$$

or, $$4(8 + 1) = x + 16$$

whence $$x = 20,$$

i.e. the B.O.D. of the sewage effluent should not exceed 20 p.p.m.

Some limitations of the B.O.D. as an indication of organic pollution must now be pointed out. Certain metals (e.g. lead, copper, mercury, chromium present as chromate) are toxic to bacteria even in low concentrations. Since the B.O.D. is so dependent on the activities of bacteria it is naturally affected to a marked degree by toxic substances which may have little or no influence on the 4 hours permanganate value. For instance, a report of an American research committee [547] shows that as regards effect in the determination of the B.O.D. of sewage by the dilution method the toxicity of mercury increases slowly from 0·02–0·2 p.p.m. of mercuric chloride, and above 0·2 p.p.m. the toxicity rises steeply until at a concentration of about 2 p.p.m. of mercuric chloride the 5-day B.O.D. of the sewage is depressed to zero. It was also found that as little as 0·1 p.p.m. of copper or zinc causes an appreciable fall in B.O.D., copper being more toxic than zinc in all concentrations from 0·1–10 p.p.m. Thus, 1 p.p.m. of zinc depresses the B.O.D. by about 17 per cent whereas the same concentration of copper lowers the B.O.D. by 33 per cent. Again, PLACAK, RUCHHOFT and SNAPP[548] have reported that as little as 0·01 p.p.m. of copper and more than 0·3 p.p.m. of chromium (present as chromate) have a marked depressing effect on the B.O.D. of sewage; in the case of copper they found that the B.O.D. was depressed by about 5 per cent by 0·01 p.p.m. of copper, and by 23 per cent by 0·05 p.p.m.

A B.O.D. of about 80 per cent of the true value was obtained in the presence of 0·9 p.p.m. of chromium (present in the hexavalent form as chromate). Some workers (e.g. COBURN[549]) have suggested that chromium present in the trivalent state does not cause much trouble biologically, but the report of an American research committee[547] suggests that as regards effect on B.O.D trivalent chromium is somewhat more toxic than chromate in the range 1–10 p.p.m. of chromium. KALABINA[550] found that as little as 0·1 p.p.m. of lead retarded the biochemical oxidation of organic matter. DAWSON and JENKINS[551] have shown that 1–100 p.p.m. of many metallic ions (e.g. zinc, copper, chromium, nickel and cadmium) caused a marked reduction in the rate of oxygen uptake by activated sludge.

It is of interest to add that MORGAN and LACKEY[552] have shown that the addition of the chelating agent EDTA can to a large extent prevent the interference of copper and trivalent chromium with the B.O.D. test since this compound forms complexes with, and so 'ties up', these metals.

As an illustration of the effect of a toxic metal on B.O.D., *Table 26* shows the analysis of stream water polluted by copper and much fatty organic material.

Table 26.   Analysis of stream water containing organic matter and copper

pH value	7·1
3 min permanganate value .	14·2 p.p.m.
4 h permanganate value . .	64·6 p.p.m.
Nitrite nitrogen . . .	nil
Nitrate nitrogen . . .	4·0 p.p.m.
Ammoniacal nitrogen . .	0·7 p.p.m.
Albuminoid nitrogen . .	0·26 p.p.m.
B.O.D. (5 days, 20° C) . .	4·3 p.p.m.
Copper (settled sample) . .	1·6 p.p.m.
Copper (shaken sample) . .	5·8 p.p.m.
Suspended solids ⎧ mineral .	30 p.p.m.
⎨ volatile .	81 p.p.m.
⎩ total . .	111 p.p.m.
Total solids	437 p.p.m.

It will be observed that, owing to the presence of copper, the B.O.D. is abnormally low in comparison with the 4 hours permanganate value.

Thus, the available evidence suggests that when small amounts of toxic metallic ions are present in organically polluted samples, an abnormally low B.O.D. figure can be expected owing to the suppression of bacterial activity. Other bactericides present in trade wastes (e.g. phenols, formaldehyde, free chlorine, cyanides, etc.) have a similar suppressing effect on B.O.D. In such cases, the B.O.D. test cannot be safely used as a measure of any organic pollution present and it is better to rely upon the permanganate test which, in general, is uninfluenced by the presence of bactericidal compounds. Among important trade wastes giving comparatively low B.O.D. values for this reason are gas liquor, wastes containing formaldehyde, TNT wastes, and plating wastes.

It is commonly accepted that the higher the 5-day B.O.D., the greater is the concentration of oxidizable organic pollution and, conversely, the smaller the B.O.D., the lower is the content of organic pollution. Although this is, in general, true it must be remembered that the work of many investigators [553-558] has demonstrated that certain types of organic material or organic degradation products (e.g. lignins, many oils, and alkylbenzenesulphonate detergents) are resistant to biochemical oxidation. Hence, these materials are not measurable by the conventional B.O.D. test and they may persist in streams for long periods. They may be objectionable on account of their toxicity, because they may impart unpleasant tastes and odours to waters, or because of their tendency to cause froth. SAWYER and his associates [558] found that tetrapropylene benzene-sulphonate (a common constituent of synthetic detergent preparations causing much froth in streams) is very resistant to biochemical oxidation and under summer conditions in river water had the rather long half-life of about 16 days.

Supernatant liquor from plants digesting sewage sludge invariably gives a 5-day B.O.D. figure which is very much below the value which might be expected from a consideration of the other analytical data. This is illustrated by *Table 27* which gives analytical results for a sample of supernatant liquor from a plant digesting a mixture of primary and activated sludges [559].

Table 27. Analysis of supernatant liquor from sludge digestion plant

pH value	. . . .	7·8
4 h permanganate value	. .	490 p.p.m.
5-day B.O.D. (18·3° C)	. .	193 p.p.m.
Ammoniacal nitrogen	. .	440 p.p.m.
Albuminoid nitrogen	.	78 p.p.m.
Suspended solids ⎰ mineral	.	320 p.p.m.
⎱ volatile	.	750 p.p.m.
total .	.	1,070 p.p.m.
Total solids	. . . .	2,930 p.p.m.

Investigation of the B.O.D. of this sample for various periods of time up to 9 days showed that a lag period occurred during the first few days resulting in an abnormally low 5-day B.O.D. After about 5 days, however, the oxygen demand increased rapidly as shown graphically in *Figure 1*. Since supernatant liquor is rich

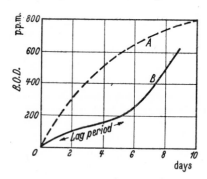

Figure 1. B.O.D. curve of digested sludge supernatant liquor.
A = B.O.D. curve of normal sewage. B = B.O.D. curve of supernatant liquor

in anaerobic organisms, it is probable that the cause of the lag period is related to a change from an anaerobic type of fermentation to an aerobic type. Any liquor which has undergone anaerobic fermentation (e.g. septic sewage) can be expected to behave in a similar way and show a tendency to yield low B.O.D. values.

Summarizing, it can be said that the B.O.D. estimation still remains the best available single test for assessing organic pollution but its errors, shortcomings and limitations must be borne in mind and the result of any test correlated with the other analytical data. When 5-day B.O.D. values are obtained which are low in relation to the permanganate value or the dichromate value, toxic or bacteriostatic substance may be present, the seed used may be unsuitable or may require acclimatization, the sample may contain substances resistant to biochemical oxidation or a preponderance of anaerobic organisms may be causing a lag period. In such cases, a study of the long-term B.O.D.–time curve may be of considerable value.

THE RATIO OF THE B.O.D. TO THE 4 HOURS PERMANGANATE VALUE

The 5-day B.O.D. of crude domestic sewage is usually about 2–4 times the 4 hours N/80 permanganate value and B.O.D.:permanganate ratios of a similar order of magnitude or even higher are generally obtained with trade wastes rich in carbohydrates and with such nitrogenous organic wastes as dairy wastes, piggery wastes and vegetable and other food processing wastes. The B.O.D.: permanganate ratio is, however, upset by the presence of certain non-nitrogenous organic trade wastes and by trade wastes containing toxic substances (e.g. gas liquor, chemical trade wastes, and wastes containing metallic contaminants). This is illustrated by *Table 28*, taken from a paper by HEWITT[560], comparing the B.O.D. and 4 hours permanganate figures for sewages at four Birmingham sewage works.

Table 28. Comparison of B.O.D. and 4 hours permanganate figures for different types of sewage (Birmingham)

Name of works	Character of sewage	5-day B.O.D. p.p.m.	4 h permanganate value p.p.m.	Ratio B.O.D.: permanganate value
Barston .	Domestic	236	59	4
Coleshill.	Domestic	229	76·5	3
Yardley .	Industrial*	222	120	1·8
Saltley .	Industrial*	264	159	1·66

* Contains large proportion of metallic trade wastes.

It will be seen from this table that there is a tendency for the trade wastes to lower the B.O.D.: permanganate ratio. To explain these results, Hewitt suggests that whilst the permanganate test indicates the actual amount of organic impurity to be treated, the B.O.D. is more of an indication of the relative ease with which biochemical oxidation takes place. Thus, when this ratio is less than about 3, the sewage will be less amenable to biochemical oxidation, whereas if the ratio is 3 or more, the sewage will be more easily treatable by aerobic biological processes.

The effect of inhibitory trade wastes in lowering the B.O.D.: permanganate ratio is also strikingly shown by results obtained at Huddersfield by GOLDTHORPE and NIXON[561]. They found that by mixing chemical trade wastes (containing iron, organic chemicals and dyestuffs) with sewage in varying proportions the B.O.D.: permanganate ratio varied from as little as 0·2, when only chemical wastes were present, to over 3·0 when only sewage was present, with intermediate values dependent on the relative proportions of chemical wastes and sewage.

Although, as a rule, when inhibitory trade wastes are absent, sewages and tank effluents as well as imperfectly purified sewage effluents give high B.O.D.: permanganate ratios (over 1·0), well-purified sewage effluents and good effluents from the treatment of nitrogenous organic trade wastes give ratios less than 1·0 (i.e. the

10—I

B.O.D. is less than the permanganate value). River waters relatively free from organic pollution (e.g. the upper reaches of many rivers known to be unpolluted) also give, in general, B.O.D.:permanganate ratios less than 1·0. When a ratio considerably greater than 1·0 is found in a river water, it is usually an indication of pollution by such discharges as sewage, farm drainage, dairy wastes, vegetable or other food processing wastes, or cotton finishing wastes containing starch, and in these cases a bad immediate effect on the river can be expected as regards deoxygenation. Obviously a river water, even if polluted, can give a ratio less than 1·0 if inhibitory trade wastes containing substances toxic to bacteria are present (acid and alkaline wastes, chemical wastes, gas liquor and metallic contaminants), and in these cases there would be a considerable adverse effect upon the self-purification of the stream.

Effect of sewage discharges to rivers on analytical results

The discharge of sewage or poorly treated sewage to a river has a pronounced effect on most of the chemical tests applied to stream waters, as shown in *Table 29* by typical examples of Lancashire and Cheshire rivers.

It will be seen that the effect of sewage or unsatisfactory sewage effluents on the analytical data is to cause decreases in dissolved oxygen and increases in the 3 minutes and 4 hours permanganate figures, chloride, suspended solids, B.O.D., and ammonia and albuminoid nitrogen. As already pointed out (page 113), the increase in the ammonia nitrogen figure affords a specially delicate chemical test for detecting sewage pollution. There is often an increase in nitrite nitrogen but nitrite being rather unstable and liable to undergo either oxidation in the stream or denitrification or reduction to nitrogen, is not always detectable. Where there is little or no nitrate present, the river below a sewage outfall is liable to fail the methylene blue stability test and to cause odour nuisance, especially if the dilution available is low.

HARDNESS

Hardness is most undesirable in river water used for steam raising and for most industrial processes. It is essential to soften hard water used as boiler feed otherwise hard scale may deposit on the boiler plates.

Hardness is due mainly to the presence of bicarbonates of calcium and magnesium ('temporary' or 'carbonate' hardness) or to sulphates and chlorides of calcium and magnesium ('permanent' or 'non-carbonate' hardness). As a rule, any hardness due to calcium predominates greatly over that due to magnesium.

Ca CO₃ handwritten: $Ca\ CO_3$

$MWt = 12 + 3(16) + 40 =$

$48 \quad 100$

Table 29.   *Analyses of some Lancashire and Cheshire rivers above and below sewage works outfalls*

River	Nature of discharge	Chloride as Cl p.p.m.	Permanganate value 3 min p.p.m.	Permanganate value 4 h p.p.m.	Suspended solids p.p.m.	Nitrogen Ammonia p.p.m.	Nitrogen Albuminoid p.p.m.	Nitrogen Nitrite p.p.m.	Nitrogen Nitrate p.p.m.	B.O.D. p.p.m.	Dissolved Oxygen. % of saturation	Methylene blue stability test
R. Keer above	—	16	0·2	1·1	nil	0·42	0·12	nil	2·8	1·6	98	Passed
R. Keer below	Crude sewage	80	88·4	246	1350	47·6	22·5	nil	1·6	860	5	Failed 1 day (H₂S)
Tributary above	—	29	1·6	6·9	4	nil	0·4	nil	2·2	6·8	71	Passed
Tributary below	Settled sewage	48	6·8	20·4	8	27·1	0·9	trace	1·0	52·8	nil	Failed 18 h (H₂S)
Stock Beck above	—	15	0·4	2·8	13	0·2	0·2	nil	2·6	3·1	93	Passed
Stock Beck below	Bad sewage effluent	45	6·4	17·4	41	14·8	1·66	1·5	6·1	20·1	18	Passed
R. Alt above	—	22	2·0	6·4	8	1·4	0·42	nil	1·3	7·4	41	Passed
R. Alt below	Poor sewage effluent	74	6·2	19·2	33	5·8	2·34	2·8	26·8	18·8	7	Passed
R. Bollin above	—	23	1·3	4·7	9	0·4	0·38	nil	2·4	6·3	76	Passed
R. Bollin below	Unsatisfactory sewage effluent	51	4·6	14·2	25	4·2	1·28	0·5	11·6	15·1	6	Passed

A convenient classification of waters according to their hardness is given in a report published for the Ministry of Health [562] given in *Table 30*.

Table 30.   *Classification of waters according to hardness (Ministry of Health [562])*

Hardness (expressed as p.p.m. of CaCO₃)	Description of water
0–50	Soft
50–100	Moderately soft
100–150	Slightly hard
150–200	Moderately hard
200–300	Hard
Over 300	Very hard

A connection between high carbonate hardness and organic pollution has been reported by HEINSEN and others [563-565] to exist in the case of ground waters, and is ascribed to the increased solubility of calcium carbonate in the presence of proteins, humus and weak acids produced by the oxidation of organic matter.

The hardness of a river water is of considerable significance in connection with the discharge of effluents containing certain toxic metallic ions to fishing streams.   In particular, zinc and lead are much less toxic to fish in hard waters containing considerable amounts of calcium salts than in soft waters [577].

ALKALINITY, ACIDITY AND pH

The pH scale affords a convenient method of expressing the *intensity* of the alkalinity or acidity of a water. On the other hand pH gives no indication of the *quantity* of alkali or acid present; this must be determined by titration with standard acid or alkali respectively. A knowledge of pH value does enable us, however, to understand the kind of acidity or alkalinity present in a water. *Table 31* shows the relation between pH and the kinds of acidity and alkalinity in river waters, but it must be borne in mind that these relationships may be somewhat modified in the presence of certain types of pollution.

Table 31. Relation between pH and kinds of acidity and alkalinity in river waters

Approximate pH	*Indicator changes*	*Indications*
<4·0 . . .	Pink to M.O.	Free mineral acid; possibly organic acids if in large quantity
Between 4·0 and 8·3	Yellow to M.O.; colourless to P.P.	Free carbon dioxide; possibly weak organic acids if pH between about 4·0 and 6·0; bicarbonate alkalinity
Between 8·3 and 9·4	Pink to P.P.; colourless to T.P.	Bicarbonate alkalinity Carbonate alkalinity
9·5 or over . .	Pink to P.P.; blue to T.P.	Carbonate alkalinity Caustic alkalinity

Abbreviations: M.O.=methyl orange; P.P.=phenolphthalein; T.P.=thymolphthalein.

Some acid discharges to rivers have a pH value as low as 1–2 and kier liquors may reach the high figure of 13–14, but dilution and buffer action (i.e. a high bicarbonate alkalinity figure) fortunately play an important part in bringing these extreme values to less harmful regions. Thus, most river waters in this country, unless grossly polluted by large volumes of acid or alkaline discharges, fall within the pH range 5·0–8·5 which is suitable for most fish. Peaty moorland waters containing organic acids or those waters highly charged with carbon dioxide may fall to pH 4·5 or even lower. Such acid waters are usually unsuitable for fish. PENTELOW [566] states that, in general, brown trout (*Salmo trutta*) grow only a few inches long and weigh only a few ounces in acid waters. Nevertheless in Sutherland, Scotland, brown trout weighing as much as 4–5 lb. are found in soft waters with a pH value as low as 4·5. Many chalk streams satisfactory for the support of fish life and other aquatic organisms are alkaline towards phenolphthalein indicator (i.e. this indicator shows a pink colour) and may attain a pH of 8·5–9·0 due to the presence of dissolved calcium carbonate*. Photosynthesis by algae and other plant life in sunny weather can also lead to rather high pH values in rivers; the utilization of the combined carbon dioxide in bicarbonates raises the pH value by disturbing the bicarbonate–carbonate equilibrium thus resulting in the formation of carbonate which can ionize to give alkaline OH' ions:

$$2HCO_3' \underset{\longleftarrow}{\xrightarrow{\hspace{2cm}}} CO_3'' + H_2O + CO_2$$
$$\text{bicarbonate ion} \qquad\qquad \text{carbonate ion}$$
$$CO_3'' + H_2O \xrightarrow{\hspace{2cm}} HCO_3' + OH'$$

Indeed, SAWYER[567] states that waters containing algae which are actively reproducing can have a pH value as high as 9·8. Even higher pH values (over 10 on sunny days) were reported by WADDINGTON[568] on the River Tweed (Scotland) after a long period of dry weather when large quantities of the filamentous alga *Cladophora glomerata* were present. During hourly sampling on one day, the pH rose to a maximum of 10·5 at 4 p.m. but fell at night to 7·8.

According to HUET[569] the best waters for the support and rearing of fish life are those with pH values between 7 and 8 and having a reserve alkalinity (to methyl orange) of 100 p.p.m. (expressed as $CaCO_3$) which helps to prevent any sudden change in pH value. Waters with an alkalinity figure of less than 25 p.p.m. are not considered advantageous for fish since owing to their low buffering action, death of fish may occur when there is a sudden fall in pH brought about by an acid discharge or by organic acids from decaying vegetation.

The significance of alkalinity in the oxidation of sewage and in the biochemical changes occurring in streams has been studied by ECKENFELDER and HOOD[570–572]. During oxidation of sewage there is a decrease in alkalinity caused by oxidation of carbonaceous matter to acidic substances, assimilation of ammonia by micro-organisms and oxidation of ammonia to nitric acid. Alkalinity determinations therefore give some indication of the degree of oxidation at any stage during the treatment of sewage. Streams receiving sewage effluents may undergo alkalinity changes owing to utilization of carbon dioxide, conversion of bicarbonates to carbonates by algae and other green plants, oxidation of ammonia and conversion of alkali nitrates to carbonates.

Determinations of pH, methyl orange alkalinity and volatile fatty acids in digesting sewage sludges and in strong organic liquors undergoing anaerobic fermentation afford useful means of controlling plant digester performance. The pH of well-digested sludge

---

* A saturated solution of calcium carbonate in pure water at 15° C has a pH value of about 9·5 and contains about 13 p.p.m. of $CaCO_3$ but, of course, these values would be altered somewhat by the presence of other salts.

is usually within the range 6·6–7·6 and the methyl orange alkalinity should not fall below 2000 p.p.m. (expressed as $CaCO_3$). The lower fatty acids are intermediates in anaerobic digestion but digestion may cease if these are permitted to accumulate. BUSWELL[573] regards 2000 p.p.m. of volatile acids (expressed as acetic acid) as the maximum limit for satisfactory digestion. It is preferable, however, to aim at keeping this figure below 500 p.p.m. if possible[574]. Any rise in volatile acids to 2000 p.p.m. is a warning sign that undesirable acid fermentation is taking place and that the plant is being overloaded. Steps should then be taken to reduce the rate of feed to the plant otherwise the volatile acids content may rise still further, gas production may fall and fermentation may stop altogether.

TOXIC POLLUTION

Some inorganic and organic substances are poisonous towards animal and vegetable life in streams and the number increases with industrial developments. Examples are many metallic ions (e.g. silver, mercury, copper, lead, zinc, chromium, arsenic, uranium etc.), cyanides, phenols, tar bases, ammonia (p. 113), free chlorine, sulphides, carbon dioxide (p. 141), formaldehyde, syndets, and insecticides (e.g. DDT, gammexane).

Table 32 gives the approximate lethal concentration to fish of a few common toxic substances. It must be emphasized that the values are given for illustration only to indicate their order of magnitude. The lethal concentration is not a fixed quantity but depends upon experimental conditions such as the species, age, size, state of health and degree of acclimatization of the fish, the chemical composition of the water, (especially pH, dissolved oxygen, hardness and dissolved mineral salts) and the temperature. Moreover some poisons may increase or reduce the toxicity of others.

Table 32.   Toxicity to fish of some common toxic substances

Substances	Approximate lethal concentration
Silver	0·004
Mercury . . .	0·01
Copper	0·02
Zinc	0·3
Cyanide (expressed as CN) .	0·02
Sulphide (expressed as H_2S) .	0·5–1
Free chlorine . . .	0·2–1
Phenols	1–10
Acridine	0·7–1
Gammexane (BHC) . .	0·035
DDT	<0·1
Toxaphene	about 0·005
Syndets	about 3–5

It will be observed from the table that the lethal concentrations are surprisingly small.

Fish food, animal and vegetable, can also be killed by very small amounts of poisons. Thus, less than 0·1 p.p.m. (expressed as Cr) of chromate can affect the crustacean *Daphnia magna*. Minute traces of copper are destructive to vegetable life, especially algae. Further information on the lethal concentration of substances to life in rivers is given in the literature (see references 575–582).

IRON

The presence of more than traces of iron in river waters generally indicates pollution by mine water or by iron-pickling wastes, especially if the pH value is low and the acidity high. These wastes may contain iron in the ferrous and/or ferric state. The presence of sulphuric acid tends to stabilize the ferrous iron and delay oxidation to the ferric state. Waters containing appreciable iron or manganese are not suitable for domestic or industrial purposes unless specially treated. The U.S. Public Health Service has a maximum permitted limit of 0·3 p.p.m. for the sum of the iron and manganese in drinking water. For process water used by most industries, the content of iron + manganese should not exceed about 0·1 p.p.m., otherwise some staining of the finished products may occur.

Iron in solution in trade effluents really constitutes potential suspended matter since a yellow to reddish-brown precipitate of ferric hydroxide will form when the waste reacts with the natural alkalinity of a river water. This precipitate blankets the stream bed and has a most objectionable appearance. The Mersey River Board has a trade effluent standard (linked up with the suspended solids content) for iron, aluminium and other metals in solution which give precipitates with the natural alkalinity of stream water, viz. suspended solids + dissolved metals must not exceed 40 p.p.m. (non-fishing stream), or 30 p.p.m. (fishing stream).

According to Ellis[575], iron up to 100 p.p.m. in a river water is not specially harmful to fish or to the crustacean *Daphnia magna* (the common water flea).

CARBON DIOXIDE

Carbon dioxide can exist in streams: (a) in the combined state ('fixed carbon dioxide') as bicarbonates and carbonates of calcium and other basic ions in which form it is harmless to fish; and (b) as free carbon dioxide which is rather toxic to fish.

Ellis[575] states that about 90 per cent of the waters of the U.S.A. containing good fish populations have a free carbon dioxide content of less than 4 p.p.m. and that where the content exceeds 6 p.p.m. there is usually some evidence of pollution.   Acid wastes discharging to chalk streams can produce concentrations of carbon dioxide lethal to fish.   There is, however, considerable disagreement in the literature about the toxicity threshold of carbon dioxide which apparently depends upon a number of factors such as the content of dissolved oxygen and ammonia.   Experiments by ALABASTER, HERBERT and HEMENS [583] have shown that concentrations of carbon dioxide liable to occur in rivers polluted by organic matter affect adversely the dissolved oxygen requirements of fish; for instance there was a considerable increase in the minimum dissolved oxygen concentration needed for the survival of 50 per cent of rainbow trout in 24 hours.   Alabaster and Herbert [509] have reported that carbon dioxide in amounts up to 30 p.p.m. was not toxic to rainbow trout within 12 hours but concentrations of 60 p.p.m. were toxic.   The presence of CO_2 greatly reduces the toxicity of ammonia.

SUSPENDED SOLIDS, DISSOLVED SOLIDS
AND TOTAL SOLIDS

Suspended solids are very objectionable in rivers for many reasons. If the suspended solids contain much organic matter, putreiaction may occur and the stream may be denuded of dissolved oxygen. Mineral and organic suspended matter can lead to silting and by blanketing the stream bed can cause destruction of plant and animal life.   Gritty material can have an abrasive action on pumps, may cause physical injury to fish, and can render the stream bed unsuitable for spawning.

In order to limit the quantity of suspended matter passing to rivers, the Royal Commission on Sewage Disposal [546] recommended that sewage effluents discharging to streams, where the dilution was at least 8-fold, should have a suspended solids content not exceeding 30 p.p.m.   In the case of trade effluents, the corresponding figure was 40–60 p.p.m., depending on the nature of the original waste.

The dissolved solids in a stream depend in part upon the geological character of the watershed, on the rainfall, and partly on the amount of pollution taking place.   A sudden rise in the content of soluble solids at a particular point on a stream often indicates pollution by an effluent.

The figure for the total solids (=suspended solids + dissolved solids) in a stream indicates the total amount of organic and mineral matter which is non-volatile at the temperature at which the determination is carried out.   A sudden rise in this figure may be due to pollution and a fall may be caused by heavy rainfall.   In making comparisons of B.O.D. and other determinations of river samples in different years, it is necessary to take into account the total solids figures. If these figures are roughly of the same degree of magnitude, then it can be assumed that the samples are being compared under equivalent rainfall conditions.

PHENOLS

The presence of phenols in rivers is generally caused by discharges from gas works (e.g. spent and crude gas liquors, coke-oven effluents) but many chemical waste liquors are also liable to contain phenols.

The chief effects noticeable in a river below the point of discharge of gas liquor are the presence of phenols in the river water and increases in the content of ammoniacal nitrogen and in the 4 hours permanganate value. There are also increases in the B.O.D. (not so marked as the rise in permanganate value owing to inhibition of bacterial activity by phenols and other toxic substances in the gas liquor) and pH value, the development of a considerable alkalinity to phenolphthalein indicator, and a decrease in the 4 h/3 min permanganate value ratio. These facts are illustrated by analytical data for two Lancashire rivers shown in *Table 33*. Naturally the magnitude of the effects of gas liquor on a stream depends upon the composition of the liquor (e.g. spent liquor will have a smaller effect than crude liquor) and upon the dilution factor.

Although laboratory experiments have shown that fish can tolerate a few p.p.m. of phenols, KALABINA[584] states that fish are not generally found in waters containing more than 0·2 p.p.m. of phenol. Fortunately, phenols do undergo slow biochemical change in a stream. Experiments by ETTINGER and RUCHHOFT[585] on the persistence of phenols and cresols in polluted and unpolluted river waters in the U.S.A. have shown conclusively that the gradual disappearance of the phenols is due largely to the biochemical action of micro-organisms. Among the factors affecting the breakdown of phenols are temperature, the characteristics of the flora and fauna present, time lags in the development of the organisms, the nature and amount of the phenolic compound present and the presence of nutrient materials (e.g. nitrogen and phosphorus). Breakdown is, in general, more rapid at 20° C than at 4° C. Biochemical oxidation of phenols is also favoured by recent phenolic pollution (which appears to provide phenol-consuming organisms) and sewage pollution (which provides the necessary nutrients). Phenols therefore persist for much longer periods of time in unpolluted streams than in polluted streams. These authors[586] also obtained rather similar results using *o*- and *p*-chlorophenols but the breakdown of these substituted phenols is much slower and appears to require the establishment of a specialized microflora.

Table 33. *Effect of gas liquor discharges on two Lancashire rivers*

	R. Irwell		R. Douglas	
	Above discharge	*Below discharge*	*Above discharge*	*Below discharge*
pH value	8·2	9·1	7·6	8·8
Permanganate value. 3 min p.p.m. . .	3·6	19·0	8·0	29·6
Permanganate value. 4 h p.p.m. . .	12·0	40·0	19·4	51·2
Alkalinity to methyl orange. p.p.m. of CaCO₃.	60	125	235	323
Alkalinity to phenolphthalein. p.p.m. of CaCO₃.	nil	50	nil	70
B.O.D. (5 days, 20° C) p.p.m. . . .	14·6	28·8	25·2	40·4
Ammoniacal nitrogen p.p.m. . . .	0·8	17·0	0·7	33·9
Phenols (as cresols) p.p.m.	trace	1·5	nil	7·5

BIBLIOGRAPHY

Recommended or standard methods of analysis

1 Ministry of Housing and Local Government. *Methods of chemical analysis as applied to sewage and sewage effluents.* 2nd Ed. H.M.S.O., London, 1956

2 *Standard methods for the examination of water, sewage and industrial wastes.* 10th ed. American Public Health Association, New York, 1955

3 *Recommended methods for the analysis of trade effluents.* (Recommended by the joint committee of the Association of British Chemical Manufacturers and the Society for Analytical Chemistry.) The Society for Analytical Chemistry, London, 1958

4 *Approved methods for the physical and chemical examination of water.* 2nd ed. Institution of Water Engineers, London, 1953. [For potable waters and untreated natural waters]

5 Ministry of Health and Ministry of Housing and Local Government. Reports on Public Health and Medical Subjects No. 71. *The Bacteriological examination of Water Supplies.* 3rd ed. H.M.S.O., London, 1956

6 ROBERTS, C. H., GRINDLEY, J. and WILLIAMS, E. H., *Fishery Investigations,* Series I, Vol. IV, No. 2. 'Chemical methods for the study of river pollution.' Ministry of Agriculture and Fisheries. H.M.S.O., London, 1940. [For river waters]

7 ELLIS, M. M., WESTFALL, B. A. and ELLIS, M. D., *Determination of water quality.* Research Report 9. U.S. Fish and Wildlife Service. U.S. Govt. Printing Office, Washington, 1948. [For natural and polluted waters]

8 *Manual on Industrial Water.* 2nd revised ed. American Society for Testing Materials, Philadelphia, 1954

9 HAASE, L. W. and Gesellschaft Deutscher Chemiker E.V. German standard methods for the examination of water, sewage, and sludge, with section on bacteriological methods (in German). Verlag Chemie, Weinheim, 1954

10 B.S. 1427: 1949. 'Tests for water used in steam generation.' British Standards Institution, London, 1949

11 B.S. 2455: 1954. 'Methods of sampling and testing boiler-water deposits.' British Standards Institution, London, 1954

12 B.S. 1170: 1947. 'Treatment of water for marine boilers.' British Standards Institution, London, 1947

13 B.S. 2690:1956. 'Methods of testing water used in industry.' British Standards Institution, London, 1956

Other books and papers on methods of analysis of waters, sewage and trade effluents

14 TAYLOR, E. W., *Examination of waters and water supplies.* 7th ed. Churchill, London, 1958. [A standard work known as 'Thresh, Beale and Suckling', after the original authors]

145

[15] SUTTON, F., *Systematic Handbook of Volumetric Analysis*. 13th ed. Revised by J. Grant. Butterworths, London, 1955. [Section on analysis of natural waters and sewage]

[16] DICKINSON, D., *The chemical analysis of waters, boiler and feed waters, sewage and effluents.* 2nd ed. Blackie & Son, London, 1950. 3rd ed. in preparation. [An excellent and inexpensive little handbook]

[17] THEROUX, F. R., ELDRIDGE, E. F. and MALLMANN, W. L., *Laboratory manual for chemical and bacterial analysis of water and sewage.* 3rd ed. McGraw-Hill, New York and London, 1943

[18] LOVETT, M. and FISH, H., 'Some notes on the analysis of sewage and trade effluents', *J. Inst. Sew. Purif.*, 1 (1950) 5–13

[19] WISHART, J. M. and LOVETT, M., 'The chemistry of sewage containing trade wastes, with demonstrations of analytical methods and tests', *J. Inst. Sew. Purif.*, 1 (1935) 152–63

[20] KEY, A., *Gas works effluents and ammonia.* 2nd Ed. Revised by GARDINER, P. C. Institution of Gas Engineers, London, 1956. [Section on analysis of Gas liquors]

[21] ISAAC, P. C. G. (Ed.). *The treatment of trade waste waters and the prevention of river pollution.* Section on 'The analysis of trade-waste waters' by BURGESS, S. G., pp. 65–84. University of Durham and *Contract Rec.*, London, 1957

Micro-analytical methods in water and sewage analysis

[22] DAWSON, P. S. S. and JENKINS, S. H., 'Application of micro-analytical methods to the examination of sewage', *Sewage Wks J.*, 17 (1945) 525–37. [Deals with micro-estimation of ammonia, nitrite, nitrate, phosphorus, dissolved oxygen, B.O.D., and grease]

[23] TOMIYAMA, T., 'Microchemical methods for water analysis. I. Micro-volumetric determination of oxygen, alkalinity and chloride in water', *J. agric. chem. Soc. Japan*, 13 (1936) 1023. Also *Summ. curr. Lit. Wat. Pollut.*, 11 (1938) 302–3

[24] TOMIYAMA, T. and SUETOMI, H., 'Microchemical methods for water analysis. II. A new micro-method for the estimation of oxygen consumed by permanganate', *J. agric. chem. Soc. Japan*, 13 (1936) 1034. Also *Summ. curr. Lit. Wat. Pollut.* 11 (1938) 302–3

[25] CONWAY, E. J., *Microdiffusion analysis and volumetric error.* 4th ed. Crosby Lockwood and Son, London, 1957

Sampling
(see also references 1, 2 and 3)

[26] WEBBER, H. F. P., 'Some sanitary aspects of waters and water supplies', *Brewers' J., Lond.*, 89 (1953) No. 1053, 242–6

[27] VELZ, C. J., 'Sampling for effective evaluation of stream pollution', *Sewage industr. Wastes*, 22 (1950) 666–84

[28] WOODWARD, F. L., 'Unique sampler for deep-water surveys', *Sewage Wks J.*, 20 (1948) 720–2

[29] GRAY, S. C., TROST, R. J. and MOSES, D. V., 'Automatic wastes sampler', *Sewage industr. Wastes*, 22 (1950) 1047–8

30 HYDE, A. C., 'Pressure cooker stream sampler', *Sewage industr. Wastes*, 22 (1950) 1068

31 WILKINSON, R. and BRIGGS, R., 'A simple automatic sampler for water', *Chem & Ind. (Rev.)*, (1953) 886–7

32 WILKINSON, R., 'An automatic sampler for intermittent flows of water', *Instrum. Pract.*, 8 (1954) 414–15

33 NEWBOULD, D. A. and HEWITT, C. H., 'Automatic sampling at sewage works', *Surveyor, Lond.*, 117 (1958) 463–6

34 WISHART, J. M. and WILKINSON, R., 'Purification of settled sewage in percolating filters in series, with periodic change in the order of the filters'. (Section VIII. Effect of storing samples of settled sewage and settled filter effluent at various temperatures before analysis.) *J. Inst. Sew. Purif.*, (1941) 36–7

35 Ministry of Housing and Local Government. Circular No. 58/52. H.M.S.O., London, 1952

35A HANEY, P. D. and SCHMIDT, J., 'Representative sampling and analytical methods in stream studies', *Sewage industr. Wastes*, 30 (1958) 812–20

Calculations, physical and chemical constants and data, mathematical tables

36 MELLOR, J. W., *Higher mathematics for students of chemistry and physics.* 4th ed. Longmans, Green, London, 1912

37 B.S. 350: 1944, incorporating Addendum No. 1, 1949. 'Conversion factors and tables.' British Standards Institution, London

38 HODGMAN, C. D. (Ed.), *Handbook of Chemistry and Physics.* A ready-reference book of chemical and physical data. 40th ed. Chemical Rubber Pub. Co., Cleveland, Ohio, 1958

39 FORSYTHE, W. E., *Smithsonian Physical Tables.* 9th ed. Smithsonian Institution, Washington, 1954. [A valuable collection of mathematical and physical tables]

40 BAYLEY, T., *A Pocket Book for Chemists.* 10th ed. Spon, London, 1948

41 COMRIE, L. J. (Ed.), *Barlow's tables of squares, cubes, square roots, cube roots, and reciprocals of all integers up to 12,500.* 4th ed. Spon, London, 1947

42 Ministry of Supply. *Five-figure logarithm tables.* H.M.S.O., London, 1944

43 COMRIE, L. J., *Chamber's shorter six-figure mathematical tables.* Chambers, Edinburgh and London, 1950

44 PRYDE, J., *Chamber's seven-figure logarithms of numbers up to 100,000* Chambers, Edinburgh and London, 1922

Physical methods

General (see also references 100–104)

45 REILLY, J. and RAE, W. N., *Physico-chemical methods.* Vol. I and Vol. II. 5th ed. Methuen, London, 1954

46 GIBB, T. R. P., *Optical methods of chemical analysis.* McGraw-Hill, New York and London, 1942

Colour (see also reference 2)

[47] RUDOLFS, W. and HANLON, W. D., 'Colour in Industrial Wastes. I. Determination by Spectrophotometric method', *Sewage industr. Wastes*, 23 (1951) 1125–32

[48] RUDOLFS, W. and HANLON, W. D., 'Colour in Industrial Wastes. II. Determination by Filterphotometric method', *Sewage industr. Wastes*, 23 (1951) 1291–7

[49] PALIN, A. T., 'Photometric determination of colour and turbidity of water', *Wat. & Wat. Engng*, 59 (1955) 341–5; *Wat. & Sewage Wks*, 104 (1957) 492–5

Turbidity (see also reference 49)

[50] SCRAGG, L. J., BRIGGS, R. and KNOWLES, G., 'A submersible photo-electric absorptiometer', *J. sci. Instrum.*, 31 (1954) 75–7

[51] RIES, H. S., 'Measurements of turbidity, a possible method for the rapid and easy determination of alterations in waters. I. Flowing inland waters', *Arch. Hydrobiol. (Plankt.)*, 47 (1953) 489–515. Also *Wat. Pollut. Abstr.*, 27 (1954) 238

[52] ABCM-SAC Joint Committee, 'Sampling and physical examination of the sample', *Analyst*, 81 (1956) 492–8

pH *value*

[53] SNELL, F. D. and SNELL, C. T., *Colorimetric methods of analysis*. Vol. I. Theory, Instruments, pH. 3rd ed. D. Van Nostrand, New York, 1948

[54] BATES, R. G., *Electrometric pH determinations: theory and practice*. Wiley and Sons, New York; Chapman and Hall, London, 1954

[55] BRITTON, H. T. S., *Hydrogen ions*. 4th ed. Vol. I and II. Chapman and Hall, London, 1955–6

[56] B.S. 1647: 1950. 'pH scale.' British Standards Institution, London, 1950

[57] MEDLOCK, R. S., 'The determination of hydrogen ion concentration', *J. Inst. Sew. Purif.*, 1 (1938) 71–94

[58] TOMICEK, O., *Chemical indicators* (translated by A. R. Weir). Butterworths, London, 1951

[59] HITCHCOCK, D. I. and TAYLOR, A. C., 'The standardisation of hydrogen ion determinations. II. A standardisation of the pH scale at 38°', *J. Amer. chem. Soc.*, 60 (1938) 2710–14

[60] SCHAAL, R. and SOUCHAY, P., 'Readily prepared pH standards', *Mikrochem. Acta*, 3–4 (1954) 371–5. Also *Analyt. Abstr.*, 1 (1954) Abstr. No. 2318

[61] BATES, R. G., PINCHING, G. D. and SMITH, E. R., 'pH standards of high acidity and high alkalinity and the practical scale of pH', *J. Res. nat. Bur. Stand.*, 45 (1950) 418–29

[62] LAUCHLAN, A. D. E., 'Borax as a standard buffer solution', *Nature, Lond.*, 154 (1944) 577

[63] Anon., 'A highly alkaline pH standard', *Sewage industr. Wastes*, 29 (1957) 804

Oil and immiscible liquids

64 KIRSCHMAN, H. D. and POMEROY, R., 'Determination of oil in oil-field waste waters', *Analyt. Chem.*, 21 (1949) 793–7

65 SHERRATT, J. G., 'Determination of volatile oil in effluents', *Analyst*, 81 (1956) 518–25

66 ABCM-SAC Joint Committee, 'Determination of non-volatile matter extractable by light petroleum and determination of volatile immiscible liquids', *Analyst*, 82 (1957) 123–6

67 SCOTT, W. W., *Standard Methods of Chemical Analysis*. 5th ed., Vol. II, p. 2078. Technical Press, London, 1939

67A 'Determination of oil in refinery effluent waters', Report of refinery effluent water analytical methods subcommittee, Amer. Petroleum Inst., *Analyt. Chem.*, 30 (1958) 36–40

68 PRINGLE, C. P., 'The determination of small quantities of oil in water', *J. Soc. chem. Ind. Lond.*, 60 (1941) 173–4

69 POMEROY, R., 'Floatability of oil and grease in waste waters. Part I. Analytical standard', *Sewage industr. Wastes*, 25 (1953) 1304–7

70 HOLLAENDER, H., 'Determination of oil content of condensate', *Seifen-Öle*, 79 (1953) 546; *Chem. Abstr.*, 48 (1954) 5407; *Wat. Pollut. Abstr.*, 28 (1955) 51

71 *Standard methods for testing petroleum and its products (excluding engine test methods for rating fuels)*. 17th ed. The Institute of Petroleum, London, 1958

72 *Standard methods for testing tar and its products*. 4th Ed. Standardisation of Tar Products Tests Committee, Gomersal, near Leeds, 1957

Electrical conductivity

73 WILCOX, L. V., 'Electrical conductivity', *J. Amer. Wat. Wks Ass.*, 42 (1950) 775–6

74 GUSTAFSON, H. and BEHRMAN, A. S., 'Determination of total dissolved solids in water by electrical conductivity', *Industr. Engng Chem.*, (*Anal.*), 11 (1939) 355–7

75 SANDELS, E. G., 'An instrument for the measurement of salinity in estuaries', *J. sci. Instrum.*, 33 (1956) 424–8

76 MACKERETH, F. J. H., 'Rapid micro-estimation of the major anions of freshwater. Appendix. A conductivity measuring instrument for ion-exchange resin columns' (by W. H. Moore), *Proc. Soc. Wat. Treatm. Exam.*, 4 (1955) 27–43

Suspended solids, Total solids

77 DEGEN, J. and NUSSBERGER, F. E., 'Notes on the determination of suspended solids', *Sewage industr. Wastes*, 28 (1956) 237–40

77A CHANIN, G., CHOW, E. H., ALEXANDER, R. B. and POWERS, J., 'Use of glass fibre filter medium in the suspended solids determination', *Sewage industr. Wastes*, 30 (1958) 1062–6

77B NUSBAUM, I., 'New method for determination of suspended solids', *Sewage industr. Wastes*, 30 (1958) 1066–9

[78] RUDOLFS, W. and BALMAT, J. L., 'Colloids in sewage. I. Separation of sewage colloids with the aid of the electron microscope', *Sewage industr. Wastes*, 24 (1952) 247–56

[79] BOUQUIAUX, J., MERTENS, A., LECLERC, E. and BEAUJEAN, P., 'Determination of suspended solids in water', *Bull. mens. Centre belge Et. Document Eaux*, 4 (1953) 66–9, 87–91

[80] LECLERC, E., BOUQUIAUX, J. and BEAUJEAN, P., 'The determination of suspended solids in water', *Bull. mens. Centre belge Et. Document. Eaux*, 1955, No. 59–60, 334–9

[81] FRASCHINA, K., 'Filter paper method for suspended solids determination', *Sewage Wks J.*, 21 (1949) 221–7

[82] SETTER, L. R., PRICE, F., GROSSMAN, C. and DEGRAZIA, C., 'Photoelectric estimation of suspended solids in sewage', *Sewage Wks J.*, 21 (1949) 14–22

[83] LUMB, C., 'Some developments in sewage works analysis', *J. Inst. Sew. Purif.*, 1 (1936) 121–36

[84] LUMB, C., 'Improved apparatus for determination of moisture in sludges etc., using perchlorethylene', *J. Inst. Sew. Purif.*, 1 (1938) 146

[85] BARR, T. and YARWOOD, J. I., 'Distillation apparatus for moisture determination', *Chem. & Ind.*, 1957, 803–5

[86] SMITH, J. I., 'Investigation of rapid methods for sludge solids estimation', *Sewage Wks J.*, 6 (1934) 908–19

[87] WISHART, J. M., JEPSON, C. and KLEIN, L., 'Dewatering of sewage sludge by coagulation and vacuum filtration. II', *J. Inst. Sew. Purif.* 1 (1947) 140–60

Radioactivity

[88] GRUNE, W. N. and ELIASSEN, R., 'Studies on the effect of radioactive phosphorus on the biochemical oxidation of sewage', *Sewage industr. Wastes*, 23 (1951) 141–54. [Design of laboratory and determination of B.O.D. of radioactive effluents]

[89] FIELDS, P. R. and PYLE, G. L., 'Detection of trace quantities of radio-active materials in waste streams', *Analyt. Chem.*, 23 (1951) 1004–8

[90] American Water Works Association Task Group E5W-12. 'Instrumentation and methods for testing radioactive contamination in water', *J. Amer. Wat. Wks Ass.*, 44 (1952) 583–94

[91] SETTER, L. R., GOLDIN, A. S. and NADER, J. S., 'Radioactivity assay of water and industrial wastes with internal proportional counter', *Analyt. Chem.*, 26 (1954) 1304–6. [Determination of α- and β-activity at low levels]

[92] SETTER, L. R. and GOLDIN, A. S., 'Measurement of low-level radioactivity in water', *J. Amer. Wat. Wks. Ass.*, 48 (1956) 1373–9

[93] KAHN, B. and GOLDIN, A. S., 'Radiochemical procedures for the identification of the more hazardous nuclides', *J. Amer. Wat. Wks Ass.*, 49 (1957) 767–71

[94] LOVERIDGE, B. A. and THOMAS, A. M., 'The determination of radio-strontium in effluents', *U.K. At. Energy Auth., Research Group Rep. No. C/R 2294.* Harwell, 1957

95 SMALES, A. A., *et al.*, 'The monitoring of effluent for alpha emitters. Part 2. Methods for the determination of Uranium, Polonium and other alpha emitters. U.K. At. Energy Auth., Research Group *Rep. No. C/R 2223.* Harwell, 1957

96 COOK, G. B. and DUNCAN, J. F., *Modern Radiochemical Practice.* Oxford University Press, London, 1952

97 WHITEHOUSE, W. J. and PUTNAM, J. L., *Radioactive Isotopes.* Oxford University Press, London, 1953

Froth

98 OKURA, T., 'Rapid estimation of water pollution by paper and pulp wastes', *Japan Analyst*, 5 (1956) 96–8; also *Wat. Pollut. Abstr.*, 30 (1957) 322

99 MUNRO, L. A., YATABE, M. and ABRAMS, W. J., 'Pilot plant studies of frothing in sewage treatment plants', *Sewage industr. Wastes*, 28 (1956) 1232–9

Other physical methods

100 WILLARD, H. H., MERRITT, L. L. and DEAN, J. A., *Instrumental methods of analysis.* 3rd Ed. Van Nostrand, New York, 1958

101 EWING, G. W., *Instrumental methods of chemical analysis.* McGraw-Hill, New York and London, 1954

102 HARLEY, J. H. and WIBERLEY, S. E., *Instrumental analysis.* Wiley and Sons, New York, 1954

103 BERL, W. G., *Physical methods in chemical analysis.* 2 vols. Academic Press, New York, 1950–1

104 STROUTS, C. R. N., GILFILLAN, J. H. and WILSON, H. N., *Analytical Chemistry: the working tools.* 2 vols. Oxford University Press, London, 1955

105 LEDERER, E. and LEDERER, M., *Chromatography: a review of principles and applications.* 2nd Ed. Elsevier Publishing Co., London and New York, 1957

106 GRANT, R. A., 'A recording dielectrometric method for column chromatography', *J. appl. Chem.*, 8 (1958) 136–40

107 HOLLUTA, J. and TALSKY, J., 'The chromatographic determination of organic substances in natural waters', *Vom Wasser*, 22 (1955) 212–42; also *Wat. Pollut. Abstr.* 30 (1957) 197–8

108 MELLON, M. G., *Analytical absorption spectroscopy.* Wiley and Sons, New York, 1950

109 LOTHIAN, G. F., *Absorption spectrophotometry.* Hilger and Watts, London, 1958

109A HOATHER, R. C., 'Applications of spectrophotometry in the examination of waters', *Proc. Soc. Wat. Treatm. Exam.*, 2 (1953) 9–19

110 DINGLE, H., *Practical applications of spectrum analysis.* Chapman and Hall, London, 1950

111 CHRIST, W., 'Emission spectrum analysis in water chemistry', *Chem. Techn.*, 8 (1956) 280–5; also *Wat. Pollut. Abstr.*, 30 (1957) 230

112 *Methods for emission spectrochemical analysis.* American Society for Testing Materials. Philadelphia, 1957

[113] BARNES, R. B., RICHARDSON, D., BERRY, J. W. and HOOD, R. L., 'Flame Photometry: a rapid analytical procedure', *Industr. Engng Chem. (Anal.)*, 17 (1945) 605–11

[114] BURRIEL-MARTÍ, F. and RAMÍREZ-MUÑOZ, J., *Flame Photometry*. Elsevier Publishing Co., New York, London, Amsterdam, Brussels; Cleaver-Hume Press, London; Van Nostrand Co., New York, 1957

[115] ISAAC, P. C. G. (Ed.), *The treatment of trade waste waters and the prevention of river pollution*. Section on 'Photoelectric instruments in the measurement of trade wastes', by Boxall, S. J., pp. 91–98 [Description of Flame Photometer] University of Durham and Contract. Rec., London, 1957

[116] MILNER, G. W. C., *The Principles and Applications of Polarography and other Electroanalytical Processes*. Longmans Green, London, 1957

[117] KOLTHOFF, I. M. and LINGANE, J. J., *Polarography*. 2 vols. 2nd. ed. Interscience Publishers, New York and London, 1952

[118] BUTTS, P. G. and MELLON, M. G., 'Polarographic determination of metals in industrial wastes', *Sewage industr. Wastes*, 23 (1951) 59–63

Chemical methods

General reference works on chemical analysis

[119] HILLEBRAND, W. F. and LUNDELL, G. E. F., *Applied Inorganic Analysis (with special reference to metals, minerals and rocks)*. 2nd ed. revised by G. E. F. Lundell, H. A. Bright and J. I. Hoffman. Wiley and Sons, New York, 1953

[120] SCOTT, W. W., *Standard Methods of Chemical Analysis*. Edited by N. H. Furman. 2 vols. 5th ed. Technical Press, London, 1939. Reprinted 1952

[121] MELLOR, J. W. and THOMPSON, H. V., *A Treatise on Quantitative Inorganic Analysis*. 2nd ed. Griffin, London, 1938.

[122] VOGEL, A. I., *Text-book of Quantitative Inorganic Analysis*. 2nd ed. Longmans, Green, London, 1951

[123] KOLTHOFF, I. M. and SANDELL, E. B., *Text-book of Quantitative Inorganic Analysis*. 3rd ed. Macmillan, New York, 1952

[124] KOLTHOFF, I. M. and STENGER, V. A., *Volumetric Analysis*. 2nd Ed. Vol. I. Theoretical Fundamentals, 1942. Vol. II. Titration methods (acid-base, precipitation, and complex-formation reactions), 1947. Interscience Publishers, London and New York

[125] KOLTHOFF, I. M. and BELCHER, R., *Volumetric Analysis*. Vol. III. Titration methods (oxidation-reduction reactions). Interscience Publishers, London & New York, 1957

[126] SNELL, F. D. and BIFFEN, F. M., *Commercial methods of analysis*. McGraw-Hill, New York and London, 1944

[127] VOGEL, A. I., *Text-book of Macro and semi-micro qualitative Inorganic Analysis*. 4th ed. Longmans, Green, London, 1954

[128] ALLEN, A. H., *Commercial Organic Analysis*. 10 vols. 5th ed. Churchill, London, 1924–33

[129] MILTON, R. F. and WATERS, W. A., *Methods of quantitative micro-analysis*. 2nd ed. Arnold, London, 1955

130 CHARLOT, G. and BEZIER, D., *Quantitative Inorganic Analysis*. Translated by Murray, R. C. Methuen, London, 1957 [a useful survey of methods with particular reference to recent advances]

Works on colorimetric methods of analysis (see also reference 324)

131 ALLPORT, N. L., *Colorimetric Analysis*. Chapman and Hall, London, 1945 [Vol. I of a 2nd Ed. appeared in 1957]

132 SANDELL, E. B., *Colorimetric determination of traces of metals*. 3rd ed. Interscience Publishers, London and New York, 1958. [An indispensable reference work containing a critical selection of the best modern methods]

133 SNELL, F. D. and SNELL, C. T., *Colorimetric Methods of Analysis (including some turbidimetric and nephelometric methods)*. Vol. II. Inorganic. 3rd ed. 1949; Vol. III. Organic. Pt 1. 3rd ed. 1953; Vol. IV. Organic. Pt. 2. 3rd ed. 1954. Also Vol. IIA, *Colorimetric and Photometric methods of analysis*, 1959. D. Van Nostrand, New York. [A monumental reference work on the subject]

134 BOLTZ, D. F. (Ed.)., *Colorimetric Determination of Non-metals*. Interscience Publishers, London & New York, 1958

134A The B.D.H. book of organic reagents. 10th Ed. British Drug Houses Ltd., Poole, England, 1958

135 MONIER-WILLIAMS, G. W., *Trace elements in food*. Chapman and Hall, London, 1949

136 FEIGL, F., *Spot tests in Inorganic Analyses*. 5th ed. Transl. R. E. Oesper. Elsevier Publishing Co., London and New York, 1958

137 FEIGL, F., *Spot tests in Organic Analysis*. 5th ed. Transl. R. E. Oesper. Elsevier Publishing Co., London and New York, 1956

138 WENGER, P. E., DUCKERT, R., VAN NIEUWENBURG, C. J. and GILLIS, J., *Reagents for Qualitative Inorganic Analysis*. 2nd Report of the International Committee on New Analytical Reactions and Reagents of the International Union of Chemistry. Elsevier Publishing Co., New York, London, Amsterdam, Brussels, 1948.

139 *Handbook of colorimetric chemical analytical methods for industrial, research and clinical laboratories* (developed for use with the Lovibond comparator and the B.D.H. Lovibond nesslerizer). 3rd ed. Tintometer Ltd., Salisbury, 1953

140 *Colour measurement and public health* (control and analytical procedures discussed and explained). Tintometer Ltd., Salisbury, 1956

141 CHAMBERLIN, G. J., *Colorimetry and Food-stuffs in Britain*. Paper read at The Symposium on Colour in Foods held on 28–29 October 1953 at Chicago, U.S.A. Tintometer Ltd., Salisbury.

*

Dissolved oxygen

142 Water Pollution Research Laboratory (Staff of). 'Some notes on the determination of dissolved oxygen', *Wat. Sanit. Engr*, 4 (1953) 48–52, 78; *J. Inst. Sew. Purif.*, 1 (1953) 15–22

143 WINKLER, L. W., 'The determination of dissolved oxygen in water', *Ber. dtsch. chem. Ges.*, 21 (1888) 2843–54

[144] RIDEAL, S. and STEWART, C. G., 'Determination of dissolved oxygen in waters in the presence of nitrites and of organic matter', *Analyst*, 26 (1901) 141–7. [Permanganate modification of Winkler method]

[145] THERIAULT, E. J. and McNAMEE, P. D., 'Dissolved oxygen in presence of organic matter, hypochlorites and sulphite wastes', *Industr. Engng Chem.*, (*Anal.*), 4 (1932) 59–64. [Alkaline hypochlorite modification of Winkler method]

[146] ALSTERBERG, G., 'Method for the determination of dissolved oxygen in water in presence of nitrous acid', *Biochem Z.*, 159 (1925) 36–47

[147] RUCHHOFT, C. C., MOORE, W. A. and PLACAK, O. R., 'Determination of dissolved oxygen. Rideal–Stewart and Alsterberg modifications of the Winkler method', *Industr. Engng Chem.*, (*Anal.*), 10 (1938) 701–3

[148] COHEN, S. and RUCHHOFT, C. C., 'Sulphamic acid modification of the Winkler method for dissolved oxygen', *Industr. Engng Chem.*, (*Anal.*), 13 (1941) 622–5

[149] HARPER, E. L., 'Semi-microdetermination of dissolved oxygen', *Analyt. Chem.*, 25 (1953) 187–8

[150] POTTER, E. C., 'The microdetermination of dissolved oxygen in water', I and II, *J. appl. Chem.* 7 (1957) 285–97, 297–308;
POTTER, E. C. and WHITE, J. E., 'The microdetermination of dissolved oxygen in water', III and IV, *J. appl. Chem.*, 7 (1957) 309–17, 317–28

[151] BRIGGS, R., KNOWLES, G. and SCRAGG, L. J., 'A continuous recorder for dissolved oxygen in water', *Analyst*, 79 (1954) 744–52. [Adaptation of Winkler method to automatic working]

[152] TRUESDALE, G. A., DOWNING, A. L. and LOWDEN, G. F., 'The solubility of oxygen in pure water and sea-water', *J. appl. Chem.*, 5 (1955) 53–62

[153] WHEATLAND, A. B. and SMITH, L. J., 'Gasometric determination of dissolved oxygen in pure and saline water as a check of titrimetric methods', *J. appl. Chem.*, 5 (1955) 144–8

[154] MILLER, J., 'A field method for determining dissolved oxygen in water', *J. Soc. Chem. Ind. Lond.*, 33 (1914) 185–6. Also 35 (1916) 457 (Note)

[155] THOMPSON, J. T., 'Recent developments in methods of sewage works analysis', *J. Inst. Sew. Purif.*, 2 (1933) 43–66. [Modified Miller's method]

[156] MOHR, F., *Lehrbuch der Chemisch-Analytischen Titrirmethoden.* 7th ed., pp. 268–9. Revised by A. Classen. Vieweg, Braunschweig, 1896

[157] LETTS, E. A. and ADENEY, W. E., Royal Commission on Sewage Disposal. 5th Report. Appendix VI, pp. 221–5. Cmd. 4284. H.M.S.O., London, 1908

[158] ADENEY, W. E., *The principles and practice of the dilution method of sewage disposal*, pp. 119–22. Cambridge University Press, London, 1928

[159] SYROKOMSKII, V. S. and BONDAREVA, T. N., 'Ceriometric method for determination of dissolved oxygen in water', *Zavod. Lab.*, No. 10 (1950) 1194–9. Also *Wat. Pollut. Abstr.*, 25 (1952) 130

[160] GAD, G., 'Titrimetric determination of dissolved oxygen in water without using reagents containing iodine', *Gesundheitsing.*, 69 (1948) 22–3

[161] ISAACS, M. L., 'Colorimetric method for the determination of dissolved oxygen', *Sewage Wks J.*, 7 (1935) 435–43

[162] GILCREAS, F. W., 'Colorimetric method for the determination of dissolved oxygen', *J. Amer. Wat. Wks Ass.*, 27 (1935) 1166–77

163 ELLIS, M. M. and ELLIS M. D., 'Photoelectric determination of dissolved oxygen with amidol', *Sewage Wks J.*, 15 (1943) 1115–18

164 OULMAN, C. S. and BAUMANN, E. R., 'A colorimetric method for determining dissolved oxygen', *Sewage industr. Wastes*, 28 (1956) 1461–5

165 SPLITTGERBER, A., MÜLLER, K. R., ULRICH, E. and RELING, E., 'Determination of dissolved oxygen in water using *o*-tolidine', *Chem.-Ing.-Tech.*, 22 (1950) 542–4; *Wat. Pollut. Abstr.*, 25 (1952) 130

166 MEYER, H. J. and BRACK, C., 'Simplified determination with *o*-tolidine of dissolved oxygen in water,' *Chem.-Ing.-Tech.* 22 (1950) 545 ; *Wat. Pollut. Abstr.*, 25 (1952) 130

167 BANKS, J., 'The absorptiometric determination of dissolved oxygen,' *Analyst*, 79 (1954) 170–3

168 INGOLS, R. S., 'Determination of dissolved oxygen by the dropping mercury electrode *Sewage*', *Wks J.*, 13 (1941) 1097–109

169 MOORE, E. W., MORRIS, J. C. and OKUN, D. A., 'Polarographic determination of dissolved oxygen in water and sewage', *Sewage Wks J.*, 20 (1948) 1041–53

170 SEAMAN, W. and ALLEN, W., 'Polarographic determination of dissolved oxygen in water containing industrial effluent,', *Sewage industr. Wastes*, 22 (1950) 912–21

171 RAND, M. C. and HEUKELEKIAN, H., 'Determination of dissolved oxygen in industrial wastes by the Winkler and polarographic methods', *Sewage industr. Wastes*, 23 (1951) 1141–9

172 LEVINE, H. S. and KLEINSCHMIDT, R. S., 'Principles and problems in development of a dissolved oxygen analyser', *Sewage industr. Wastes*, 29 (1957) 856–63

173 BRIGGS, R., DYKE, G. V. and KNOWLES, G. 'Use of the wide-bore dropping-mercury electrode for long-period recording of concentration of dissolved oxygen', *Analyst*, 83 (1958) 304–11; see also *Chem. & Ind.*, 1957, 223–4

Potassium permanganate methods

174 McGOWAN, G., FLORIS, R. B. and FINLOW, R. S., Royal Commission on Sewage Disposal. 4th Report. Vol. IV. Pt V, pp. 37–41. Cmd. 1886–IV. H.M.S.O., London, 1904

175 ROBERTS, R. F., '"Oxygen absorbed" from acid permanganate in the presence of chloride', *Analyst*, 80 (1955) 517–19

176 NIEDERCORN, J. G., KAUFMAN, S. and SENN, H., 'Rapid procedure for estimating organic materials in industrial wastes', *Sewage industr. Wastes*, 25 (1953) 950–2

Sodium hypochlorite methods

177 GIBSON, M., 'The differentiation between animal and vegetable pollution of water', *Analyst*, 67 (1942) 125–30

178 BUYDENS, R., 'Determination of the amount and kind of the organic substances in drinking water', *J. Pharm. Belg.*, 17 (1935) 343, 359. Also *Summ. curr. Lit. Wat. Pollut.*, 9 (1936) 51

179 DIXON, F. and JENKINS, D. C., 'Note on use of hypochlorite in water analysis', *Analyst*, 64 (1939) 735–6

Potassium dichromate methods and methods using other oxidizing agents

180 ADENEY, W. E. and DAWSON, B. B. (Miss), 'The estimation of organic matter in water by means of potassium bichromate and sulphuric acid', *Sci. Proc. R. Dublin Soc.*, 18 (1926) No. 17, 199–202. Also ADENEY, W. E., *The dilution method of sewage disposal.* pp. 130–4. Cambridge University Press, London, 1928

181 ABBOTT, W. E., 'Estimation of organic matter in sewage and effluent: modification of Adeney's acid dichromate method', *Industr. Engng Chem. (Industr.)*, 19 (1927) 919–21

182 LOVETT, M. and GARNER, J. H., 'Strength of sewage', *J. Inst. Sew. Purif.*, 2 (1935) 283–98

183 KLEIN, L., 'The strength of sewage : some comparative results', *J. Inst. Sew. Purif.*, (1941) 174–85

184 RHAME, G. A., 'Determination of B.O.D. values by chemical oxidation', *Wat. & Sewage Wks*, 94 (1947) 192–4

185 INGOLS, R. S. and MURRAY, P. E., 'An oxygen consumed test for sewage', *Wat. & Sewage Wks*, 95 (1948) 113–17

186 MOORE, W. A., KRONER, R. C. and RUCHHOFT, C. C., 'Dichromate reflux method for determination of oxygen consumed', *Analyt. Chem.*, 21 (1949) 953–7

187 PORGES, N., PEPINSKY, J. B., HENDLER, N. C. and HOOVER, S. R., 'Biochemical oxidation of dairy wastes. I. Methods of study', *Sewage industr. Wastes*, 22 (1950) 318–25

188 MOORE, W. A., LUDZACK, F. J. and RUCHHOFT, C. C., 'Determination of oxygen-consumed values of organic wastes', *Analyt. Chem.*, 23 (1951) 1297–300

189 ROBERTS, H. V. and SANDERSON, W. W., 'Evaluation of the oxygen-consumed test', *Sewage industr. Wastes*, 25 (1953) 793–7

190 ABCM–SAC Joint Committee, 'Determination of oxygen demand', *Analyst*, 82 (1957) 683–708

191 CAMERON, W. M. and MOORE, T. B., 'The influence of chloride on the dichromate-value test', *Analyst*, 82 (1957) 677–82

192 FLAY, R. B., 'Periodate oxidation of pea cannery wastes', *Sewage industr. Wastes*, 25 (1953) 953–7

Biochemical oxygen demand
(see also references 1, 2, 3 and 190)

Dilution method

193 McGOWAN, G., FRYE, C. C. and KERSHAW, G. B., Royal Commission on Sewage Disposal. 8th Report. Vol. II. Appendix. Pt II. Sect. 2. 'Determination of dissolved oxygen absorption in 5 days', pp. 93–9. Cmd. 6943. H.M.S.O., London, 1913.

194 BARNETT, G. R. and HURWITZ, E., 'The use of sodium azide in the Winkler method for the determination of dissolved oxygen', *Sewage Wks J.*, 11 (1939) 781–7

195 PLACAK, O. R. and RUCHHOFT, C. C., 'Determination of Biochemical Oxygen Demand. Comparative study of Azide and Rideal–Stewart modifications of Winkler method', *Industr. Engng Chem., (Anal.)*, 13 (1941) 12–15

196 RUCHHOFT, C. C. and MOORE, W. A., 'Determination of B.O.D. and dissolved oxygen of river mud suspensions', *Industr. Engng Chem.*, *(Anal.)*, 12 (1940) 711–14

197 SAWYER, C. N., CALLEJAS, P., MOORE, M. and TOM, A. Q. Y., 'Primary standards for B.O.D. work', *Sewage industr Wastes*, 22 (1950) 26–30

198 HEUKELEKIAN, H. and RAND, M. C., 'B.O.D. of pure organic compounds', *Sewage industr. Wastes*, 27 (1955) 1040–53

199 GELLMAN, I. and HEUKELEKIAN, H., 'Studies of biochemical oxidation by direct methods. V. Effect of various seed materials on rates of oxidation of industrial wastes and organic compounds', *Sewage industr. Wastes*, 27 (1955) 793–801

200 HATFIELD, R., 'Biological oxidation of organic compounds', *Industr. Engng Chem. (Industr.)* 49 (1957) 192–6

Manometric methods

201 DIXON, M., *Manometric methods (as applied to the measurement of cell respiration and other processes).* 3rd ed. Cambridge University Press, London, 1951

202 WOOLDRIDGE, W. R. and STANDFAST, A. F. B., 'Use of Barcroft differential manometer in the estimation of the oxygen absorption of sewage', *Biochem. J.*, 30 (1936) 141–8

203 CALDWELL, D. H. and LANGELIER, W. F., 'Manometric measurement of the B.O.D. of sewage', *Sewage Wks J.*, 20 (1948) 202–18. [Deals with various forms of manometric apparatus, with particular reference to the Warburg constant-volume manometer]

204 SIERP, F., 'A new method for determining B.O.D.', *Industr. Engng Chem. (Industr.).* 20 (1928) 247. ['Sierp apparatus']

205 GELLMAN, I. and HEUKELEKIAN, H., 'Studies of biochemical oxidation by direct methods. I. Direct method for B.O.D.', *Sewage industr. Wastes*, 23 (1951) 1267–81. [Warburg manometer and Sierp apparatus]

206 LEE, E. W. and OSWALD, W. J., 'Comparative studies of the dilution and Warburg methods for determining B.O.D.', *Sewage industr. Wastes*, 26 (1954) 1097–1108

207 WHEATLAND, A. B. and LLOYD, R., 'A respirometer for the study of the oxygen demand of polluted water and sewage', *Lab. Pract.*, 4 (1955) No. 1, 6–10

Other methods

208 BRYAN, E. H. and ROHLICH, G. A., 'Biological reduction of sodium chlorate as applied to measurement of sewage B.O.D.', *Sewage industr. Wastes*, 26 (1954) 1315–24

Organic carbon

209 MOHLMAN, F. W. and EDWARDS, G. P., 'Determination of carbon in sewage and industrial wastes', *Industr. Engng Chem. (Anal.)*, 3 (1931) 119–23

210 ABCM-SAC Joint Committee, 'Methods for the determination of Organic carbon, chloride (chlorion), acidity, alkalinity, and manganese', *Analyst*, 81 (1956) 721–8

[211] MILLS, E. V., 'The determination of organic carbon in sewage', *J. Soc. chem. Ind., Lond.*, 50 (1931) 375T–377T

[212] JENKINS, S. H. and ROBERTS, S. J., 'Wet combustion method for determination of organic carbon in sewage liquors and sludges', *J. Inst. Sew. Purif.*, 2 (1938) 175–80

Stability

(see also references 1 and 2)

[213] McGOWAN, G., FLORIS, R. B. and FINLOW, R. S., Report to Commission on methods of chemical analysis as applied to sewage and sewage effluents. 4th Report, Royal Commission on Sewage Disposal. Vol. IV. Pt V., p. 41. Cmd. 1886–IV. H.M.S.O., London, 1904

[214] STODDART, F. W., 'The incubator test for sewage effluents', *Analyst*, 26 (1901) 281–3

[215] SCUDDER, F., 'Estimation of dissolved oxygen', *Proc. Ass. Sewage Disp. Wks* (1927) 201–3. (See also 5th Report of Royal Commission on Sewage Disposal, 1908. Appendix I, 'Minutes of Evidence', p. 684. Cmd. 4279. H.M.S.O., London)

[216] DE VAAL, H. M. and STANDER, G. J., 'The utility and limitations of the Methylene Blue Stability Test for sewage effluents', *J. Inst. Sew. Purif.*, 2 (1939) 355–60

[217] LEDERER, A., 'A serious fallacy of the standard methylene blue putrescibility test', *Amer. J. publ. Hlth*, 4 (1914) 241–8 (Old Series 10)

[218] HOPPER, S. H. and BRISCOE, O. W., 'Modifications of the relative stability test for sewage.' *Sewage Wks J.*, 16 (1944) 558–70

[219] TIDWELL, W. L. and SORRELS, J. H., 'The relative stability test', *Sewage industr. Wastes*, 28 (1956) 136–9

Ammoniacal nitrogen

[220] HOULIHAN, J. E., 'Rapid method of estimation of ammonia nitrogen in sewages and effluents', *Analyst*, 74 (1949) 511–13

[221] ABCM-SAC Joint Committee, 'Method for the determination of combined nitrogen', *Analyst*, 82 (1957) 276–84

[222] JENKINS, S. H., 'Determination of ammoniacal nitrogen in sewage, sewage effluents, and river water', *J. Inst. Sew. Purif.*, 2 (1950) 144–5

[223] JENKINS, S. H., 'Effect of urea on the determination of ammonia in sewage', *J. Inst. Sew. Purif.*, 2 (1950) 149–52

[224] CROWTHER, A. B. and LARGE, R. S., 'Improved conditions for the sodium phenoxide—sodium hypochlorite method for the determination of ammonia', *Analyst*, 81 (1956) 64–5

[225] KRUSE, J. and MELLON, M. G., 'Colorimetric determination of free ammonia with a pyridine-pyrazolone reagent', *Sewage industr. Wastes*, 24 (1952) 1098–1100

[226] ATKINS, W. R. G., 'The direct estimation of ammonia in sea water, with notes on nitrate, copper, zinc and sugars', *J. Cons. int. Explor. Mer.*, 22 (1957) 271–7

Albuminoid nitrogen and organic nitrogen

227 WATSON, W., 'A criticism of the albuminoid ammonia determination', *J. Inst. Sew. Purif.*, 1 (1935) 191–9

228 MA, T. S. and ZUAZAGA, G., 'Micro-Kjeldahl determination of nitrogen: a new indicator and an improved rapid method', *Industr. Engng Chem., (Anal.)*, 14 (1942) 280–2

229 KLEIN, L., 'Semi-micro determination of nitrogen in sewage sludges', *J. Soc. chem. Ind. Lond.*, 66 (1947) 376. Also *J. Inst. Sew. Purif.*, 1 (1947) 223–5

230 JENKINS, S. H., 'The determination of organic nitrogen in sewage, sewage effluents, and river water', *J. Inst. Sew. Purif.*, 2 (1950) 147–9

231 MORGAN, G. B., LACKEY, J. B. and GILCREAS, F. W., 'Quantitative determination of organic nitrogen in water, sewage, and industrial wastes', *Analyt. Chem.*, 29 (1957) 833–5

Nitrogen as nitrite and nitrate ('oxidized nitrogen')

232 RIDER, B. F. and MELLON, M. G., 'Colorimetric determination of nitrites', *Industr. Engng Chem. (Anal.)*, 18 (1946) 96–9. [Griess–Ilosvay method]

233 KLEIN, L., 'Observations on the determination of nitrite in sewage effluents', *J. Inst. Sew. Purif.*, 2 (1950) 153–5

234 SHINN, M. B., 'Colorimetric method for determination of nitrite' *Industr. Engng Chem. (Anal.)*, 13 (1941) 33–5. [Use of N-(1-naphthyl)-ethylene diamine dihydrochloride]

235 BENDSCHNEIDER, K. and ROBINSON, R. J., 'New spectrophotometric method for determination of nitrite in sea water', *J. Mar. Res.*, 11 (1952) 87–96. Also *Wat. Pollut. Abstr.*, 26 (1953) 291

236 CARON, H. and RAQUET, D., 'Colorimetric determination of nitrates in water in presence of chlorides', *J. Pharm. Chim., Paris*, 23 (1936) 446–7

237 LOVETT, M., 'Chemical tests and the small sewage works', *Sewage Purif.*, 1 (1939) 124–8

238 JENKINS, S. H., 'Determination of nitrite plus nitrate in sewage, sewage effluents and river water', *J. Inst. Sew. Purif.* 2 (1950) 145–7

239 NOLL, C. A., 'Determination of nitrate in boiler water by brucine reagent', *Industr. Engng Chem. (Anal.)*, 17 (1945) 426–8

240 HAASE, L. W., 'Colorimetric determination of nitrate', *Chem. Ztg*, 50 (1926) 372. [Brucine method]

241 LEWIN, V. H., 'The estimation of nitrous and nitric nitrogen in sewage effluents', *J. Inst. Sew. Purif.*, 1942, 266–70

242 SWAIN, J. S., 'Determination of nitrates in boiler water by 1:3-xylen-4-ol (2:4-xylenol)', *Chem. & Ind.*, 1957, 479–80

243 PAPPENHAGEN, J. M., 'Colorimetric determination of nitrates', *Analyt. Chem.*, 30 (1958) 282–4

244 ZWICKER, B. M. G. and ROBINSON, R. G., 'Photometric determination of nitrate in sea water with a strychnidine reagent', *J. Mar. Res.*, 5 (1944) 214–32

[245] HARVEY, H. W., 'Nitrate in the sea', *J. Mar. biol. Ass. U.K.*, 14 (1926) 55–61; 15 (1928) 183

[246] ATKINS, W. R. G., 'Nitrate in sea water and its estimation by means of diphenylbenzidine', *J. Mar. biol. Ass. U.K.*, 18 (1932) 167–9; *Summ. curr. Lit. Wat. Pollut.*, 5 (1932) 380–1

Sulphide

[247] MUELLER, P. K. and RAND, M. C., 'Qualitative spot test for sulphides' *Sewage industr.Wastes*, 25 (1953) 1405

[248] POMEROY, R., 'Determination of sulphides in sewage', *Sewage Wks J.*, 8 (1936) 572–91. [Methylene blue method]

[249] POMEROY, R., 'Hydrogen sulphide in sewage', *Sewage Wks J.*, 13 (1941) 498–505. [Methylene blue method]

[250] POMEROY, R., 'Determination of sulphides in petroleum waste waters', *Pet. Engr*, 15 (1944) No. 13, 156–64. Also *Summ. curr. Lit. Wat. Pollut.*, 19 (1946) 251–2. [Iodine titration method with correction for non-sulphide demand]

[251] HOULIHAN, J. E. and FARINA, P. E. L., 'A method of estimating sulphides in waters', *Sewage industr. Wastes*, 24 (1952) 157–63

[252] WHEATLAND, A. B. and LOWDEN, G. F., 'Apparatus for determination of dissolved sulphide and iron in river waters', *Chem. & Ind. (Rev.)*, No. 46 (1955) 1469–70

Sulphite and sulphate (see also reference 274)

[253] KOHOUT, M., 'The iodine numbers of river waters', *Chem. Listy*, 33 (1939) 129; *Chem Abstr.*, 33 (1939) 5953; *Summ. curr. Lit. Wat. Pollut.*, 12 (1939) 410–11

[254] ABCM-SAC Joint Committee, 'Determination of phosphorus and acid-soluble sulphate', *Analyst*, 83 (1958) 50–2

[255] BELCHER, R., GIBBONS, D. and WEST, T. S., 'The evaluation of barium sulphate precipitates by a titrimetric method', *Chem. & Ind. (Rev.)*, (1954) 127–8. Also JACKSON, P. J., *ibid.*, p. 435

[256] SCHROEDER, W. C., 'Direct titration for sulphate: tetrahydroxyquinone as an internal indicator', *Industr. Engng Chem. (Anal.)*, 5 (1933) 403–6

[257] ALLEN, L. A., 'Determination of inorganic sulphates in sewage', *J. Soc. chem. Ind., Lond.*, 63 (1944) 89–94. [Rapid semi-micro volumetric benzidine method]

[258] McCONNELL, J. W. and INGOLS, R. S., 'Sulphate ion determination with benzidine dihydrochloride', *Wat. & Sewage Wks*, 97 (1950) 330–2

[259] KLEEMAN, C. R., TABORSKY, E. and EPSTEIN, F. H., 'Improved method for the determination of inorganic sulphate in biologic fluids', *Proc. Soc. exp. Biol., N.Y.*, 91 (1956) 480–3

[260] BELCHER, R., NUTTEN, A. J., PARRY, E. and STEPHEN, W. I, 'The titrimetric determination of sulphate with 4-amino-4'-chlorodiphenyl hydrochloride as reagent', *Analyst*, 81 (1956) 4–8

[261] THOMAS, J. F. and COTTON, J. E., 'A turbidimetric sulphate determination', *Wat. & Sewage Wks*, 101 (1954) 462–5

Alkalinity and Acidity
(see also references 1, 3, 52, 54, 57)

262 FEHNEL, E. A. and AMSTUTZ, E. D., 'Ethyl *bis*-2:4-dinitrophenyl-acetate, a new pH indicator', *Industr. Engng Chem.*, (*Anal.*), 16 (1944) 53–5

263 HICKMAN, K. C. D. and LINSTEAD, R. P., 'A modified methyl orange indicator', *J. chem. Soc.*, 121 (1922) 2502–6

264 HARDEN, W. C. and DRAKE, N. L., 'A new series of sulphonephthaleins', *J. Amer. chem. Soc.*, 51 (1929) 562–6, 2278–9

265 BUSWELL, A. M., 'A note on the determination of volatile acids in digesting sludges', *Sewage Wks J.*, 20 (1948) 845

266 HEUKELEKIAN, H. and KAPLOWSKI, A. J., 'Improved method of volatile acid recovery from sewage sludges', *Sewage Wks J.*, 21 (1949) 974–83

267 FROOK, J. E., 'Volatile acids by direct phosphoric acid distillation', *Sewage industr. Wastes*, 29 (1957) 18–23

268 BULEN, W. A., VARNER, J. E. and BURRELL, R. C., 'Separation of organic acids from plant tissues: chromatographic technique', *Analyt. Chem.*, 24 (1952) 187–90

269 MUELLER, H. F., BUSWELL, A. M. and LARSON, T. E., 'Chromatographic determination of volatile acids', *Sewage industr. Wastes*, 28 (1956) 255–9; See also *Analyt. Chem.*, 30 (1958) 41–4

270 MANGANELLI, R. M. and BROFAZI, F. R., 'Quantitative determination of volatile acids by paper chromatography for application to sewage sludge digestion', *Analyt. Chem.*, 29 (1957) 1441–3

Free carbon dioxide
(see also references 2, 4, 13, 14)

271 PARKHOUSE, D., 'Determination of free and combined carbon dioxide in condensates and boiler feed waters and standardisation of the method against known amounts of carbon dioxide', *Chem. & Ind.* (*Rev.*), (1953) 1197–9

272 KOZMA, A. B., 'Sludge digestion—operation and control', *Sewage Wks J.*, 16 (1944) 700–4

273 DYE, J. F., 'Calculation of effect of temperature on pH, free carbon dioxide and the three forms of alkalinity', *J. Amer. Wat. Wks Ass.*, 44 (1952) 356–72

Free chlorine

274 ABCM-SAC Joint Committee, 'Methods for the determination of residual chlorine, cyanides and thiocyanate, fluoride, formaldehyde, and sulphite and thiosulphate', *Analyst*, 83 (1958) 230–41

275 PALIN, A. T., 'The estimation of free chlorine and chloramine in water', *J. Instn Wat. Engrs*, 3 (1949) 100–22

276 PALIN, A. T., 'Symposium on the sterilisation of water. (B) Chemical aspects of chlorination', *J. Instn Wat. Engrs*, 4 (1950) 565–81, 587–99

277 PALIN, A. T., 'The determination of free and combined chlorine in water by the use of diethyl-p-phenylene diamine', *J. Amer. Wat. Wks Ass.*, 49 (1957) 873–80; also *Proc. Soc. Wat. Treatm. Exam.*, 6 (1957) 133–6

[278] MILTON, R. F., 'New test for free chlorine or bromine', *Nature, Lond.*, 164 (1949) 448

[279] MORRIS, H. A. L. and GRANT, P. K., 'Modification of Milton's method for estimation of total available chlorine in water', *Analyst*, 76 (1951) 492–4

[280] BELCHER, R., NUTTEN, A. J. and STEPHEN, W. I., 'Determination of chlorine in water: suggested use of 3:3'-dimethylnaphthidine', *Analyt. Chem.*, 26 (1954) 772–3

[281] KUL'BERG, L. M. and BORZOVA, L. D., 'New method for the specific determination of chlorine', *Zh. analyt. Khim.*, 11 (1956) 470–8; also *Analyt. Abstr.*, 4 (1957) Abstr. No. 1537

[282] MARKS, H. C., JOINER, R. R. and STRANDSKOV, F. B., 'Amperometric titration of chlorine residual in sewage', *Wat. & Sewage Wks*, 95 (1948) 175–8

[283] STRANDSKOV, F. B., MARKS, H. C. and HORCHLER, D. H., 'Application of a new residual chlorine method to effluent chlorination', *Sewage Wks J.*, 21 (1949) 23–30

[284] MARKS, H. C. and JOINER, R. R., 'Determination of residual chlorine in sewage', *Analyt. Chem.*, 20 (1948) 1197–9

Chloride (see also reference 210)

[285] MOHR, F., 'New volumetric method for the estimation of chloride in compounds', *Ann. Chemie u Pharm.*, 97 (1856) 335–8

[286] TARAS, M. J., 'Interference by industrial wastes in the Mohr test for chlorides', *Wat. & Sewage Wks*, 102 (1955) 442–6

[287] HARVEY, H. W., 'The chemistry and fertility of sea waters'. Cambridge University Press, London, 1955

[288] BARNES, H., 'The analysis of sea water: a review', *Analyst*, 80 (1955), 573–92

[289] KNUDSEN, M., Hydrographic tables. Gad, Copenhagen, and Williams & Norgate, London, 1901

[290] LANDINGHAM, J. W. V., 'A modification of the Knudsen method for salinity determination', *J. Cons. int. Explor. Mer*, 22 (1957) 174–9

[291] SCHNEEBELI, W. and STABU, M., 'Determination of chlorides in water (new colorimetric method)', *Mitt. Lebensm. Hyg. Bern*, 36 (1945) No. 1, 20–24; *Summ. curr. Lit. Wat. Pollut.*, 19 (1946) 300

[292] THOMAS, J. F., 'Mercurimetric determination of chloride', *J. Amer. Wat. Wks Ass.*, 46 (1954) 257–62

[293] UNGAR, J., 'Mercurimetric determination of chlorides', *Chem. & Ind. (Rev.)*, (1954) 453–4, 787

Fluoride (see also reference 274)

[294] BOND, A. M. and MURRAY, M. M., 'Direct titrimetric determination of fluoride in natural waters', *Biochem. J.*, 53 (1953) 642–5

[295] MILTON, R. F., LIDDELL, H. F. and CHIVERS, J. E., 'A new titrimetric method for the estimation of fluorine', *Analyst*, 72 (1947) 43–7

[296] MILTON, R. F., 'Titrimetric estimation of fluoride', *Analyst*, 74 (1949) 54

297 LAMAR, W. L. and DRAKE, P. G., 'Factors affecting the determination of fluoride in water with zirconium–alizarin', *J. Amer. Wat. Wks Ass.*, 47 (1955) 563–72

298 TARAS, M. J., CISCO, H. D. and GARNELL, M., 'Interferences in alizarin method of fluoride determination', *J. Amer. Wat. Wks Ass.*, 42 (1950) 583–8

299 MEGREGIAN, S. and SOLET, I., 'Critical factors in fluoride distillation technique', *J. Amer. Wat. Wks Ass.*, 45 (1953) 1110–16

300 SHOUP, R. E., 'Removal of interferences in the Scott-Sanchis fluoride determination', *Analyt. Chem.*, 29 (1957) 1216–8

301 LAMAR, W. L., 'Determination of fluoride in water', *Industr. Engng Chem. (Anal.)*, 17 (1945) 148–9

302 MEGREGIAN, S. and MAIER, F. J., 'Modified zirconium–alizarin reagent for determination of fluoride in water', *J. Amer. Wat. Wks Ass.*, 44 (1952) 239–46

303 LONGWELL, J., 'Fluoridation of domestic water supplies', *Proc. Soc. Wat. Treatm. Exam.*, 4 (1955) 44–56

304 WILLARD, H. H. and HORTON, C. A., 'Fluorometric determination of traces of fluoride', *Analyt. Chem.* 24 (1952) 862–5

305 VENKATESWARLU, P. and NARAYANARAO, D., 'Estimation of fluoride in waters containing excessive amounts of interfering ions', *Indian J. med. Res.*, 45 (1957) 273–5; *Wat. Pollut. Abstr.*, 31 (1958) 48–9

Hardness

306 ABCM-SAC Joint Committee, 'Methods for the determination of hardness, calcium and magnesium', *Analyst*, 82 (1957) 197–200

307 SCHWARZENBACH, G., BIEDERMANN, W. and BANGERTER. F, 'Com-, plexones. VI. A new titration method for the estimation of the hardness of water', *Helv. Chim. acta*, 29 (1946) 811–18. [Complexometric method using ethylene diamine tetra-acetic acid]

308 SCHWARZENBACH, G., *Complexometric titrations*. Translated by Irving, H. Methuen, London, 1957

309 WELCHER, F. J., *The analytical uses of ethylenediaminetetra-acetic acid*. Van Nostrand, New York, 1958

310 DIEHL, H., GOETZ, C. A. and HACH, C. C., 'Versenate titration for total hardness', *J. Amer. Wat. Wks Ass.*, 42 (1950) 40–8

311 BETZ, J. D. and NOLL, C. A., 'Total hardness determination by direct colorimetric titration', *J. Amer. Wat. Wks Ass.*, 42 (1950) 49–56

312 BETZ, J. D. and NOLL, C. A., 'Further studies with the direct colorimetric hardness titration', *J. Amer. Wat. Wks Ass.*, 42 (1950) 749–54

313 HOULIHAN, J. E., 'Total hardness of water by the versenate method— direct titration with ethylene diamine tetra-acetate (EDTA)', *Analyst*, 77 (1952) 158–9

314 KNIGHT, A. G., 'The estimation of calcium in water', *Chem. & Ind. (Rev.)*, (1951) 1141. [Modification of Schwarzenbach method, using murexide screened with Naphthol Green B as indicator]

315 CROOK, L. R., *Sequestric acid and sequestric acid disodium salt*. Monograph No. 10. Messrs. Hopkin and Williams, Chadwell Heath, Essex, 1953

[316] DISKANT, E. M., 'Stable indicator solutions for complexometric determination of total hardness in water', *Analyt. Chem.*, 24 (1952) 1856–57

[317] GANS, D. and RAHAMIMOFF, R., 'The precipitation of calcium oxalate in acetic acid medium', *Chem. & Ind. (Rev.)*, (1956) 32–4

[318] LINGANE, J. J., 'Volumetric determination of calcium in presence of silica, iron, aluminium, magnesium, phosphorus, titanium and manganese', *Industr. Engng Chem. (Anal.)*, 17 (1945) 39–41

[319] DIEHL, H. and ELLINGBOE, J. L., 'Indicator for titration of calcium in presence of magnesium using disodium dihydrogen ethylenediamine-tetra-acetate, *Analyt. Chem.*, 28 (1956) 882–4

[320] TUCKER, B. M., 'Calcein as an indicator for the titration of calcium with EDTA', *Analyst*, 82 (1957) 284–5

Metallic contaminants

General references (see also references 1–3, 131–133)

[321] RIEHL, M. L., 'Analytical procedures for the determination of metals affecting sewage treatment', *Sewage Wks J.*, 20 (1948) 629–39

[322] BUTTS, P. G., GAHLER, A. R. and MELLON, M. G., 'Colorimetric determination of metals in sewage and industrial wastes', *Sewage industr. Wastes*, 22 (1950) 1543–62. [Methods for Cd, Pb, Zn, Cr, Cu, Fe, Mn, and Ni]

[323] FOULKE, D. G., 'Colorimetric methods for analysis of electroplating baths', *Metal Finish.*, 47 (1949) No. 10, 58–67. [Methods for Al, Co, Cd, Cu, Fe, Mn, Ni and Zn]

[324] *Organic reagents for metals and other reagent monographs.* Vol. I. Edited by W. C. Johnson. 5th ed. Hopkin and Williams, Chadwell Heath, Essex, 1955

[325] ABCM-SAC Joint Committee, 'Preparation of sample: destruction of organic matter; and methods for the determination of arsenic and copper', *Analyst*, 81 (1956) 59–63

Arsenic (see also references 2 and 3)

[326] SACCHETTA, R. A. and MACHADO, A. O., 'Detection of traces of arsenic in potable waters', *Rev. asoc. bioquim. argent.*, 17 (1952) 27–9. Also *Chem. Abstr.*, 46 (1952) 8791f

[327] '1st Report of the Sub-Committee on the determination of arsenic, lead and other poisonous metals in food colouring materials to the Standing Committee on the uniformity of analytical methods. I. The determination of arsenic', *Analyst*, 55 (1930) 102–9. Also *ibid.*, 81 (1956) 60

Barium

[328] ABCM-SAC Joint Committee, 'Determination of antimony, barium soluble in dilute hydrochloric acid, and cadmium', *Analyst*, 82 (1957) 764–7

[329] WILSKA, S., 'Quantitative spectral analysis of trace elements in water.' *Acta chem. scand.*, 5 (1951) 1368–74. Also *Chem. Abstr.*, 47 (1953) 2405; *Wat. Pollut. Abstr.*, 26 (1953) 229

Cadmium (see also reference 328)

330 FAIRHALL, L. T. and PRODAN, L., 'Colorimetric determination of traces of cadmium in organic matter,' *J. Amer. chem. Soc.*, 53 (1931) 1321–3; *Analyst*, 56 (1931) 412. [Determination as colloidal CdS]

331 SERFASS, E. J., MURACA, R. F. and GARDNER, D. G., 'Colorimetric determination of cadmium in effluents', *Plating*, 40 (1953) 148–50; *Chem. Abstr.*, 47 (1953) 4241; *Wat. Pollut. Abstr.*, 26 (1953) 229 [Dithizone method]

332 MULLIN, J. B. and RILEY, J. P., 'The occurrence of cadmium in sea water and in marine organisms and sediments', *J. Mar. Res.*, 15 (1956) 103–22

Chromium (see also reference 372)

333 EGE, J. F. and SILVERMAN, L., 'Preparation of stable colorimetric reagent for chromate', *Analyt. Chem.*, 19 (1947) 693–4. Also *Analyst*, 73 (1948) 413

334 STONES, T., 'Estimation of small quantities of chromium in sewage', *J. Inst. Sew. Purif.*, (1944) 241

335 DICKINSON, D., 'Determination of Chromates in sewage liquors', *Analyst*, 65 (1940) 409–10

Copper (see also reference 325)

336 CALLAN, T. and HENDERSON, J. A. R., 'A new reagent for the colorimetric determination of minute amounts of copper', *Analyst*, 54 (1929) 650–3. [Sodium diethyldithiocarbamate]

337 HAMENCE, J. H., 'The influence of salts on the adsorption of cupric ions by ferric hydroxide. *Trans. Faraday Soc.*, 30 (1934) 299–303

338 SWOPE, H. G., HATTMAN, B. and PELLKOFER, C., 'Determination of copper in sewage and industrial wastes', *Sewage Wks J.*, 21 (1949) 1016–27. [Dithizone method]

339 CHOW, T. J. and THOMPSON, T. G., 'The determination of copper in sea water. I. The spectrophotometric determination of copper in sea water', *J. Mar. Res.*, 11 (1952) 124–38

340 JEWSBURY, A., 'Determination of copper with sodium diethyldithiocarbamate in presence of nickel and other interfering elements', *Analyst*, 78 (1953) 363–7

341 BRECKENRIDGE, J. G., LEWIS, R. W. J. and QUICK, L. A., '2:2'-Diquinolyl as a reagent for copper', *Canad. J. Res.*, 17B (1939) 258; *Quart. J. Pharm.*, 13 (1940) 277–8; *Analyst*, 66 (1941) 32

342 HARRAP, K. R., *2:2'-Diquinolyl ('cuproine'), reagent for copper. Monograph No. 31.* Hopkin & Williams, Chadwell Heath, Essex, 1957

343 ELWELL, W. T., 'A colorimetric method for the determination of copper in alloyed steels with 2:2'-diquinolyl', *Analyst*, 80 (1955) 508–14

344 RILEY, J. P. and SINHASENI, P., 'The determination of copper in sea water, silicate rocks and biological materials', *Analyst*, 83 (1958) 299–304

345 NILSSON, G., 'A new colour reaction for copper with certain carbonyl compounds', *Acta chem. scand.*, 4 (1950) 205. [*bis*-cyclohexanone oxalyldihydrazone]

346 WETLESEN, C. U. and GRAN, G., 'The determination of copper in pulp and paper', *Svensk PappTidn.*, 55 (1952) 212–6. Also *Wat. Pollut. Abstr.*, 26 (1953) 126–7

347 SMITH, G. F. and McCURDY, W. H., '2:9-Dimethyl-1:10-phenanthroline: new specific in spectrophotometric determination of copper', *Analyt. Chem.*, 24 (1952) 371–3

348 BORCHARDT, L. G. and BUTLER, J. P., 'Determination of trace amounts of copper: application of bathocuproine reagent to pulp, paper, and pulping liquors', *Analyt. Chem.*, 29 (1957) 414–9

Iron

349 FAIR, G. M., MOORE, E. W. and THOMAS, H. A. (jun.), 'Determination of ferrous iron in river muds and pollutional sediments', *Sewage Wks J.*, 13 (1941) 779

350 WOODS, J. T. and MELLON, M. G., 'Thiocyanate method for iron: a spectrophotometric study', *Industr. Engng Chem. (Anal.)*, 13 (1941) 551–4

351 POMEROY, R., 'The determination of iron in sewage', *Sewage Wks J.*, 14 (1942) 651–2.   [Thiocyanate method using methyl cellosolve as solvent]

352 ABCM-SAC Joint Committee, 'Methods for the determination of iron, mercury and nickel', *Analyst*, 81 (1956) 176–180

353 SMITH, G. F., McCURDY, W. H. (jun.) and DIEHL, H., 'Colorimetric determination of iron in raw and treated municipal water supplies by use of 4:7-diphenyl-1:10-phenanthroline', *Analyst*, 77 (1952) 418–22

354 COOPER, L. H. N., 'Iron in the sea and in marine plankton', *Proc. roy. Soc.*, B, 118 (1935) 419–38.   [Tripyridyl]

355 MORRIS, R. L., 'Determination of iron in water in the presence of heavy metals', *Analyt. Chem.*, 24 (1952) 1376–8.   [Tripyridyl method]

356 HEISIG, G. B., 'Volumetric determination of ferrous ion by means of potassium iodate', *J. Amer. chem. Soc.*, 50 (1928) 1687–91

357 ANDREWS, L. W., 'Titrations with potassium iodate', *J. Amer. chem. Soc.*, 25 (1903) 756–61

358 JAMIESON, G. S., *Volumetric iodate methods.* Chemical Catalog Co., New York, 1926

359 SMITH, G. F., *Analytical applications of periodic acid and iodic acid and their salts.* 5th ed. Chap. VI. G. Frederick Smith Chemical Co., Columbus, Ohio, 1950

360 SMITH, G. F. and WILCOX, C. S., 'New indicators for iodate—iodine monochloride Andrews analytical procedures.' *Industr. Engng Chem. (Anal.)*, 14 (1942) 49–53

Lead (see also reference 372)

361 '2nd Report of the Sub-Committee on the determination of arsenic, lead and other poisonous metals in food-colouring materials to the Analytical Methods Committee of the Society of Public Analysts. II. The determination of lead', *Analyst*, 60 (1935) 541–52

362 GAD, G., 'Simple method for determination of lead in potable water', *Gas-u. Wasserfach*, 79 (1936) 105. Also *Summ. curr. Lit. Wat. Pollut.*, 9 (1936) 199

Manganese (see also reference 210)

363 NYDAHL, F., 'Determination of manganese by the peroxidisulphate [persulphate] method', *Analyt. chim. acta.*, 3 (1949) 144–57

Mercury (see also reference 352)

364 JOHANSSON, A., 'Determination of mercury in pulps, paper, white water, etc.', *Svensk. PappTidn.*, 53 (1950) 231–3; *Wat. Pollut. Abstr.*, 24 (1951) 90. [Dithizone method]

Nickel (see also reference 352)

365 TSCHUGAEFF, L., 'A new reagent for nickel', *Analyst*, 30 (1905) 378–9. Abstracted from *Ber. dtsch. chem. Ges.*, 38 (1905) 2520–1. [Dimethylglyoxime]

366 JOHNSON, W. C. and SIMMONS, M., '1:2-Cyclohexanedione dioxime ("nioxime") as a reagent for nickel,' *Analyst*, 71 (1946) 554–6

367 JONES, B., 'The determination of small amounts of nickel in steel', *Analyst*, 54 (1929) 582–9

368 MAKEPEACE, G. R. and CRAFT, C. H., 'Colorimetric determination of nickel in steel', *Industr. Engng Chem. (Anal.)*, 16 (1944) 375–7

369 SANDELL, E. B. and PERLICH, R. W., 'Determination of nickel and cobalt in silicate rocks', *Industr. Engng Chem. (Anal.)*, 11 (1939) 309–11

370 GARDNER, D. G., SERFASS, E. J. and MURACA, R. F., 'Colorimetric determination of nickel in effluents', *Plating*, 41 (1954) 782–4. Also *Wat. Pollut. Abstr.*, 28 (1955) 236

Selenium

371 FOGG, D. N. and WILKINSON, N. T., 'Determination of selenium in effluents', *Analyst*, 81 (1956) 525–31

372 ABCM-SAC Joint Committee, 'Methods for the determination of chromium, lead and selenium', *Analyst*, 81 (1956) 607–14

373 LAMBERT, J. L., ARTHUR, P. and MOORE, T. E., 'Determination of trace amounts of selenium in water', *Analyt. Chem.*, 23 (1951) 1101–6

Silver

374 JELLEY, E. E., 'The colorimetric determination of small amounts of silver', *J. Soc. chem. Ind., Lond.*, 51 (1932) 191T–193T

375 GAD, G. and NAUMANN, K., 'Determination of silver in artificial mineral waters and lemonades', *Gesundheitsing.*, 68 (1947) 29–31. Also *Wat. Pollut. Abstr.*, 23 (1950) 226–7

Titanium

376 YOE, J. H. and ARMSTRONG, A. R., 'Colorimetric determination of titanium with disodium 1:2-dihydroxybenzene-3:5-disulphonate', *Analyt. Chem.*, 19 (1947) 100–2

[377] REYNOLDS, R. J., *Tiron, reagent for iron, titanium and molybdenum, Monograph No. 28.* Hopkin & Williams, Chadwell Heath, Essex, 1956

Uranium

[378] Department of Scientific and Industrial Research. *Chemical methods for the determination of uranium in minerals and ores.* H.M.S.O., London, 1950

[379] CURRAH, J. E. and BEAMISH, F. E., 'Colorimetric determination of uranium with thiocyanate', *Analyt. Chem.*, 19 (1947) 609–12

[380] TUCKER, H. T., 'The absorptiometric determination of uranium in solutions by an improved thiocyanate method', *Analyst*, 82 (1957) 529–30

[381] CLINCH, J. and GUY, M. J., 'The extraction and absorptiometric determination of uranium as thiocyanate', *Analyst*, 82 (1957) 800–7

[382] YOE, J. H., WILL, F. and BLACK, R. A., 'Colorimetric determination of uranium with dibenzoylmethane', *Analyt. Chem.*, 25 (1953) 1200–4

[383] BLANQUET, P., 'Colorimetric determination of uranium with dibenzoylmethane', *Analyt. chim. acta*, 16 (1957) 44–56

[383A] CHENG, K. L., 'Determination of traces of uranium with 1-(2-pyridylazo)-2-naphthol', *Analyt. Chem.*, 30 (1958) 1027–30

[384] PRICE, G. R., FERRETTI, R. J. and SCHWARTZ, S., 'Fluorophotometric determination of uranium', *Analyt. Chem.*, 25 (1953) 322–30

[385] THATCHER, L. L. and BARKER, F. B. 'Determination of uranium in natural waters', *Analyt. Chem.*, 29 (1957) 1575–8

Vanadium

[386] BELCHER, R., NUTTEN, A. J. and STEPHEN, W. I., '3:3'-Dimethylnaphthidine as a reagent for the detection of vanadium', *Analyst*, 76 (1951) 430–1

[387] BACH, J. M., 'Identification of small quantities of vanadium', *An. Asoc. quim. argent.*, 28 (1940) 108–10. Also *Analyst*, 66 (1941) 130. [8-hydroxyquinoline test]

[388] BACH, J. M. and TRELLES, R. A., 'Quantitative estimation of vanadium in water', *An. Asoc. quim. argent.*, 28 (1940) 111–22. Also *Analyst*, 66 (1941) 130–1. [8-hydroxyquinoline method]

[389] BACH, J. M. and TRELLES, R. A., 'A new method for the quantitative determination of vanadium in water', *Bol. Obras sanit. Nac.*, *B. Aires*, 7 (1940) No. 38, 135; 'Vanadium: its determination in waters', *ibid.*, 9 (1941) No. 50, 127. Also *Summ. curr. Lit. Wat. Pollut.*, 21 (1948), 224. [8-hydroxyquinoline method]

[390] SWOPE, G. H., HATTMAN, B. and PELLKOFER, C., 'Determination of metals in industrial wastes. II. Chromium, vanadium, and cyanide', *Wat. & Sewage Wks*, 97 (1950) 172–4. [Volumetric method using ceric sulphate]

Zinc

[391] FISCHER, H. and LEOPOLDI, G., 'Detection and estimation of small amounts of zinc with dithizone', *Z. anal. Chem.*, 107 (1936) 241–69

[392] ABCM-SAC Joint Committee, 'Methods for the determination of aluminium and zinc', *Analyst*, 82 (1957) 443–8

393 MURACA, R. F., GARDNER, D. G. and SERFASS, E. J., 'The colorimetric determination of zinc in effluents', *Plating*, 41 (1954) 155–6, 161–3. Also *Wat. Pollut. Abstr.*, 28 (1955) 236

394 RUSH, R. M. and YOE, J. H., 'Colorimetric determination of zinc and copper with 2-carboxy-2'-hydroxy-5'-sulphoformazylbenzene', *Analyt. Chem.*, 26 (1954) 1345–7; see also *Wat. Pollut. Abstr.*, 29 (1956) 156

395 HOUGHTON, G. U., 'The colorimetric determination of zinc in water using brilliant green and thiocyanate', *Proc. Soc. Wat. Treatm. Exam.*, 6 (1957) 60–5

Cyanide, Thiocyanate, and Cyanate
(see also reference 274)

396 SERFASS, E. J., FREEMAN, R. B., DODGE, B. F. and ZABBAN, W., 'Analytical methods for the determination of cyanides in plating wastes and in effluents from treatment processes', *Plating*, 39 (1952) 267–73

397 KRUSE, J. M. and MELLON, M. G., 'Colorimetric determination of cyanide', *Sewage industr. Wastes*, 23 (1951) 1402–7

398 RATHENASINKAM, E., 'Detection of small quantities of cyanogen compounds. Test-paper modification of the Prussian blue test', *J. Inst. Chem. (India)*, 18 (1946) 151–3. Also *Analyst*, 73 (1948) 394

399 ALDRIDGE, W. N., 'New method for the estimation of micro-quantities of cyanide and thiocyanate', *Analyst*, 69 (1944) 262–4; 70 (1945) 474–5. [Bromine-pyridine-benzidine method]

400 KRAWCZYK, D. F., 'Review of methods for cyanide determination in sewage', *Sewage industr. Wastes*, 26 (1954) 1388–92

401 KÖNIG, W., 'On a new class of dyestuff derived from pyridine', *J. prakt. Chem.*, 69 (1904) (2), 105–37

402 NUSBAUM, I. and SKUPEKO, P., 'Determination of cyanide in sewage and polluted waters', *Sewage industr. Wastes*, 23 (1951) 875–9. [Aldridge method modified by butyl alcohol extraction]

403 EPSTEIN, J., 'Estimation of micro-quantities of cyanide', *Analyt. Chem.*, 19 (1947) 272–4. [Pyridine-pyrazolone method]

404 KRUSE, J. M. and MELLON, M. G., 'Colorimetric determination of cyanide, cyanate and thiocyanate in sewage and plating wastes'. *Sewage industr. Wastes*, 24 (1952) 1254–9

405 FASKEN, J. E., 'Determination of small amounts of cyanide in water', *J. Amer. Wat. Wks Ass.*, 32 (1940) 487–93. [Thiocyanate method]

406 FRIEL, F. S. and WIEST, G. J., 'Cyanide removal from metal-finishing wastes', *Waterwks & Sewerage*, 92 (1945) 97–8. [Prussian blue method]

407 WEEHUIZEN, F., 'Phenolphthalin as reagent for hydrogen cyanide', *Pharm. Weekb.*, 42 (1905) 271–2

408 NICHOLSON, R. I., 'Estimation of hydrocyanic acid by the phthalin method', *Analyst*, 66 (1941) 189–92. [Cresolphthalin method]

409 ROBBIE, W. A., 'An improved phenolphthalin technique for the microdetermination of cyanide', *Arch. Biochem.*, 5 (1944) 49–58; Also *Summ. curr. Lit. Wat. Pollut.*, 18 (1945) 175

410 *Water Pollution Research, 1950*, p. 31. H.M.S.O., London, 1951. [Phenolphthalin method]

410A SCHILT, A. A., 'Colorimetric determination of cyanide: *tris*-(1:10-phenanthroline)-iron (II) ion as a selective and sensitive reagent', *Analyt. Chem.*, 30 (1958) 1409–11

411 RYAN, J. A. and CULSHAW, G. W., 'Use of *p*-dimethylaminobenzylidene-rhodanine as an indicator for the volumetric determination of cyanides', *Analyst*, 69 (1944) 370–1

411A ARCHER, E. E., 'The argentimetric titration of halide and cyanide ions with dithizone as indicator', *Analyst*, 83 (1958) 571–79

412 GARDNER, D. G., MURACA, R. F. and SERFASS, E. J., 'Analytical determination of trace constituents in metal finishing effluents', XV. The colorimetric determination of cyanates in effluents', *Plating*, 43 (1956) 743–6

Formaldehyde (see also reference 274)

413 FÜRST, K., 'Rapid and simple test for formaldehyde using *ortho*-condensed pyrroles', *Mikrochemie*, 33 (1948) 348–51

414 REYNOLDS, J. G. and IRWIN, M., 'The determination of formaldehyde and other aldehydes', *Chem. & Ind. (Rev.)*, (1948) 419–24

415 BRICKER, C. E. and JOHNSON, H. R., 'Spectrophotometric method for determining formaldehyde', *Industr. Engng Chem. (Anal.)*, 17 (1945) 400–2. [Chromotropic acid method]

416 SCHRYVER, S. B., 'The photochemical formation of formaldehyde in green plants', *Proc. roy. Soc.*, B, 82 (1910) 226–32

417 TANENBAUM, M. and BRICKER, C. E., 'Microdetermination of free formaldehyde', *Analyt. Chem.*, 23 (1951) 354–7. [Schryver method]

418 DOWSE, C. M. and SAUNDERS, J. A., 'Estimation of formaldehyde by Schryver's method, *Biochem. J.*, 60 (1955) Proc. xxi

419 OWENS, D. K., 'Method for determination of free formaldehyde', *Sewage Industr. Wastes*, 27 (1955) 939–40

420 FUKUYAMA, T., SATO, T., WATANABE, A. and KIMURA, H., 'Estimation of toxic gases in air. IX. Formaldehyde', *Bull. Inst. Publ. Health, Tokyo*, 5 (1956) 1–6; *Analyt. Abstr.* 4 (1957) Abstr. No. 3470

421 NASH, T., 'The colorimetric estimation of formaldehyde by means of the Hantzsch reaction', *Biochem. J.*, 55 (1953) 416–21

Phenols

422 MILLON, M. E., 'On a peculiar reaction of proteins', *C. R. Acad. Sci. Paris*, 28 (1849) 40–42

423 NASSE, O., Detection of proteins, *Z. anal. Chem.*, 40 (1901) 193–4

424 FOLIN, O. and CIOCALTEU, V., 'Tyrosine and tryptophane determinations in proteins', *J. biol. Chem.*, 73 (1927) 627–50

425 Anon. 'A review of phenol analysis', *Chemical Age, Lond.*, 66 (1952) 301–4, 333–6; 67 (1952) 89–93, 113–16, 181–6, 219–26, 287–9, 357–61

426 FOX, J. J. and GAUGE, A. J. H., 'Determination of tar acids in drainage from tarred roads', *J. Soc. chem. Ind., Lond.*, 39 (1920) 260T; 'Determination of tar acids and tar bases in road drainage and mud', *ibid.*, 41 (1922) 173T–176T

427 BEIER, E., 'A colorimetric process for the control of phenol removal plants', *Gas-u. Wasserfach*, 98 (1957) 262–5

428 GIBBS, H. D., 'Phenol tests. III. The indophenol test', *J. biol. Chem.*, 72 (1927) 649–64

429 ETTINGER, M. B. and RUCHHOFT, C. C., 'Determination of phenol and structurally related compounds in polluted waters by the Gibbs method', *Analyt. Chem.*, 20 (1948) 1191–6

430 RIEHL, M. L. and WILL, E. G., 'Determination of phenols in water and trade wastes', *Sewage industr. Wastes*, 22 (1950) 190–5. [Gibbs method]

431 HOUGHTON, G. U. and PELLY, R. G., 'Colorimetric method for the determination of traces of phenols in water', *Analyst*, 62 (1937) 117–20. [*p*-nitrosodimethylaniline method]

432 HILL, R. H. and HERNDON, L. K., 'Determination of phenols by *p*-nitrosodimethylaniline method', *Sewage industr. Wastes*, 24 (1952) 1389–96

433 NUSBAUM, I., 'Determination of phenols by the *p*-nitrosodimethylaniline method—a discussion', *Sewage industr. Wastes*, 25 (1953) 311–13

434 ABCM-SAC Joint Committee, 'Methods for the determination of phenols and sulphide', *Analyst*, 82 (1957) 518–21

435 DANNIS, M., 'Determination of phenols by amino-antipyrine method', *Sewage industr. Wastes*, 23 (1951) 1516–22

436 ETTINGER, M. B., RUCHHOFT, C. C. and LISHKA, R. J., 'Sensitive 4-amino-antipyrine method for phenolic compounds', *Analyt. Chem.*, 23 (1951) 1783–8

437 SHAW, J. A., 'Determination of phenols in aqueous wastes from coke plants', *Analyt. Chem.*, 23 (1951) 1788–92. [4-amino-antipyrine method]

438 EMERSON, E., 'The condensation of amino-antipyrine. II. A new colour test for phenolic compounds', *J. org. Chem.*, 8 (1943) 417–28

439 MOHLER, E. F., jun. and JACOB, L. N., 'Determination of phenolic-type compounds in water and industrial waste waters', *Analyt. Chem.*, 29 (1957) 1369–74

440 DRABEK, R., 'Estimation of phenols by means of 4-amino-phenazone', *Chem. Tech. Berl.*, 9 (1957) 77–81

Tar bases

441 KRONER, R. C., ETTINGER, M. B. and MOORE, W. A., 'Determination of pyridine and pyridine-base compounds in river water and industrial wastes', *Analyt. Chem.*, 24 (1952) 1877–81

Hydrocarbons

442 WEDGWOOD, P., 'Notes on humus', *J. Inst. Sew. Purif.*, 1 (1952) 20–31

443 WEDGWOOD, P., 'The nature or composition of sewage and trade effluents', *J. Inst. Sew. Purif.*, 1 (1953) 5–11

444 WEDGWOOD, P. and COOPER, R. L., 'Detection and determination of traces of polynuclear hydrocarbons in industrial effluents and sewage. I', *Analyst*, 78 (1953) 170–3

445 WEDGWOOD, P. and COOPER, R. L., 'Detection and determination of traces of polynuclear hydrocarbons in industrial effluents and sewage. II. Sewage humus and treated effluents', *Analyst*, 79 (1954) 163–9

[446] WEDGWOOD, P. and COOPER, R. L., 'Detection and determination of traces of polynuclear hydrocarbons in industrial effluents and sewage. III. The examination of some gasworks effluents', *Analyst*, 80 (1955) 652–5

[447] WEDGWOOD, P. and COOPER, R. L., 'Detection and determination of traces of polynuclear hydrocarbons in industrial effluents and sewage. IV. The quantitative examination of effluents', *Analyst* 81 (1956), 42–4

[448] MEDIN, A. L. and HERNDON, L. K., 'Determination of naphthalene in industrial wastes', *Sewage industr. Wastes*, 24 (1952) 1260–5

Synthetic Insecticides

[449] BERCK, B., 'Micro-determination of DDT in river water and suspended solids', *Analyt. Chem.*, 25 (1953) 1253–6

[450] SCHECHTER, M. S., SOLOWAY, S. B., HAYES, R. A. and HALLER, H. L., 'Colorimetric determination of DDT. Colour test for related compounds', *Industr. Engng Chem. (Anal.)*, 17 (1945) 704–9

[451] SCHECHTER, M. S. and HORNSTEIN, I., 'Colorimetric determination of benzene hexachloride', *Analyt. Chem.*, 24 (1952) 544–8

[452] HANCOCK, W. and LAWS, E. Q., 'The determination of traces of benzene hexachloride in water and sewage effluents', *Analyst*, 80 (1955) 665–74

Synthetic detergents

[453] Ministry of Housing and Local Government. *Report of the Committee on Synthetic Detergents*. H.M.S.O., London, 1956.

[454] JONES, J. H., 'Colorimetric method for determination of small quantities of sulphonated or sulphated surface-active compounds', *J. Ass. off. agric. Chem. Wash.*, 28 (1945) 398–409

[455] EVANS, H. C., 'Determination of anionic synthetic detergents in sewage', *J. Soc. chem. Ind. Lond.*, Suppl. Issue No. 2, 69 (1950) S76–S80. [Methylene blue method at pH values 3·25 and 0·7, extrapolating to pH minus 2·0]

[456] KAY, S. E., 'Evans' modified methylene blue method for the estimation of anionic detergents in sewage', *J. Inst. Sew. Purif.*, 4 (1950) 403–7

[457] LESTER, W. F. and RAYBOULD, R. D., 'Sewage analysis. I. Determination of anion-active detergents in sewage and effluents', *J. Inst. Sew. Purif.*, 4 (1950) 392–8

[458] DEGENS, P. N. (jun.), EVANS, H. C., KOMMER, J. D. and WINSOR, P. A., 'Determination of sulphate and sulphonate anion-active detergents in sewage', *J. appl. Chem., Lond.*, 3 (1953) 54–61

[459] DEGENS, P. N. (jun.), VAN DER ZEE, H. and KOMMER, J. D., 'Routine method for determination of sulphate and sulphonate anion-active detergents in sewage', *Sewage industr. Wastes*, 25 (1953) 24–5

[460] LONGWELL, J. and MANIECE, W. D., 'Determination of anionic detergents in sewage, sewage effluents, and river waters', *Analyst*, 80 (1955) 167–71

[461] ABCM-SAC Joint Committee, 'Method for the determination of synthetic detergents', *Analyst*, 82 (1957) 826–34

462 FAIRING, J. D. and SHORT, F. R., 'Spectrophotometric determination of alkyl benzenesulphonate detergents in surface water and sewage', *Analyt. Chem.*, 28 (1956) 1827–34

463 Sub-committee on analytical methods, Technical advisory committee, Association of American Soap and Glycerine Producers, Inc., *Analyt. Chem.*, 28 (1956) 1822–26

464 LEWIS, G. R. and HERNDON, L. K., 'The determination of surface active agents. *Sewage industr. Wastes*, 24 (1952) 1456–66

465 EDWARDS, G. P. and GINN, M. E., 'Determination of synthetic detergents in sewage', *Sewage industr. Wastes*, 26 (1954) 945–53

466 BARR, T., OLIVER, J. and STUBBINGS, W. V., 'Determination of surface active agents in solution', *J. Soc. chem. Ind., Lond.*, 67 (1948) 45–8

467 SCHAFFER, C. B. and CRITCHFIELD, F. N., 'Solid polyethylene glycols (carbowax compounds): quantitative determination in biological materials', *Analyt. Chem.*, 19 (1947) 32–4

468 HEATLEY, N. G. and PAGE, E. J., 'Some experiments on the estimation of non-ionic detergents of the polyglycol type in sewage', *Wat. Sanit. Engr.*, 3 (1952) 46–9

469 TSCHOPP, Ernst and TSCHOPP, Emilio, 'The reduction of phosphomolybdic acid to molybdenum blue and the quantitative determination of phosphates in the presence of silicates and arsenates', *Helv. chim. acta*, 15 (1932) 793–809

Fats and grease

470 KNECHTGES, O. J., PETERSON, W. H. and STRONG, F. M., 'The lipids of sewage sludge', *Sewage Wks J.*, 6 (1934) 1082–93

471 LUMB, C. and HIRST, J., 'The determination of grease in sludges', *J. Inst. Sew. Purif.*, 1 (1936) 134–5

472 ARDERN, E., JEPSON, C. and KLEIN, L., 'Short period mesophilic sludge digestion at Davyhulme', *J. Inst. Sew. Purif.*, (1940) 126–30

473 HOLROYD, A., Written contribution to discussion on reference 472., *J. Inst. Sew. Purif.*, (1941) 157–8

474 GEHM, H. W. and TRUBNICK, E. H., 'Grease in sewage, sludge and scum. I. Determination of total and non-saponifiable grease', *Sewage Wks J.*, 13 (1941) 467–84

475 POMEROY, R. and WAKEMAN, C. M., 'Determination of grease in sewage, sludge and industrial wastes', *Industr. Engng Chem. (Anal.)*, 13 (1941) 795–801

476 STEPHENSON, R. J., 'Estimation of grease in sewage sludges', *Analyst*, 74 (1949) 257–60

477 B.S. 684: 1958. 'British Standard methods of analysis of oils and fats', British Standards Institution, London, 1958

478 GRIBKOFF, G. P. and NAKADA, S. J., 'A system for the qualitative analysis of sewage greases', *Sewage industr. Wastes*, 29 (1957) 821–6

Other chemical methods

479 DAUES, G. W. and HAMNER, W. F., 'Determination of small amounts of acrylonitrile in aqueous industrial streams', *Analyt. Chem.*, 29 (1957) 1035–7

[480] FOOTE, F. J., 'Determination of boron in water', *Industr. Engng Chem.* (*Anal.*), 4 (1932) 39–42

[481] POWELL, W. A., HARDCASTLE, E. and POINDEXTER, E. H., Curcumin (turmeric) method for spectrophotometric determination of boron', *U.S. Atomic Energy Comm.*, Rep. CCC-1024-TR-230, 1957

[482] HOUGHTON, G. U., 'The bromide content of underground waters. I. Determination and occurrence of traces of bromide in water', *J. Soc. chem. Ind. Lond.*, 65 (1946) 277–80

[483] RUCHHOFT, C. C., KACHMAR, J. F. and MOORE, W. A., 'Studies of sewage purification. XI. The removal of glucose from substrates by activated sludge', *Sewage Wks J.*, 12 (1940) 31 (footnote)

[484] HINDIN, E., 'Determination of lactose in dairy wastes', *Sewage industr. Wastes*, 25 (1953) 188–90

[485] FOGG, D. N. and WILKINSON, N. T., 'The colorimetric determination of phosphorus', *Analyst*, 83 (1958) 406–14

[486] WELLS, W. N., ROHRBAUGH, P. W. and DOTY, G. A., 'Determination of total and reducing sugars in citrus wastes', *Sewage industr. Wastes*, 24 (1952) 212–14

[487] LYNE, F. A. and McLACHLAN, T., 'Contamination of water by tri-chloroethylene', *Analyst*, 74 (1949) 513

[488] SANDERSON, W. W. and HANSOM, A. M., 'Colorimetric determination of tin in industrial wastes and receiving waters', *Sewage industr. Wastes*, 29 (1957) 422–7

Interpretation of results of chemical analysis

[489] DOWNING, A. L. and TRUESDALE, G. A., 'Aeration in aquaria', *Zoologica, N.Y.*, 41 (1956) 129–143

[490] WHIPPLE, G. C. and WHIPPLE, M. C., 'Solubility of oxygen in sea water', *J. Amer. chem. Soc.*, 33 (1911) 362–5

[491] FOX, C. J. J., 'On the coefficients of absorption of nitrogen and oxygen in distilled water and sea-water, and of atmospheric carbonic acid in sea-water', *Trans. Faraday Soc.*, 5 (1909) 68–87

[492] TRUESDALE, G. A. and DOWNING, A. L., 'Solubility of oxygen in water', *Nature, Lond.*, 173 (1954) 1236. (June 26th)

[493] MORTIMER, C. H., 'The oxygen content of air-saturated fresh waters and aids in calculating percentage saturation', *Mitt. int. Ver. Limnol.*, No. 6, 1956 (20 pp.)

[494] GAMESON, A. L. H. and ROBERTSON, K. G., 'The solubility of oxygen in pure water and sea-water', *J. appl. Chem., Lond.*, 5 (1955) 502

[495] TRUESDALE, G. A. and GAMESON, A. L. H., 'The solubility of oxygen in saline water', *J. Cons. int. Explor. Mer.*, 22 (1957) 163–6

[496] Royal Commission on Sewage Disposal. 8th Report. Vol. II, Appendix, Sect. 4, p. 111. Cmd. 6943. H.M.S.O., London, 1913

[497] COKER, R. E., *Streams, Lakes, Ponds.* Chapel Hill, University of N. Carolina Press, 1954

[498] PRICE, D. H. A., 'Practical aspects of river pollution', *J. Inst. Sew. Purif.*, 2 (1956) 145–8

[499] MOHLMAN, F. W., HERRICK, T. L. and SWOPE, H. G., 'Technique of stream pollution investigations', *Ind. Engng Chem.*, 23 (1931) 209–13

500 SCHROEPFER, G. J., 'An analysis of stream pollution and stream standards', *Sewage Wks J.*, 14 (1942) 1030–63

501 BRIGGS, R., KNOWLES, G. and SCRAGG, L. J., 'A continuous recorder for dissolved oxygen', *Wat. Sanit. Engr*, 5 (1954) 24–5

502 DOWNING, K. M. and MERKENS, J. C., 'The influence of temperature on the survival of several species of fish in low tensions of dissolved oxygen', *Ann. appl. Biol.*, 45 (1957) 261–7

503 *Water Pollution Research, 1953.* H.M.S.O., London, 1954

503A KEY, A., 'Pollution of surface water in Europe', *Wld. Health Org. Bull.*, 14 (1956) 845–948

504 LASSLEBEN, P., 'Is supersaturation with oxygen dangerous?', *Fischbauer*, 2 (1951) 105–6. Also *Wat. Pollut. Abstr.*, 25 (1952) 144

505 Royal Commission on Sewage Disposal. 8th Report. Vol. II, Appendix. Pt II. Sect. 1, p. 63. Cmd. 6943. H.M.S.O., London, 1913

506 W. Riding of Yorkshire Rivers Board. 'Biological survey of the River Wharfe', *J. Ecol.*, 18 (1930) 273–305

507 SPICER, J. I., 'Personal impressions of the Rivers (Prevention of Pollution) Act, 1951', *J. Inst. Sew. Purif.*, 3 (1952) 181–94

508 WUHRMANN, K. and WOKER, H., 'Contributions to the toxicology of fish. II. Experimental investigations on the toxicity of ammonia and hydrocyanic acid', *Schweiz. Z. Hydrol.*, 11 (1948) 210–44. Also *Wat. Poll. Abstr.*, 25 (1952) 70–71

509 ALABASTER, J. S. and HERBERT, D. W. M., 'Influence of carbon dioxide on the toxicity of ammonia', *Nature, Lond.*, 174 (1954) 404

510 DOWNING, K. M. and MERKENS, J. C., 'Influence of dissolved oxygen concentration on the toxicity of un-ionised ammonia to rainbow trout', *Ann. appl. Biol.*, 43 (1955) 243–6

511 CAREY, W. G., *Water and Public Health. 28th Streatfield Memorial Lecture.* Royal Institute of Chemistry, London, 1946

512 KRUL, W. F. J. M. and LIEFRINCK, F. A., *Recent groundwater investigations, in the Netherlands.* Elsevier Publishing Co., New York, 1946

513 REGAN, C. J., 'The sanitary engineer and reports on chemical analyses', *Wat. Sanit. Engr*, 1 (1951) 385–7

514 BRAARUD, T. and FØYN, E., 'Nitrite in polluted sea water. Observations from the Oslo fjord, 1946–8', *Avh. norske VidenskAkad.*, No. 3 (1951). Also *Wat. Pollut. Abstr.*, 25 (1952) 144

515 TOWNEND, C. B., 'Ten years' operation of the West Middlesex Works at Mogden, England', *Sewage Wks J.*, 17 (1945) 1146–73

516 GRIFFITHS, J., 'The new treatment plant of the Colne Valley Sewerage Board', *Chem. & Ind. (Rev.)*, (1953) 421–6

517 *Colorimetric determination of oxidation–reduction balance.* 5th ed. British Drug Houses Ltd., Poole, England, 1953

518 HEUKELEKIAN, H., 'Effect of the addition of sodium nitrate to sewage on hydrogen sulphide production and B.O.D. reduction', *Sewage Wks J.*, 15 (1943) 255–61

519 JEPSON, C. and GREENE, G., 'The availability of nitrates in sewage effluents', *J. Inst. Sew. Purif.*, 2 (1951) 148–50

520 GAMESON, A. L. H. and PREDDY, W. S., 'Factors affecting the concentration of dissolved oxygen in the Thames estuary', *J. Inst. Sew. Purif.*, 4 (1956) 322–48

[521] *Annual Report for year ended 31 March 1953*. Pt VI. 'Prevention of River Pollution', pp. 3–4. Trent River Board, Nottingham, 1953

[522] WESTON, R. F., 'Problems in the application of the B.O.D. test to pulp and paper wastes—a discussion', *Sewage Wks J.*, 19 (1947) 871–4

[523] WHEATLAND, A. B. and SMITH, R. G., 'The biochemical oxygen demand test: a note on variable results from the use of stored standard dilution water', *Analyst*, 80 (1955) 899–900

[524] LAMB, C. B. and JENKINS, G. F., 'B.O.D. of synthetic organic chemicals', *Proc. 7th Industr. Waste Conf., Purdue Univ. Engng Extn. Ser. No. 79*, (1952) 326–339. Also *Wat. Pollut. Abstr.*, 26 (1953) 236

[525] GOTAAS, H. B., 'Effect of sea water on biochemical oxidation of sewage', *Sewage Wks J.*, 21 (1949) 818–39

[526] GRINDLEY, J. and WHEATLAND, A. B., 'Salinity and the B.O.D. of Estuary Water', *Wat. sanit. Engr*, 6 (1956) 10–14

[527] WISHART, J. M. and WILKINSON, R., 'The purification of settled sewage in percolating filters in series, with periodic change in the order of the filters. Results of operation of Experimental plant at Minworth, Birmingham, 1938–40', *J. Inst. Sew. Purif.*, (1941) 15–38

[528] LOCKETT, W. T., *J. Inst. Sew. Purif.*, (1941) 60. [Discussion]

[529] EDMONDSON, J. H. and GOODRICH, S. R., 'The Cyclo-Nitrifying Filter', *J. Inst. Sew. Purif.*, (1943) 57–79

[530] ABBOTT, W. E., 'Suppression of nitrification and denitrification during determination of B.O.D. II', *J. Soc. chem. Ind., Lond.*, 67 (1948) 399

[531] SAWYER, C. N. and BRADNEY, L., 'Modernisation of the B.O.D. test for determining the efficacy of sewage treatment processes', *Sewage Wks J.*, 18 (1946) 1113–20

[532] HURWITZ, E., BARNETT, G. R., BEAUDOIN, R. E. and KRAMER, H. P. 'Nitrification and B.O.D.', *Sewage Wks J.*, 19 (1947) 995–9

[533] MOHLMAN, F. W., HURWITZ, E., BARNETT, G. R. and KRAMER, H., 'Experience with modified methods for B.O.D.', *Sewage industr. Wastes*, 22 (1950) 31–40

[534] ABBOTT, W. E., 'Suppression of nitrification and denitrification during the determination of B.O.D. I', *J. Soc. chem. Ind., Lond.*, 67 (1948) 373–4

[535] ABBOTT, W. E., 'Bacteriostatic effect of methylene blue on B.O.D. test', *Wat. & Sewage Wks*, 95 (1948) 424–5

[536] STONES, T., 'The biological oxygen demand of mixed effluents', *Contract. Rec.*, 64 (1953) No. 17, 12

[537] OGINSKY, E. L. and UMBREIT, W. W., *An introduction to bacterial physiology*. W. H. Freeman, San Francisco, Calif., 1954

[538] LEA, W. L. and NICHOLS, M. S., 'Influence of substrate on Biochemical Oxygen Demand', *Sewage Wks J.*, 8 (1936) 435–47

[539] LEA, W. L. and NICHOLS, M. S., 'Influence of phosphorus and nitrogen on Biochemical Oxygen Demand', *Sewage Wks J.*, 9 (1937) 34–40

[540] HELMERS, E. N., ANDERSON, E. J., KILGORE, H. D. (jun.), WEINBERGER, L. W. and SAWYER, C. N., 'Nutritional requirements in the biological stabilisation of industrial wastes. I. Experimental method', *Sewage industr. Wastes*, 22 (1950) 1200–6

[541] HELMERS, E. N., FRAME, J. D., GREENBERG, A. E. and SAWYER, C. N., 'Nutritional requirements in the biological stabilisation of industrial

wastes. II. Treatment with domestic sewage. III. Treatment with supplementary nutrients', *Sewage industr. Wastes*, 23 (1951), 884–99; 24 (1952) 496–507

542 KILGORE, H. D. (jun.), and SAWYER, C. N., 'Nutritional requirements in the biological stabilisation of industrial wastes. IV. Treatment on high-rate filters', *Sewage industr. Wastes*, 25 (1953) 596–604

543 ZEHNPFENNIG, R. and NICHOLS, M. S., 'Inoculation studies in B.O.D. determination on sewage and pulp mill waste', *Sewage industr. Wastes*, 25 (1953) 61–5

544 TYLER, R. G. and GUNTER, S., 'Biochemical oxygen demand of sulphite waste liquor', *Sewage Wks J.*, 20 (1948) 709–19

545 LEWIN, V. H., 'The routine estimation of Biochemical Oxygen Demand', *J. Inst. Sew. Purif.*, 2 (1949) 140–48

546 Royal Commission on Sewage Disposal. 8th Report. Vol. I. 'Standards and tests for sewage and sewage effluents discharging into rivers and streams', Cmd. 6464. H.M.S.O., London, 1912.

547 Reports of the Research Committee, Sub-committee on Toxicity of Industrial Wastes, Section II. 'Toxicity of mercuric chloride, chromic sulphate and sodium chromate in the dilution B.O.D. test', *Sewage industr. Wastes*, 26 (1954) 536–8; 'Toxicity of copper and zinc ions in the dilution B.O.D. test', *ibid.*, 28 (1956) 1168–9.

548 PLACAK, O. R., RUCHHOFT, C. C. and SNAPP, R. G., 'Copper and chromate ions in sewage dilutions', *Industr. Engng Chem.*, 41 (1949) 2238–41. Also *Wat. Pollut. Abstr.*, 23 (1950) 91

549 COBURN, S. E., 'Limits for toxic wastes in sewage treatment', *Sewage Wks J.*, 21 (1949) 522–4

550 KALABINA, M. M., 'Effects of copper and lead bearing wastes on purification of sewage', *Wat. & Sewage Wks*, 93 (1946) 30

551 DAWSON, P. S. S. and JENKINS, S. H., 'The oxygen requirements of activated sludge determined by manometric methods'. II. *Sewage industr. Wastes*, 22 (1950) 490–507

552 MORGAN, G. B. and LACKEY, J. B., 'B.O.D. determinations in wastes containing chelated copper or chromium', *Sewage industr. Wastes*, 30 (1958) 283–6

553 BOGAN, R. H., 'Biochemical degradation products—a new dimension in stream pollution', *Sewage industr. Wastes*, 30 (1958) 208–14

554 ETTINGER, M. B., 'Biochemical oxidation characteristics of stream-pollutant organics', *Ind. Engng Chem.*, 48 (1956) 256–9

555 LUDZACK, F. L. and KINKEAD, D., 'Persistence of oily wastes in polluted waters under aerobic conditions: motor oil class of hydrocarbons', *Ind. Engng Chem.*, 48 (1956) 263–7

556 HAMMERTON C., 'Observations on the decay of synthetic anionic detergents in natural waters', *J. appl. Chem.*, 5 (1955) 517–24

557 HAMMERTON, C., 'Synthetic detergents and water supplies', *Proc. Soc. Wat. Treatm. Exam.*, 5 (1956) 145–74; also *J. Inst. Sew. Purif.*, 3 (1957) 280–96

558 SAWYER, C. N., BOGAN, R. H. and SIMPSON, J. R., 'Biochemical behaviour of synthetic detergents', *Ind. Engng Chem.*, 48 (1956) 236–40

559 Manchester Corporation Rivers Department. *Annual Report for year ended 31 March 1939*, pp. 48–9

560 HEWITT, C. H., 'The Barston works of the Birmingham Tame and Rea District Drainage Board', *J. Inst. Sew. Purif.*, (1940) 156–76

561 GOLDTHORPE, H. H. and NIXON, J., 'Laboratory experiments on the treatment of the chemical trade wastes at Huddersfield', *J. Inst. Sew. Purif.*, 1 (1945) 109–16

562 Ministry of Health. *Water Softening*. Report of the Water Softening Sub-Committee of the Central Advisory Water Committee, p. 8. H.M.S.O., London, 1949

563 LÜNING, O. and HEINSEN, E., 'High carbonate hardness as an indication of contamination of sub-soil water', *Z. Untersuch. Lebensmitt.*, 67 (1934) 627. Also *Summ. curr. Lit. Wat. Pollut.*, 7 (1934) 379

564 LANG, A. and BRUNS, H., 'Pollution of ground water by chemicals', *Gas-u. Wasserfach*, 83 (1940) 6. Also *Summ. curr. Lit. Wat. Pollut.*, 15 (1942) 287

565 HEINSEN, E., 'Increased hardness—an indication of pollution of ground water', *Gas- u. Wasserfach*, 83 (1940) 261. Also *Summ. curr. Lit. Wat. Pollut.*, 15 (1942) 287–8

566 PENTELOW, F. T. K., 'Growth of trout in acid waters', *Rep. Brit. Ass.*, (1937) Sect. D, 364. Also *Summ. curr. Lit. Wat. Pollut.*, 11 (1938) 164

567 SAWYER, C. N., 'Factors involved in disposal of sewage effluents to lakes', *Sewage industr. Wastes*, 26 (1954) 317–28

568 WADDINGTON, J. I., 'The first two years', *J. Inst. Sew. Purif.*, 2 (1957) 172–83

569 HUET, M., 'pH value and reserves of alkalinity', *Commun. Sta. Rech. Groenendael*, D, No. 1, 1941. Also *Summ. curr. Lit. Wat. Pollut.*, 21 (1948) 254

570 ECKENFELDER, W. W. and HOOD, J. W., 'A critical evaluation of routine sewage analyses', *Wat. & Sewage Wks*, 97 (1950) 138–41. Also *Wat. Pollut. Abstr.*, 23 (1950) 207

571 ECKENFELDER, W. W. and HOOD, J. W., 'Alkalinity significance in sewage oxidation', *Wat. & Sewage Wks*, 97 (1950) 189–93. Also *Wat. Pollut. Abstr.*, 23 (1950) 233–4

572 ECKENFELDER, W. W. and HOOD, J. W., 'Alkalinity–nitrogen relationships in sewage treatment. V', *Wat. & Sewage Wks*, 97 (1950) 507–10

573 BUSWELL, A. M., 'Important considerations in sludge digestion. II. Microbiology and theory of anaerobic digestion', *Sewage Wks J.*, 19 (1947) 28–38

574 Anon., 'Sludge digestion', *Wat. & Waste Treatm. J.*, 6 (1958) 545

575 ELLIS, M. M., 'Detection and measurement of stream pollution', *Bull. U.S. Bur. Fish*, 48 (1937), No. 22, 365–437

576 DOUDOROFF, P. and KATZ, M., 'Critical review of literature on the toxicity of industrial wastes and their components to fish. I. Alkalis, acids and inorganic gases. II. Metals, as salts', *Sewage industr. Wastes*, 22 (1950) 1432–58; 25 (1953) 802–39

577 KLEIN, L., *Aspects of river pollution*. Butterworths Scientific Publications, London, 1957

578 California State Water Pollution Control Board. 'Water quality criteria.' SWPCB Publ. No. 3. Sacramento, California, U.S.A., 1952. Addendum No. 1. Sacramento, California, U.S.A., 1954 [includes a valuable and comprehensive compilation of data on substances toxic to aquatic life]

579 WALLEN, I. E., GREER, W. C. and LASATER, R., 'Toxicity to *Gambusia affinis* of certain pure chemicals in turbid waters', *Sewage industr. Wastes*, 29 (1957) 695–711

580 ANDERSON, B. G., 'The toxicity thresholds of various substances found in industrial wastes as determined by the use of *Daphnia magna*', *Sewage Wks J.*, 16 (1944) 1156–65

581 ANDERSON, B. G., 'The toxicity thresholds of various sodium salts determined by the use of *Daphnia magna*', *Sewage Wks J.*, 18 (1946) 82–7

582 ANDERSON, B. G., 'The apparent thresholds of toxicity to *Daphnia magna* for chlorides of various metals when added to Lake Erie water', *Trans. Amer. Fish. Soc.*, 78 (1948) 96–113

583 ALABASTER, J. S., HERBERT, D. W. M. and HEMENS, J., 'The survival of rainbow trout and perch at various concentrations of dissolved oxygen and carbon dioxide', *Ann. appl. Biol.*, 45 (1957) 177–88

584 KALABINA, M. M., 'Decomposition of phenol in running and standing waters', *Z. Fisch.*, 33 (1935) 295. Also *Summ. curr. Lit. Wat. Pollut.*, 9 (1936) 215

585 ETTINGER, M. B. and RUCHHOFT, C. C., 'Removal of phenol and cresols from natural waters', *Industr. Engng Chem.*, 41 (1949) 1422–7

586 ETTINGER, M. B. and RUCHHOFT, C. C., 'Persistence of chlorophenols in polluted river water and sewage dilutions', *Sewage industr. Wastes*, 22 (1950) 1214–7

APPENDIX

THE following table of saturation values for dissolved oxygen, reproduced here by kind permission of the Director, has been compiled from recent data obtained by the Water Pollution Research Laboratory, assuming air at 100 per cent humidity and under a total pressure of 760 mm of mercury. Each entry is correct to the nearest digit. The data are calculated for air, free from carbon dioxide, and containing 20·93 per cent of oxygen.

Table 34. Solubility of oxygen in water. Dissolved oxygen. Saturation values for fresh water and mixtures of fresh water and sea-water. Milligrams of oxygen dissolved in 1 l. of water saturated with air at the stated temperatures under a pressure of 760 mm

Temp. °C	Chloride, in p.p.m. of Cl					Difference per 100 p.p.m. of Cl
	0	5000	10,000	15,000	20,000	
	Dissolved oxygen in mg/l.					mg/l.
0	14·16	13·40	12·64	11·88	11·12	0·0152
1	13·77	13·03	12·30	11·56	10·82	0·0148
2	13·40	12·68	11·97	11·26	10·54	0·0144
3	13·05	12·36	11·66	10·97	10·28	0·0138
4	12·70	12·03	11·34	10·68	10·01	0·0134
5	12·37	11·72	11·06	10·41	9·76	0·0130
6	12·06	11·43	10·79	10·16	9·53	0·0126
7	11·76	11·14	10·53	9·92	9·30	0·0124
8	11·47	10·87	10·28	9·68	9·09	0·0120
9	11·19	10·61	10·03	9·45	8·88	0·0116
10	10·92	10·36	9·80	9·23	8·67	0·0112
11	10·67	10·12	9·58	9·03	8·49	0·0110
12	10·43	9·90	9·37	8·84	8·31	0·0106
13	10·20	9·68	9·17	8·65	8·14	0·0104
14	9·98	9·48	8·98	8·48	7·97	0·0100
15	9·76	9·27	8·78	8·29	7·81	0·0098
16	9·56	9·08	8·61	8·13	7·66	0·0096
17	9·37	8·91	8·44	7·98	7·52	0·0092
18	9·18	8·73	8·28	7·82	7·37	0·0090
19	9·01	8·57	8·13	7·69	7·24	0·0088
20	8·84	8·41	7·98	7·54	7·11	0·0086
21	8·68	8·26	7·83	7·41	6·99	0·0084
22	8·53	8·12	7·70	7·29	6·88	0·0082
23	8·38	7·97	7·57	7·16	6·76	0·0082
24	8·25	7·85	7·45	7·05	6·66	0·0080
25	8·11	7·72	7·33	6·93	6·54	0·0078
26	7·99	7·61	7·22	6·83	6·45	0·0076
27	7·86	7·48	7·10	6·72	6·34	0·0076
28	7·75	7·37	7·00	6·62	6·25	0·0076
29	7·64	7·27	6·89	6·52	6·15	0·0074
30	7·53	7·16	6·79	6·42	6·05	0·0074

Table 35. Solubility of oxygen in sea water of salinity 35‰, in mg per litre, from a normal atmosphere saturated with water vapour at a total pressure of 760 mm of mercury from −2 to +40° C. $\triangle C_1$ is the change in solubility for a change of 1‰ in salinity

(Reproduced by permission from the paper by TRUESDALE, G. A. and GAMESON, A. L. H., *J. Cons. Intrnat. Explor. Mer*, 22 (1957) 163–6).

Temp. °C	0·9	0·8	0·7	0·6	0·5	0·4	0·3	0·2	0·1	0·0	$\triangle C_1$
−2										11·86	
−1	11·82	11·79	11·76	11·72	11·69	11·66	11·63	11·59	11·56	11·53	−0·088
−0	11·50	11·47	11·44	11·41	11·37	11·34	11·31	11·28	11·25	11·22	−0·085

Temp. °C	0·0	0·1	0·2	0·3	0·4	0·5	0·6	0·7	0·8	0·9	$\triangle C_1$
+0	11·22	11·19	11·16	11·13	11·10	11·07	11·04	11·01	10·98	10·95	−0·083
1	10·92	10·89	10·86	10·83	10·80	10·78	10·75	10·72	10·69	10·66	−0·080
2	10·64	10·61	10·58	10·55	10·52	10·50	10·47	10·44	10·41	10·39	−0·078
3	10·36	10·33	10·31	10·28	10·26	10·23	10·20	10·18	10·15	10·12	−0·076
4	10·10	10·07	10·05	10·02	10·00	9·97	9·95	9·92	9·90	9·87	−0·073
5	9·85	9·82	9·80	9·78	9·75	9·73	9·70	9·68	9·66	9·63	−0·071
6	9·61	9·58	9·56	9·54	9·52	9·49	9·47	9·45	9·42	9·40	−0·069
7	9·38	9·36	9·33	9·31	9·29	9·27	9·25	9·22	9·20	9·18	−0·067
8	9·16	9·14	9·12	9·10	9·07	9·05	9·03	9·01	8·99	8·97	−0·065
9	8·95	8·93	8·91	8·89	8·87	8·85	8·83	8·81	8·79	8·77	−0·063
10	8·75	8·73	8·71	8·69	8·67	8·65	8·63	8·61	8·59	8·58	−0·061
11	8·56	8·54	8·52	8·50	8·48	8·46	8·45	8·43	8·41	8·39	−0·059
12	8·37	8·36	8·34	8·32	8·30	8·29	8·27	8·25	8·23	8·22	−0·058
13	8·20	8·18	8·17	8·15	8·13	8·12	8·10	8·08	8·06	8·05	−0·056
14	8·03	8·02	8·00	7·98	7·97	7·95	7·94	7·92	7·90	7·89	−0·055
15	7·87	7·86	7·84	7·83	7·81	7·80	7·78	7·76	7·75	7·73	−0·053
16	7·72	7·70	7·69	7·67	7·66	7·65	7·63	7·62	7·60	7·59	−0·052
17	7·57	7·56	7·54	7·53	7·52	7·50	7·49	7·48	7·46	7·45	−0·051
18	7·43	7·42	7·41	7·39	7·38	7·37	7·37	7·34	7·33	7·31	−0·049
19	7·30	7·29	7·27	7·26	7·25	7·23	7·22	7·21	7·20	7·18	−0·048
20	7·17	7·16	7·15	7·13	7·12	7·11	7·09	7·08	7·07	7·06	−0·047
21	7·05	7·03	7·02	7·01	7·00	6·99	6·97	6·96	6·95	6·94	−0·046
22	6·93	6·92	6·90	6·89	6·88	6·87	6·86	6·85	6·84	6·82	−0·045
23	6·81	6·80	6·79	6·78	6·77	6·76	6·75	6·73	6·72	6·71	−0·044
24	6·70	6·69	6·68	6·67	6·66	6·65	6·64	6·63	6·62	6·61	−0·044
25	6·60	6·59	6·57	6·56	6·55	6·54	6·53	6·52	6·51	6·50	−0·043
26	6·49	6·48	6·47	6·46	6·45	6·44	6·43	6·42	6·41	6·40	−0·042
27	6·39	6·38	6·37	6·36	6·35	6·34	6·33	6·32	6·31	6·30	−0·042
28	6·29	6·28	6·27	6·26	6·25	6·24	6·23	6·22	6·21	6·20	−0·041
29	6·19	6·18	6·17	6·16	6·15	6·14	6·13	6·12	6·12	6·11	−0·041
30	6·10	6·09	6·08	6·07	6·06	6·05	6·04	6·03	6·02	6·01	−0·041
31	6·00	5·99	5·98	5·97	5·97	5·96	5·95	5·94	5·93	5·92	−0·040
32	5·91	5·90	5·89	5·88	5·87	5·86	5·85	5·84	5·83	5·82	−0·040
33	5·82	5·81	5·80	5·79	5·78	5·77	5·76	5·75	5·74	5·73	−0·040
34	5·72	5·71	5·70	5·69	5·68	5·68	5·67	5·66	5·65	5·64	−0·040
35	5·63	5·62	5·61	5·60	5·59	5·58	5·57	5·56	5·55	5·54	−0·040
36	5·53	5·52	5·51	5·51	5·50	5·49	5·48	5·47	5·46	5·45	−0·040
37	5·44	5·43	5·42	5·41	5·40	5·39	5·38	5·37	5·36	5·35	−0·041
38	5·34	5·33	5·32	5·31	5·30	5·29	5·28	5·27	5·26	5·25	−0·041
39	5·24	5·23	5·22	5·21	5·20	5·19	5·18	5·17	5·16	5·15	−0·041
40	5·14										

If the barometric pressure is markedly different from 760 mm, the solubility of oxygen can be calculated from the formula:

$$\frac{S'}{S} = \frac{P}{760}$$

where S' = solubility of oxygen at P mm pressure

and S = solubility of oxygen at 760 mm pressure (from above tables).

Table 36. Interconversion of British, American and metric units

Length

1 in.	$=2\cdot54$ cm
1 ft.	$=0\cdot3048$ m
1 mile	$=1\cdot6093$ km
1 m	$=39\cdot3701$ in.
1 mμ (millimicron)	$=10$ Angstrom units (Å) $=0\cdot000001$ mm
1 μ (micron)	$=10{,}000$ Å $=0\cdot001$ mm $=0\cdot00003937$ in.

Area

1 ft.^{2}	$=929\cdot03$ cm^2
1 acre	$=4840$ yd.$^2=0\cdot4047$ hectare
1 sq. mile	$=640$ acres $=259$ hectares
1 hectare	$=10{,}000$ m$^2=2\cdot471$ acres

Weight

1 lb. (avoir.)	$=7000$ gr $=0\cdot45359243$ kg*
1 g	$=15\cdot4324$ gr
1 ton	$=1\cdot01605$ metric tons $=1016\cdot05$ kg
1 metric ton	$=2204\cdot62$ lb. (avoir.) $=0\cdot9842$ ton

Volume and capacity

1 ft.^{3}	$=6\cdot2288$ imperial gal. $=28\cdot316$ l.
1 imperial gal.	$=4\cdot5459631$ l.* $=0\cdot16054$ ft.^{3}
	$=277\cdot42$ in.$^3=1\cdot201$ U.S. gal.
1 U.S. gal.	$=231$ in.$^3=3\cdot7853$ l.
	$=0\cdot833$ imperial gal.
1 m^3	$=1\cdot30795$ yd.$^3=219\cdot97$ imperial gal.
1 l.	$=1000\cdot028$ cm$^3=0\cdot22$ imperial gal.

Pressure

1 atm $=760$ mm of mercury (0° C) $=29\cdot921$ in. of mercury
      $=14\cdot696$ lb./in.$^2=1033\cdot3$ g/cm^2
      $=1013\cdot25$ millibars
1 bar $=1000$ millibars $=10^6$ dynes per cm^2
      $=750\cdot062$ mm of mercury †
      $=29\cdot53$ in. of mercury †

Velocity

1 ft./sec $=0\cdot6818$ m.p.h. $=1\cdot097$ km/hour
1 m.p.h. $=1\cdot4667$ ft./sec $=88$ ft./min

Flow of water

1 ft.^{3}/sec (1 cusec) $=538{,}170$ imperial gal. per 24 hours
      $=646{,}300$ U.S. gal. per 24 hours
      $=1699$ l./min
      $=101\cdot94$ m^3/hour

[For approximate work, it may be assumed that

      1 cusec $=500{,}000$ imperial gal./day
              $=1700$ l./min
and that   1 ft.^{3}/min $=9000$ imperial gal./day
              $=1\cdot7$ m^3/hour]
      1 m^3/hour $=0\cdot00981$ ft.^{3}/sec $=4\cdot4$ U.S. gal./min
      1 l./min $=0\cdot06$ m^3/hour
               $=0\cdot0005886$ cusec

Miscellaneous data

1 in. of rain over 1 acre $=22{,}624$ imperial gallons
                           $=101$ tons (approx.)
1 in. of rain over 1 sq. mile $=64{,}640$ tons (approx.)

* Board of Trade definition.   † 0° C and standard gravity.

Table 37.   Conversion table for concentration units

Grains per imperial gal.	Parts per 100,000 Centigrammes per litre	Parts per million* Grammes per million millilitres Milligrammes per litre
1	1·425	14·25
0·7	1	10
0·07	0·1	1

* Parts by weight per million parts by volume.

In the case of samples with a specific gravity significantly greater than 1 (e.g. brines, sea-water, slurries, etc.), 'parts by weight per million parts by weight' is *not* the same as 'parts by weight per million parts by volume', but is given by the expression:

$$\text{parts by weight per million parts by weight} = \frac{\text{milligrammes per litre}}{\text{specific gravity}}$$

Table 38.   Conversion table for hardness

	Grains per gal. Parts per 70,000 ° Clark	Parts per 100,000 French ° hardness	p.p.m.	German ° hardness
Grains per gallon . . ⎫ Parts per 70,000 . . ⎬ ° Clark . . . ⎭	1	1·425	14·25	0·8
Parts per 100,000 . . ⎫ French ° hardness . ⎬	0·7	1	10	0·56
p.p.m.	0·07	0·1	1	0·056
German ° hardness . . .	1·25	1·78	17·8	1

German degrees of hardness are expressed in terms of CaO (each degree of hardness = 1 part of CaO per 100,000 parts of water). All the other degrees of hardness are expressed in terms of $CaCO_3$.

Table 39.   Water: relation between weight and volume

Official definitions

10 lb. (avoir.) distilled water (62° F, 30 in. mercury pressure) occupies 1 imperial gal.

1 kg. distilled water (4° C, 760 mm mercury pressure) occupies 1 l.

Approximate relationships

1 ton = 224 imperial gal. = 35·94 ft.³ = 1·016 m³
1 ft.³ = 62·3 lb. = 0·0278 ton
1 m³ = 1000 kg = 1 metric ton = 220 gal. = 0·9842 ton

Table 40.   Sea-water: approximate weight–volume relations

Taking the specific gravity of sea-water as 1·026
1 imperial gal. = 10·26 lb.
1 ft.³   = 63·9 lb. = 0·0285 ton
1 ton   = 219 gal.

Table 41. Conversion factors for gases

Multiply	By	To obtain
p.p.m. of oxygen	0·698	ml./l.
ml./l. of oxygen	1·43	p.p.m.
p.p.m. of carbon dioxide	0·506	ml./l.
ml./l. of carbon dioxide	1·98	p.p.m.

In general, British and American units are virtually the same. When comparing British and American results, the differences shown in the following table should be noted.

Table 42. Differences in British and American units

British units	American units
1 gal. of water weighs 10 lb. 1 gal. $=277·4$ in.^{3} $=4·546$ l. 1 ton $=2240$ lb.	1 gal. of water weighs 8·33 lb. 1 gal. $=231$ in.^{3} $=3·785$ l. 1 ton $=2000$ lb.

Table 43. Alkalinity conversion factors

Multiply	By	To get	Multiply	By	To get
$CaCO_3$	0·98	H_2SO_4	CaO	1·78	$CaCO_3$
$CaCO_3$	0·8	NaOH	NaOH	1·25	$CaCO_3$
$CaCO_3$	1·06	Na_2CO_3	NaOH	1·225	H_2SO_4
$CaCO_3$	0·74	$Ca(OH)_2$	Na_2CO_3	0·943	$CaCO_3$
$CaCO_3$	0·56	CaO	H_2SO_4	1·02	$CaCO_3$
$Ca(OH)_2$	1·35	$CaCO_3$	H_2SO_4	0·816	NaOH

Table 44. Chemical volumetric factors for use in titrations

Free chlorine . .	1 ml. N/40 sodium thiosulphate	$=0·887$ mg chlorine
Sulphide . . .	1 ml. N/40 sodium thiosulphate	$=0·426$ mg H_2S
		$=0·4$ mg S
Permanganate value Dissolved oxygen	1 ml. N/40 sodium thiosulphate	$=0·2$ mg oxygen
Dissolved oxygen .	1 ml. N/80 sodium thiosulphate	$=0·1$ mg oxygen
Chromate . .	1 ml. N/40 sodium thiosulphate	$=0·434$ mg Cr
Copper . . .	1 ml. N/10 sodium thiosulphate	$=6·357$ mg copper
	1 ml. N/40 sodium thiosulphate	$=1·589$ mg copper
Phenol . . .	1 ml. N/10 sodium thiosulphate	$=1·568$ mg phenol
	1 ml. N/40 sodium thiosulphate	$=0·392$ mg phenol
Iron . . .	1 ml. N/100 potassium dichromate	$=0·558$ mg iron
Cyanide . . .	1 ml. N/100 silver nitrate	$=0·54$ mg HCN
		$=0·52$ mg CN
Calcium . . .	1 ml. N/100 potassium permanganate	$=0·2$ mg Ca
	1 ml. N/80 potassium permanganate	$=0·25$ mg Ca
Hardness . . .	1 ml. N/50 EDTA	$=1$ mg $CaCO_3$
Sulphate . . .	1 ml. N/10 NaOH	$=4·8$ mg SO_4
		$=4·0$ mg SO_3
Ammonia . .	1 ml. N/10 acid or alkali	$=1·4$ mg N

Table 45. *Conversion of Centigrade to Fahrenheit and Fahrenheit to Centigrade temperature,*

$$\frac{C}{5} = \frac{F - 32}{9}$$

Each ° C rise = 1·8° F rise
Each ° F rise = $\frac{5}{9}$° C rise

Centigrade to Fahrenheit		Centigrade to Fahrenheit	
° C	° F	° C	° F
0	32·0	21	69·8
1	33·8	22	71·6
2	35·6	23	73·4
3	37·4	24	75·2
4	39·2	25	77·0
5	41·0	26	78·8
6	42·8	27	80·6
7	44·6	28	82·4
8	46·4	29	84·2
9	48·2	30	86·0
10	50·0	31	87·8
11	51·8	32	89·6
12	53·6	33	91·4
13	55·4	34	93·2
14	57·2	35	95·0
15	59·0	36	96·8
16	60·8	37	98·6
17	62·6	38	100·4
18	64·4	39	102·2
19	66·2	40	104·0
20	68·0		

Fahrenheit to Centigrade		Fahrenheit to Centigrade	
° F	° C	° F	° C
32	0	57	13·9
33	0·6	58	14·4
34	1·1	59	15·0
35	1·7	60	15·6
36	2·2	61	16·1
37	2·8	62	16·7
38	3·3	63	17·2
39	3·9	64	17·8
40	4·4	65	18·3
41	5·0	66	18·9
42	5·6	67	19·4
43	6·1	68	20·0
44	6·7	69	20·6
45	7·2	70	21·1
46	7·8	71	21·7
47	8·3	72	22·2
48	8·9	73	22·8
49	9·4	74	23·3
50	10·0	75	23·9
51	10·6	76	24·4
52	11·1	77	25·0
53	11·7	78	25·6
54	12·2	79	26·1
55	12·8	80	26·7
56	13·3		

Table 46.   *Typical Analyses of River waters containing green algae (showing differences between B.O.D. determinations done on unfiltered and filtered samples)*

River	Temperature °C	pH value	Dissolved oxygen per cent of saturation	Chloride as Cl	N/80 Permanganate value	
					3 min.	4 hour
R. Bollin . .	10	7·2	103	18	0·6	2·8
The Sluice . .	16	9·3	145	1,640	6·0	18·4
Bridgewater Canal .	19	8·6	106	196	3·4	9·6
Bridgewater Canal .	5	8·6	132	700	2·0	4·8
Bridgewater Canal .	5	8·8	114	630	1·4	4·0

Table 46—cont.

Results in p.p.m.

			Suspended solids		Alkalinity as CaCO$_3$		Nitrogen				5-day B.O.D., 20° C	
in.	vol.	total	to p.p.	to M.O.	NH$_3$	*Alb.*	*Nitrite*	*Nitrate*	*Unfiltered*	*Filtered*
6	11	17	—	60	nil	0·32	nil	1·7	4·7	1·9
3	17	30	80	150	0·04	2·76	nil	nil	26·5	5·2
7	19	26	20	100	4·00	1·32	0·2	trace	14·2	3·4
6	19	35	25	120	0·04	0·56	nil	1·8	6·9	1·0
0	12	22	25	120	0·04	0·44	nil	2·4	5·7	1·0

Table 47. Typical analyses of nitrogenous organic wastes

Type of waste water	Appearance (settled)	pH	Transparency mm seen through		KMnO₄ value	
			Shaken	Settled	3 min	4 h
Piggery	Dark brown, opaque, foul odour; fairly large dark brown sediment	6·8	10	13	174	290
Piggery (very strong) .	Deep red-brown, opaque, very foul odour, large dark brown sediment	8·0	nil	10	1,650	3,700
Bacon factory . . .	Red, cloudy	6·9	41	62	60·8	160
Brewery	Straw, very cloudy, much sediment (yeast cells)	5·2	4	51	320	2,080
Dairy (satisfactorily treated by alternating double filtration)	Colourless, clear, trace of sediment	7·6	280	570	2·4	6·2
Dairy (poorly treated by alternating double filtration)	Almost colourless, very cloudy, much sediment	6·8	30	52	16·0	47·2
Pea vining drainage . .	Greenish-straw, opaque; foul odour; large sediment	5·1	4	8	1,120	4,600
Vegetable preparation, washings (potatoes, etc.)	Yellow-brown, opaque. Large dark brown sediment	9·8	10	12	73·6	1140
Dehydrated vegetable manufacture	Straw, turbid; very large brown sediment	4·5	5	20	146	742

Table 48. Typical analyses of textile wastes

Type of waste water	Appearance (settled)	pH	Transparency mm seen through		KMnO₄ value	
			Shaken	Settled	3 min	4 h
Cotton kier liquor . .	Deep brown, opaque	13·2	6	7	1,520	4,640
Viscose rayon . . .	Colourless, cloudy, H₂S odour	2·0	187	220	19·6	34·ᵢ
Towel bleaching . . .	Colourless, cloudy	3·9	50	100	2·0	12·ᵢ
Jute dyeing . . .	Greenish-brown, opaque	6·8	7	10	108	404
Sulphide dyeing . . .	Black, opaque	10·6	24	25	168	420
Calico printing . . .	Deep grey-straw, very cloudy	11·2	25	38	124	400
Sponge cloth cleaning . .	Brown, opaque, oily odour	11·4	2	2	128	532
Screen printing and dyeing (cotton)	Greyish-brown, very cloudy, much sediment	6·4	20	35	80	496
Woollen piece goods scouring (crude)	Greyish, opaque	11·0	3	6	319	908
Ditto, after treatment with alum and settlement	Colourless, fairly clear	6·0	190	420	13·8	38·ᵢ

Table 47—cont.

	Results in p.p.m.										Methylene blue stability test
Total solids		Suspended matter			Alkalinity as CaCO₃		B.O.D. (5 days) 20° C	Ammoni-acal N	Albumi-noid N	Other deter-mination	
Min.	Total	Min.	Vol.	Total	P.P.	M.O.					
236	2,527	42	95	137	—	—	1,275	20·0	260	—	Failed at once (much H₂S)
420	24,640	132	504	636	—	—	13,260	3,600	304	—	Failed at once (much H₂S)
914	1,857	24	187	211	—	250	898	108	28·8	—	Failed in 2 h (H₂S)
811	1,937	435	344	779	—	—	4,550	—	—	—	Failed in 6 h (H₂S)
—	—	10	16	26	—	—	9·0	—	—	Nitrate N = 9·8	Passed
704	1,370	20	128	148	—	530	432	—	—	Nitrate N = Nil	Failed in 2 h (much H₂S)
450	27,250	34	104	138	—	—	12,880	—	—	—	Failed at once (much H₂S)
050	4,400	32	383	415	180	650	3030	18·0	38·6	—	Failed in 2 days
040	5,860	490	3,480	3,970	—	215	950	—	—	—	Failed in 2 h

Table 48—cont.

	Results in p.p.m.										
Total solids		Suspended matter			Alkalinity as CaCO₃		Sulphide (as H₂S)	Zinc	B.O.D. (5 days) 20° C	Free chlorine	Oil
Min.	Total	Min.	Vol.	Total	P.P.	M.O.					
240	19,890	3	8	11	6,600	9,500	—	—	—	—	—
500	5,840	48	30	78	*Acidity* 1,370	1,130	5·7	120	—	—	—
318	2,037	46	59	105	*Acidity* 180	100	—	—	—	8·9	—
802	2,113	174	289	463	*Alkalinity* —	200	—	—	—	—	—
308	3,173	32	61	93	200	644	32·9	—	—	—	—
019	2,020	31	101	132	500	710	—	—	—	—	—
990	5,429	134	819	953	425	2,150	—	—	—	—	2,080
400	2,885	998	1,135	2,133	—	150	—	60	683	—	—
—	—	16	179	195	441	—	—	—	—	—	—
—	—	7	24	31	Nil	—	—	—	—	—	—

Table 49. *Typical analysis of miscellaneous wastes*

Type of waste water	Appearance (settled)	pH	Transparency mm seen through		KMnO₄ value	
			Shaken	Settled	3 min	4 h
Salt works . . .	Colourless, clear	8·0	>600	>600	0·4	4
Coal washery (Bad) . .	Pale yellow, very large black sediment	8·3	Nil	25	4,880	19,400
Coal washery (Unsatisfactory)	Colourless, slightly cloudy	8·5	24	314	9·2	31·
Coal washery (Satisfactory)	Colourless, slightly cloudy	8·4	146	385	1·8	7·
Straw kier liquor . .	Dark brown, opaque	14·2	2	2	29,000	74,000
Paper works (paper making dept.)	Colourless, slightly cloudy	4·8	130	364	7·2	25·
Sulphite cellulose liquor (wood pulp)	Reddish brown, cloudy	3·4	39	47	17,200	58,000
Crude gas liquor . .	Deep orange, cloudy, tarry odour	8·8	114	140	15,600	20,400
Spent gas liquor . .	Reddish-brown, cloudy, phenolic odour	8·6	14	50	7,520	11,800
Gas-holder water (seal liquor)	Straw, fairly clear	8·4	445	445	77·2	128
Organic chemical manufacture (neutralized and settled)	Colourless, clear, phenolic odour	7·8	600	600	94	196
Organic chemical manufacture	Straw, clear, aromatic odour	13·5	7	>600	90	212
Latex foam manufacture .	Milky, opaque, rubber odour	6·9	2	2	146	1,368
Sand and gravel washing (badly settled)	Straw-yellow, very cloudy, very large sandy sediment	7·5	1	62	254	1,000
Sand and gravel washing (well settled)	Pale straw, rather cloudy, small sediment	7·4	92	117	1·8	4··
Penicillin and Streptomycin	Pale fawn, opaque	6·8	7	15	214	1,180·
Chrome tanning (crude) .	Pale greenish, very cloudy	9·0	32	56	86·4	178··
Electroplating . . .	Yellow, clear	1·4	412	>600	0·6	6··
Vinegar brewing (swillings)	Greyish, cloudy, sour putrescent odour, large grey sediment	5·3	10	75	95	460

Table 49—cont.

Results in *p.p.m.*

Total solids		Suspended matter			Alkalinity as CaCO₃		Chloride (as Cl)	Phenols (as cresols)	Ammoniacal N	Albuminoid N	Other Determinations
in.	*Total*	*Min.*	*Vol.*	*Total*	*P.P.*	*M.O.*					
360	63,300	2	1	3	—	150	38,000	—	—	—	—
000	169,000	108,000	58,900	166,900	—	—	—	—	—	—	—
428	2,596	178	50	228	20	300	—	—	—	—	—
130	1,280	22	10	32	20	245	—	—	—	—	—
000	213,800	212	4,570	4,782	37,500	75,000	—	—	—	—	—
600	1,030	16	16	32	—	10	—	—	—	—	—
						Acidity					
580	99,700	36	68	104	850	9,250	—	—	—	—	—
						Alkalinity					
104	26,050	4	17	21	8,400	15,800	—	12,500	14,000	260	CNS' = trace, H₂S = trace
110	12,220	25	377	402	1,600	2,100	—	2,500	2,600	200	—
26	94	—	—	trace	200	3,540	—	10·0	901	6·6	CNS' = trace
730	10,410	2	3	5	—	170	—	26·0	—	—	B.O.D. = 308
700	191,500	3,717	811	4,528	5,700	5,900	—	—	—	—	B.O.D. = 20
433	2,383	49	58	107	—	170	—	—	—	—	B.O.D. = 206
070	40,820	35,820	4,640	40,460	—	450	—	—	—	—	—
298	388	16	4	20	—	90	—	—	—	—	—
688	4,874	180	952	1,132	—	440	—	—	—	—	B.O.D. = 1,750, Crⁱⁱⁱ = trace
080	4,690	190	300	490	98	510	—	—	—	—	B.O.D. = nil, Cromate (as Cr) = 14
						Acidity					
582	14,480	12	12	24	10,900	10,400	—	—	—	—	Copper = 15, Nickel = 22·5, Cyanide (as HCN) = 8
090	3,467	662	2,087	2,749	—	170	—	—	—	—	B.O.D. = 1,545

14

Table 50. Ministry of Health (now Ministry of Housing and Local Government) requirements for low-rate percolating filter plants. (Abridged from table given by J. H. GARNER *in paper on 'Sewage Treatment in England' in* (a) Modern Sewage Disposal. *Anniversary Book of the Federation of Sewage Works Associations. Chap. xxvii, New York, 1938; and* (b) J. Inst. Sew. Purif., 2 *(1939) 374)*

System	Tank capacity	Percolating filters* [see Note (1)]		
		Strong sewage	Average sewage	Weak sewage
Detritus tank . .	2 or more equal to $\frac{1}{100}$ D.W.F.§	15	25	40
Septic tank † . .	2 or more, total equal to 1 day D.W.F.	45 ‡	70	100
Continuous settling tank	2 or more, total equal to 10–15 hours D.W.F.	45 ‡	70	100
Continuous chemical precipitation tank	2 or more, total equal to 8 hours D.W.F.	65	100	150

* Using coarse filter media (not to pass 1 in. sieve), or medium filter media (passing through 1 in. sieve but not through $\frac{1}{4}$ in. sieve).
† Only used for very small works.
‡ Reduce by 10 if medium sized media used.
§ D.W.F.=Dry Weather Flow in gallons per day of 24 hours.

Notes on Table 50

(1) Minimum cubical contents (in yards) for treating $3 \times$ D.W.F.

$$= \frac{\text{D.W.F.}}{\text{appropriate figure in table}}$$

(2) *Storm overflows.* To operate at $6 \times$ D.W.F. (this is now varied according to local circumstances). No overflows at or near disposal works.

(3) *Screening.* All sewage must be screened, including storm water.

(4) *Storm water.* Sewage flows in excess of $3 \times$ D.W.F. to be treated by settlement in two or more storm tanks (total capacity $= \frac{1}{4}$ D.W.F.). No further treatment normally required. Land irrigation can be substituted for tanks.

(5) *Land.* Contents of filters may be reduced to one-half where sufficient suitable land is available. In wet weather, $1\frac{1}{2} \times$ D.W.F. should be treated in filters and the rest on land. Depending on the quality of the land, 3,000–30,000 gal. D.W.F. per acre per day of 24 hours.

(6) *Humus tanks.* Where the effluent from percolating filters is not irrigated on land, humus tanks (capacity $= 4$ h D.W.F.) must be provided.

(7) *Strength of sewage.* Can be based upon the McGowan strength figure (p. 29), upon B.O.D., or upon the 4 hours N/80 acid permanganate figure. Approximate values for domestic sewage are as follows:

Sewage	McGowan Strength (parts per 100,000)	5-day B.O.D. (p.p.m.)	4 hours Permanganate value (p.p.m.)
Weak	60	210	50
Average	100	350	100
Strong	170	600	150

(8) Although the figures in the table are used as a basis for design, they are not necessarily rigidly followed but may be varied according to local circumstances.

AUTHOR INDEX

SUBJECT INDEX

TAKE CARE

Also by Eunice Andrada

Flood Damages

EUNICE ANDRADA

TAKE CARE

NEW POEMS

First published 2021
from the Writing and Society Research Centre
at Western Sydney University
by the Giramondo Publishing Company
PO Box 752
Artarmon NSW 1570 Australia
www.giramondopublishing.com

Cover and design by Jenny Grigg
Typesetting by Andrew Davies
in 9/15 pt Tiempos Regular

Printed and bound by Ligare Book Printers
Distributed in Australia by NewSouth Books

A catalogue record for this
book is available from the
National Library of Australia.

ISBN: 978-1-925818-79-6

The Giramondo Publishing Company acknowledges the support
of Western Sydney University in the implementation of its book
publishing program.

This project has been assisted by the Commonwealth Government
through the Australia Council, its arts funding and advisory body.

For kapwa, by blood and experience

Contents

iv. : CARE

i. TAKE:

The only way to know tenderness is to dismantle it.
Diane Seuss

Echolalia

Beyond a dilated island, bodies rise
as if summoned in rapture. Explosions tear
through the current, hunting softness.

Science declares we come from a detonation
like this. From their boats, the men hurl dynamite
into the water. Wait for the end of the roar.

We swim across suckling reefs of infancy,
encoding sound. Gravity releases
its gilled subjects. They float up

for the taking, airbladders honeycombed
by noise, eyeballs tilted to the sun.
We rise, thinking, *so close*.

Years later, a full sentence ruptures inside.
The bursts resound from my mouth.
Then the hands. Not mine.

I want the *no* to petrify all movement.
For my human body to be seen as the centre
of a poem, it must be buoyant.

Sexual Assault Report Questionnaire: Describe your hair.

What would happen if one woman told the truth about her life?
The world would split open.
Muriel Rukeyser, 'Käthe Kollwitz'

Of the sixteen kinds of breakage, often it chooses
to crack into right angles. What this says about me:
I coil my crown into unforgiving shapes.
The categories of damage creeping up my hair:
basic splits, baby splits, deep splits, long splits,
triple splits, double y splits, like a roll call

for failed efforts of resistance. The counsellor calls
for our regular phone sessions, asks me to choose
what I want to talk about. I reach up to my uncombable hair:
knots, trees, candles, feathers, offshoots, incomplete splits.
The reminders come. I'm told to notice what's around me.
Tally the yellow objects in the room. Note the pattern of shapes.

In the recurring math problem, it asks which shape
of vessel can hold the heaviest shame. I call
a friend—white spots, thickened ends, crinkle splits,
right angles—*why did you have to come to me?*
The beeping admits a worthier emergency. I must choose
for myself. I wring the answer from my hair.

On average, women spend 1.5 years doing their hair
with their unique combination of scorched shape
-shifting, chemical colouring—Vivian compliments me

on my buzzed head outside the library. I choose
not to submit the report. What will they call
a girl not the right colour or demeanour, no split

hem? I tell the truth and expect the world to split
open. Fissures crawl up the length of my hair
to prove its tolerance. When I was younger, I'd choose
to spend summers chewing on my ponytail. They'd call
me away from my gnawing, not knowing what shaped
the daydreams: my lineage or me.

When I watch robins plummet from the sky, it's just me.
A poet asks, what feminine part of yourself did you split
off clean so you wouldn't be catcalled?
Even in garish light I can't recognise the shapes
behind car windows. The growth cycle of hair
on your scalp is 2 to 7 years. You can't choose.

Pipeline Polyptych

makeshift
kingdoms allow
portable royalty. scholars
who called us 'children of
the nanny nation' must not
have seen you on a Sunday.
cardboard marking your
territory in the halls, the
subway steps, the parks:
your dominion. how can
you resist pageantry?
the homemade gowns
and potluck-purchased
crowns, the admiration of
strangers. no employers
on a day holy enough
for freedom. tourists take
photos to post on Twitter:
behold the mess of
saints sprawled out
in the open, prone.

history
begins with what we
can take but cannot afford.
lustrous orbs forged when
an outsider settles where it
shouldn't. the state sends
Filipino men to dive into
these waters and give up their
bounty. in a recipe called
'to make a pearl', MFK Fisher
lists as ingredients: 1 diving
girl and an unnameable
astringent. soon warming
waters will cease all radiance
and the diving girls it brings.
I love and accumulate while
I can. I decide on a future
and research the daily
cost of living. the ones I
love are determined to die
in the right country. our
absence ossifies in the water.
the harvest outlives us.

after WWII,
Filipinos are sent
to work as domestic
care-givers in Palestine.
in 1993, Israeli forces seal
Palestinian territories,
then haul in cheap labour
from Southeast Asia,
Africa, South America
and Eastern Europe. new
arrivals take jobs once held
by Palestinians killed or
forced out of their homes.
at the checkpoint to leave
Ramallah, Palestinians are
made to line up outside the
bus. a soldier moves down
the aisle, demanding to be
shown our right to be here.
he asks to see a permit from
the woman beside me. she
mutters under her breath,
bato ko to sa mukha mo.

supply
chains ensure
America will never
be forsaken. pre-WWII
medical training in
English means they are
export-ready. Filipinos
comprise a third of all
COVID fatalities in the
US healthcare industry.
our historians call it a
time of war. in war, I am
mistaken for a nurse or
someone's property: a
degree separated from
death. when he discovers
where I'm from, he asks
about the brothels in
Angeles. insists I must
visit. o world, how you
shine with our spit.

Subtle Asian Traits

Come autumn, it's a woman's face that flutters
down a decaying timeline, instead of the blue
-eyed rapist they insisted on calling a *swimmer*.

When Emily Doe's identity is revealed,
a man posts on the SAT page,
I just had a feeling she was Asian—

I log out and leave my apartment in outdoor
tsinelas to take out the trash. When I return,
I wear my home tsinelas.

That evening, while washing up after dinner,
I shatter the lip of a glass against the faucet.
In a home for one, perhaps I should instead

drink and eat from plastic, single-use
and disposable. Red sap weeps from my finger.
I hold it under the running spout.

Most days I don't look at the nature
of my subtle animations and label them.
I try: my Asian swimming,

my Asian insomnia, my Asian speechlessness,
my Asian exhaustion—I keep labelling until
the words run clear.

Take Care

Night terrors descend as I sleep in Jerusalem.
A woman offers salvation in the morning.

At the Filipino grocery store, she eavesdrops
into my conversation at the register, catches

me by the steps and introduces herself.
She comments on my weight, the bones beetling

from my wrists. I must go to her party that evening
and eat. She texts me the address.

Her guests stream in two hours late, tired relief
at seeing each other when their days off align.

They shiver as they crowd her apartment,
cosied by the warmth of food reheating, the smell

of liempo, courtesy of the Russian grocery store.
Neglecting the coats suspended mid-air like mocking

phantoms, it's almost like we're meant to be here:
where Christ himself had lived and laboured.

Some had arrived to care for Holocaust survivors
before I was born, now past the age of birthing their own.

Some don't plan on going back, their children old
enough to be cut off from Western Union payments.

They recommend churches I must visit, the ones
where sermons are most convincing.

On the hissing TFC, Kuya Kim introduces
an endangered species of eagle. The child actors marvel

according to script. I remember the Palestinians being killed
and forced to leave. My titas and titos delivered

to their land as carers : taking care : caring : taking :
over the pop biology lesson on TV, everyone shouts

for attention. The night's dispersal marked by chimes
of ingat. We spill onto the concrete, listening

for what the wind will corroborate.
Moonlight settles viscous like the grease

of machinery. They tell me to ingat
with the men, the checkpoints, the soldiers.

Take care. Take care. Take care.

In my temporary room, I let myself rest,
believing I could be safe.

Valentine's Day at the Women's Baths

after Warsan Shire

my skin pristine at that point in time
friends tell me he looks 'so *nice*' after meeting him
on Valentine's Day I slough off layers next to Soo-Min
she coats her garnet tattoo with sunblock
her laughter cracking against the cliff face
my thighs don't rub together till the next summer
animal fabric in protest against contagion
for months I wedge cotton, velvet, satin between
dotted scars singed by liquid nitrogen
I erase lines unflattering to my ego
sea-carved rock blots us from their view of the water

sea-carved rock blots us from their view of the water
I write lines unflattering to my ego
dotted scars singed by liquid nitrogen
months after I wedge cotton, velvet, satin between
no ghost of fabric in protest against contagion
my thighs rub together all summer
her laughter cracking against the cliff face
she coats her garnet tattoo with sunblock
on Valentine's Day I slough off layers next to Soo-Min
friends told me he looked 'so *nice*' after meeting him
my skin pristine at that point in time

On Invasion Day

My beloved wait at the meeting place
of grand bullets. Their softness dissonant
with towering steel.

In Quezon City, rifles salivate for my skull
on the avenue my mother was promised
a delivery room. I am twice delivered

to Neptune Street, not far enough
from where men on the overpass
manoeuvre their weapons.

I can't get too far before another
of his doppelgangers drag in front of me
on the train, the pedestrian crossing,

the airport security line.
The same silhouette caught
leaving.

On Invasion Day he stands proud
as a violent flag, chanting *no justice,
no peace*. He sees me and cannot hold

my gaze. From shining horses,
vulturing cops search
for convenient fare.

Hi-vis obstructions.
Someone's shoulder exhumes me
from the moment.

My beloved have left, coursing down the path.
Sunlight glints from the wall of hooves
yearning for pasture.

No matter out of place
where invasion is so everyday
it is unremarkable.

Nothing remains private in the eye
of the colonizer : the rapist : the man
behind the rifle on the overpass.

I resist desirability.
My sight dismantles
what sees me.

Screen Time

After the announcement of a false alarm,
PornHub use surges by 48 per cent.

Earlier that day, emergency alerts pealed
carnelian and unmistakable, declaring

incoming missiles. What was not reported:
how panic cradled the island. How its people said

goodbye. I imagine the last thing I'd do
in this skin before annihilation.

Which desires to evacuate before they refract
into other matter? No one calls for me

in the same timezone. Sometimes an old lover will
ask where I am. Those who used force prefer not

to think of me. While I vigil, I doomscroll,
block myself from apps, then find another way back.

Thumbing past blue-lit triggers,
on the wall my shadow shock-still.

Trick Mirror

In horror, the audience clicks out of Zoom.
I do not let shame creep up to me.

Two men keep their names and invade our space.
They flaunt a photo of a brown woman,

her legs spread, magnificent dark
vulva gleaming on screen.

The participant number crashes.
I begin to resent those who leave,

disgusted by the way bodies like mine
can corrupt a room.

The men dagger their taunts.
Panels eclipse, domain reformulating.

The woman jolts against her static frame.
She blinks out of a reverie,

processing. Motion resurrects her
in increments.

I move closer. She mirrors.
In the background, voices swarm

in their undecipherable whirr.
The woman traces her thumb over

the lens, verifying her reflection.
We do not banish one another.

Now bored of executing assault, the men blip
out of view, a slurry of black in their wake.

The screen pivots to my face, the making
of apology. She lingers to hear the poems.

instead of finding water

el niño drones past its deadline
bearing a surplus　　　of 10,000,000 mangoes
their candied rot　　littering the streets

instead of finding water
I divine juice from a yellow stone fruit
my foraging habitual　　　after another biopsy
without the silver　　nitrate to mend

I am ancestor
to supervirus　　microplastic
more radiation

for chemical soil
where we　　　　tumble
burp　　　play　　　alive

I suppose a life after mine
will still be a life　　though to
whom

will I describe the delicate sugar
of mangoes　　　　　or
the exact way to strike

the fullest part
of a watery fruit　　to hear

                    its age
        I am a forgetful   maker
        I was going   to make
                    the bed

        I was going   to make myself
                    last

Nature Is Healing

elephants guzzle a stash of corn wine and snore on a field
in Yunnan, while this time elsewhere, la niña begins, and in Australia,
my mother's lungs fill with rain, as ministers argue over how to divide
a river, I bring her meals, wash my hands for 20 seconds afterwards,
parliament discusses whether they should mine under our supply
of drinking water, I sanitise the counters with Dettol wipes, register
their deliberations, her face so young behind an N95 mask, but no
one questions the future of our bodies, Filipino women die
so heroically, our nation's infinite natural resource, the doctor
comments she doesn't need a large dosage for my mother's
'tiny' frame, at 8 pm everyone stands on their balconies to clap
for healthcare workers, applause smattering the gloom with useless
detonations, reminding the pigeons of private property,
but don't worry, *nature is healing*, a viral meme says,
humans are the real virus, researchers say they don't yet know
the long-term effects of January's smoke, PM 2.5 lingering
in the bloodstream, leading to heart disease, diabetes, dementia,
by her bedside, I stow inhalers in dependable plastic, our own
futures up for debate, but the elephant story was fake,
the dolphins in Venice, too, their sparkling heads
photoshopped into the dross of canals,
their true routes remote from the fact
of our bodies, essential even
when not at work, taking
all the air needed
to float

ii. : COMFORT

For Jennifer Laude
Fabel Pineda
Liliosa Hilao
Mhelody Bruno
& all those whose suffering
was not named and remembered
but is still carried through generations

Another statue dedicated to 'comfort women' who were
enslaved and raped in wartime has been removed in the
Philippines. The two met ˻   ˼culpture depicting a
blindfolded, grieving v   ts Filipino 'comfort
women' enslaved by   ɩerial Army during
World War II. Less th˷   its establishment,
the Department of P   ˑhways removed
the statue at 10 p.m   for a 'drainage
improvement pr˓   ˑrol. Duterte
expressed his s˹   statue, saying,
'That issue   ɔos na iyan.'
It's over.'
Manila, th˷   ˷ɩ˵˷ɩ˵ce to Japan's
title as the '   ˏ   statue did not face
the sea when the   ɩ Laguna, another
'comfort woman'   ˒ two days after its
unveiling. The r˷   Japanese embassy
in Manila expre   the statue. In the
1930s, it was di˷   ɔops would go on
raping sprees. I   ɔreading sexually
transmitted di˷   al Army devised
a system to r˷   ugh the use of
full-time slave   ˖ women.' The
euphemism 'c˷   y incorrect as
most of the sex˷   ˒ 13 to 18 when
they were abd˵   en classified
under Japane˷   ɩmunition',
sometimes, 'am˷   ɩno women
were enslaved   Japanese
occupation of   ˖ these
memorials ca˙   since
the state w   ˑs.

close
enough to the
water, I could have
leapt to meet the
tide. their machines
scraped the ground until
it gurgled with rubble. they
trust you will not mourn what
you cannot recall. tell me who
racked their mind for this euphemism
but could not bear to look anyway.
memory antagonizes. the
act of rape: acceptable
savagery. the reminder
of a woman raped: in-
tolerable, too real too real
too real too real too real
too real too real too real too
real too real too real too real
too real too real too real too
real too real too real too real
too real too real too real too
real too real too real too real
too real too real too real too real
too real too real too real too real
too real too real too real too real
too real too real too real too real too
real too real too real too real too real
too real too real too real too real too real
too real too real too real too real too real

rape

: late 14c., rapen – 'seize prey; abduct, take by force'
from Anglo-French raper or Old French rapir :
'to seize, abduct,' a legal term :
from Latin rapere – «seize, carry off by force, abduct»
from which come the words

: rapiña – Spanish for 'looting or predatory behaviour'
: rapaz – Portuguese for 'young man'

in Bontoc, there was no rape
in Iloilo, there was no word for rape
in Hiligaynon or Kinaray-a until

rape is a structure :
not monstrous
not excess

rape is a logical conclusion
sovereignty ends
and ends
and

rape becomes *access to amenities*
slavery becomes *polo y servicio*
colonisation becomes *benevolent assimilation*
murderous intent becomes *a bad day*

I attempt love
in my tender vernacular :
vernaculus : domestic, native
verna : a home-born slave

o, how they explode our lexicon
and warp our needful
sound

In Iloilo, on the island of Panay, two comfort stations existed. In 1942, the first contained 12–16 enslaved women, while the second contained 10–11 enslaved women. As tourists pass through Panay to visit the popular island of Boracay, a statue representing women raped by Japanese soldiers will welcome them in Aklan's jetty port.

is this a warning or welcome
to islands named after a brutal dead man
and his living imagination?

holy paradise of rape
ruled by a president
who encourages your investment
and awaits his commission

The rate of gender-based violence and sexual assault
rises in times of natural disaster and displacement.

they take home upon home
until every one is uninhabitable

we have no choice but to be
intimate with disaster

:

the conversation turns to the supernatural
as I mince garlic into dull jewels

my lola sits by the twisting neck
of the electric fan while I prepare dinner

I ask her if she believes in the aswang
by day, an ordinary woman

by dusk, a shape-shifting hunter
who drains blood with her proboscis tongue

she shoots back, hurt diffusing
in her voice like dye through water

If they were real, why didn't they do anything
when the soldiers came to Panay?

Rapists are immortalised at the park.
I can't even scarf down a grainy salad
on my lunch break without being under
a rapist's surveillance. The city council
can't get rid of the statues
because *it's part of our culture*.
A rapist steals my coffee order
then smiles as he returns it to me.
I recite a rapist's love poems and send
a picture of the page to my friends.
The rapist qualified to be a doctor
is too eager to enter me. He laughs at my socks
while a metal speculum gawks into my vagina.
A rapist teaches me how to drive.
A rapist decides what I do with my body
after rape. A rapist on trial doesn't believe
he's a rapist. A rapist doesn't like being called
a rapist. A rapist raping doesn't believe in rape,
its perversion of simpler ideas like cold seedless
grapes, eggs ripe for hatching, nape of beast
for slaughter. A rapist tells me to be careful
of what I say.

2:30 speech:

I was angry. ~~that she was raped.~~
~~But~~ She was ~~so beautiful.~~
~~I should have been~~
~~the first.~~
~~What a waste.~~

~~If you go down, I go down.~~
~~But for this martial law~~
~~and the ramifications of martial law~~
~~I and~~ I alone. ~~would be responsible~~
~~just do your job~~
~~I will take care~~
~~of the rest.~~

:

~~unremarkable facts:~~

All American military bases spread
across the islands are typhoon-safe.

Under the Visiting Forces Agreement,
the condition of legal immunity
to commit rape is agreed upon.

When a rapist dies, the incumbent rapist
declares a period of national mourning.

During this period, Philippine flags
fly at half mast for ten days.

When the woman who raised my lola dies,
she is buried as cheaply as possible.

:

In another speech, he tells soldiers
to shoot female guerrilla fighters
in their bisong. Bisaya for vagina.

In the official government transcript,
the word is replaced with a dash.
The transcript records laughter
from the audience.

:

Tita throws a party in Miag-ao.
It doesn't matter what anyone wears.
The soldiers come down from the base
to get drunk.

Dragonflies zip over the creek.
Even without breeze, sound crackles
through blades of balete.

Kota Batu

Miag-ao, Iloilo, Panay Island

We did not see the perfect yolks spill from the river
into the straits. Leftovers from building their churches
of limestone and egg whites. How the thousands
of golden pupils must have stared back.

Or the oil that flooded the mangroves and changed
the harvest forever. Hair trimmings from salon floors
across the islands: swept up and sent in cargo loads.
Black soaking in the black.

Perhaps it was a blessing not to see the image
of dead women drifting face down, their hair undulating,
soft pollutants. Still the fruit from Guimaras bloats
with putrid nectar. If you held the land inside you,

you would become the land: sick.
Fruitbats fly to the forests of Antique.
The weavers fly to Hong Kong.
The last binukot dies.

This is where we observe who comes to take
and who leaves alive. From our monument of rain
trapped in coralline, we watch the boats sever
the water, release the cruelty it cannot hold.

Shrivel

The birds flee. Mountains are whittled to baby teeth,
calcium pulverised to the ground. Where the horizon
submits to the water, creation proceeds: they spurt
new islands like semen, crude appendages of sand
and concrete and steel, dripping colonies made
crystal-hard in the heat. When they finish,
doves land on the throbbing neon
casinos, singing to each other,
how everything soused
in salt will soon
shrivel.

Kundiman

And a senator orders: every radio station broadcasting
over the sea should air our music in Tagalog
so invaders know whose waters they're on.

As if our love songs alone could thwart a battalion.
Our serenades would lull night guards to sleep before
the noise of extraction numbed them once more.

I want to be there with a love song
not to wield as a weapon,
but as a comfort to the water.

The Yield

after Sonia Feldman

When I read there were 170 women
seized from brothels in the Gardenia
district, loaded into police wagons
and crammed into the hull of a ship,
I wonder if they held hands. Or prayed.
If they cried when their lurching cage
docked, and when next morning
they were forced to till the dizzying
fields. I wonder how they felt
when told it was a waste
for pleasure to bear no fruit,
how they must instead keep
the earth fertile with their hands.
I wonder about the small protests:
if they slashed open the mouths
of green coconuts to drink in
the juice in croaking afternoons,
if, while wrenching cassava from
the dirt, they spat jokes about the men
who must be asking for them, if they
sang ballads under their breath
while they worked, if they made
love to each other and did not wait
for the yield.

iii. : REVENGE

Fine print: you can own
my labor, but not my defiance.
Carmen Gimenez Smith

Revenge is more decolonial than justice.
Billy-Ray Belcourt

Vengeance Sequence

I obliterate the pixels of my body.
Phones combust in their pockets.

The smoke sucks out files from hidden folders
of the iCloud. Every photo of me disappears.

:

The Home Shopping Network advertises another
anti-rape device. Its alarm blares whenever

a rapist is in the room. It beeps until it finds the perpetrator.
It comes with a KILL button. All you need to do is point.

:

Jaundiced maggots follow wherever they go,
squirming in their cups of tea,

spewing from their pens
when they try to write another poem.

The 40-year-old poet who pulled me close
and kissed me when I was 17.

The poet who came up to me from behind and draped
his arms around me because *he just had to.*

The married professor in his fifties
who asked me to send him photographs

of myself. Maggots infest
his dead animal eyes.

:

Catcalls clot under the uvula.
The men must hack out the blockage

or choke on the barbed thing scraping
crimson into their throats.

I hurry to the train station on pavements
spattered with blood and spittle.

The day comes when the paths are clear.

:

When I hear Mariah Carey was paid at least $5,000,000
as an inconvenience fee for the tedium of her divorce

proceedings, I consider what the world owes me.
My bank account will fatten whenever someone tells me

their maid, nanny, wife or ex is Filipino.
Extra charges:

when people ask me if I'm a nurse

when they say they've been to the Philippines
and list the names of islands they visited

all of them mispronounced

when they ask me if I know their one Filipino friend
and are disappointed when I don't

:

The most dignified rape scene on TV
is where the rape doesn't happen.

He attempts to do it but can't get hard,
stroking his cock, pliant as shore-washed

seagrass. She can't stop laughing.
The bliss surges from her throat,

a carafe unfractured, her cackles
erupting and erupting.

:

I take naps to undo the myth I am hardworking.

:

In my dreams, there is a nibbling at the ends of my hair.
I wake to the Pasig River flowing once more.

A fry of catfish come alive in my belly and suckle
on the lining of my stomach.

They follow the bend of my fallopian tubes,
dropping to the bowl at my next menstruation.

It takes them a few seconds to adapt to the water,
shaking off ruby wisps from their fins.

They keep swimming, pullulating as they paddle.
They begin their procession back to the river.

                                                    :

                          Filipino women stop working.
                          Empires shut down in a tantrum,

                              refusing to care for themselves.
                              We do not go back to work.

:

Military bases dissolve in the tide.
The balete trees look on.

:

I care for my beloved
until the collapse of empires
and beyond
beyond
beyond

:

The girl has emerged
from the murk of red clay.

She breathes in the steam, looking at me
for what comes next. For weeks now, the town

can't drink the water, or bathe, or boil it clean.
The people let their faucets run to free thousands of clumps

of her black hair. They stare at the wet thudding
of inky urchins in their sinks. One by one,

the tangles of hair gather strength. They stand
on their legs like newborn spiders,

skittering out of tiny holes and crevices. They click
together like magnets, pulling their stygian hearse

to the dam where he dumped her corpse.
The spiders in the water keep coming.

From the dam to their sinks and back.
She speaks.

Who did this to me? I take her hand and we rise,
heavy

:

:

:

To Be of Use

They sprout tails under the sprinkle of water
gushing colour like scalded lagundi leaves.
The stream batters them pink and pinker
until they dart to the drain, succumbing to their girldeaths.
Doctor's orders to cast loose my month's tablespoons:
a backlog of blood unlocked by orgasms, lazy stretches,
an emmenagogue diet. She miscalculates the volume.
The same doctor prescribes a pill two other governments
had banned after she sees my facial hair and says, *too much*.
I let her nick nascent berries from my pelvis.
She shows me the live-feed as she judges
how much of my anatomy can be of use.
I fill the tunnels with dirt. Nothing else can be devoured.
The ends scab over like nodes of ginger.

The Chismis on Warhol

Art is the letters you send home
about the man you serve.
Alfred A. Yuson, 'Andy Warhol speaks to his two Filipino maids'

Did you hear the canned sopas
was a hit at the galleries?
How they ate that shit up.

Wonder what he eats at home,
what Nena and Aurora must prepare
for his guests.

While he's with guests, who cares
for his mother? And while he slurps
oysters with Imelda? Didn't they

tell him to be careful of Imelda?
Who cares for their children
while they're gone?

When he's gone, do they parade
down the halls wearing his silver
slip-hazard wigs?

Mop the floor with his wigs? Did you hear
he calls them 'girls'? Just girls alone
a few moments, all theirs.

Uninhabitable

From the book of Jonah,
people remember the whale
and the prophet swallowed
in equal measure.

They forget about the anger
that ends his book. The kind
I'm not allowed if I'm not a king
or prophet, or a son

who ransacks the sullied temple
of his father. Proverbs say it is better
to live in the wilderness than with
an angry woman.

Rage is the whale I must dwell in
when I move through cities my body
cannot inhabit.

This is no hero's journey.
The objective of my wrath is not
to save.

Don't you hate it when women

kill the herbs on the windowsill / devote their year's salary
to take-out / put in the work and it isn't called 'women's work' /
depend on rechargeable limbs to stretch an aeon / invent
new vocabularies / aren't interrupted / coast on the high
seas of their depression / are in each other's gaze /
no longer products of myth / sleep safe on the late train /
sleep the slumber of the wicked / as empires succumb / take
selfies from a million angles / each one the perfect angle / revolt /
kill the cop / the colonizer / the capitalist / living rent-free
in their heads / demolish the altar built on their backs /
without blame / walk away

iv. : CARE

This is the only kingdom.
The kingdom of touching;
the touches of the disappearing, things.
Aracelis Girmay

Repatriation

In my mind, you arrive before dawn.
Heaven bruised purple when my mother
would return by surprise and wake me.

Instead of an election promise, a virus
brings you home, overworked women
who could be my sisters, cousins, aunts,

women I can ask for directions wherever I go,
women whose care the world feeds on,
your mouths behind the cheerful hue

of surgical masks. You stand in a procession
of hundreds. The largest remittance of kin
in our history of organised exile.

The terminal wi-fi connects—slow pour
of Bikolano, Tagalog, Cebuano, so blood-
close I call you 'te

wherever we are. You come back
to changing hands: passport-stealer father,
wasteful son, balikbayan box spirit

duct-taped for safety. The reliable
syrup of humidity. In unison, the clocks
on your phones reset.

To Be Left Alone

A woman reminds me she is real
by smashing her elbow into my chin.
The jolt of delight after an hour of mock punches.
She is a foot shorter than me and doesn't smile back.

We switch partners. I go through the sequence
with someone who hesitates to punish me
for my daring to punch her. She shrugs
a sweat-soaked fishtail braid off her glistening
shoulder, and I do it again, adore a woman
not there to be adored.

The krav maga instructor does her rounds.
Bold white letters announce *BEAST MODE*
on her chest. She commands breakneck
repetition, thrusting hypotheticals:
if they   you must

                 you must

                 you must

Padded floors groan under
the rhythm of shifting feet.
The room crowds with breath
galloping forth, rewilding.

When the session is over, the women
reassemble the rings on their knuckles,

rewrap damp hair. I measure tonight's
transformation, the military tactics to deploy
over conquerable space. In between fight,
flight, or freeze: deciding what will beget
my keys into the lock.

We break off into different directions
at the parking lot, alone again, perspiration
drying in the brisk air, striding
into separate provinces
of a ruthless habitat.

Visitations

At any moment, it might still right its capsized
musculature and zip into my mouth. Punishment
for staring. Every two years, my landlord pays
a discounted rate of $99 to rid my home of all
non-human dwellers. In the balcony,
I sweep ladybugs, cockroaches, cicadas,
stag beetles and moths into a purple dustpan,
their rigid figures rattling like keychain toys
disturbed by the claw.
After their anonymous years,
cicadas call for a mate, crackling the air
with honeyed voltage. I warn them to cloak
their arias in foliage. It is the eternal season
my kind determines who survives.
Yet creatures appear in their daily visitations.
Before I leave for work, the magpie lands on
the ledge, drinks the tap water I set down each
morning. They regurgitate a bundle of seeds,
undigested, wadded in spit. I sweep the gifts
into the trash. By circadian instinct, they come,
proceed their faithful churning, spasming hidden
passages to divulge the day's offerings to me,
their wingless dependant, idle, familiar.

Flight Path

When the sun slows its trickle like molasses,
I take the manta ray out on walks.
They recoil from the crowds,

hugging closer to my cheeks.
We sigh when the breeze finally comes.
I am turning the corner of Charlotte St

when the scent visits. I reach up
to pinch a tiny blossom from the shrub
of orange jasmine.

If I close my eyes, I am back in Molo, standing
in a churchyard cluttered with sampaguita.
Pulling a fin back, I drop the petals,

like plankton, into their waiting mouth.
They hum all the way to the clinic.
Embracing my face as I talk to Esther,

they catch falling saltwater.
A few blocks away from home,
when there's no one else in sight,

I unpeel the sticky manta ray from my cheeks.
They twirl around my finger for the rest
of the walk. In the bathroom, twin rays swim

in an aquarium of suds. I wrap each fin around
my knuckles, lather their slippery tails
with soap.

I leave them to glide around the basin
as I try to write the poem. Past the hour
of lorikeets and magpies, the manta rays

hang from a rack on my balcony.
Clouds twist into their pandemic
of colour, elaborating wreckage.

The manta rays billow in the wind, wings straining
to flap until they wriggle free from the clothespins.
They fly into the wound.

Nocturnal

A girl from the internet gives me her old bedside lamp
for free. Pink velvet shield circling the hot bulb.
When I cannot sleep, I stare at the glow until my vision
blurs. I catch them from the corner of my eye.
From the craters burned into my thigh, they crawl
into the treacle of heat, annealing. Lush limbs jitter
in electric climate. Some beings clawed, some lanterned,
some propelled into the dust by invisible engines, some
velutinous, rustling the hairs on my leg as they move.
The ones I love sweetest return incantation
to the warbling in my ears. I have come to accept
the revelations that nest in my body. They bear
no omen, no lament. Obedient to unknowable laws
of their creation, they abandon me in herds, orbiting
in the air, sucked into the torrent of shadow,
plodding on the carpet, away, away, leaving me
to tend to my most prolific aches
until they quiet.

I Write the Poem

I write the poem so it lives
outside of my body.

The poem where he is intent
on a doom I already know.

The poem where I'm another star
in the steady opera of vanishing girls.

People will say I deserved it
because I got into the wrong car

but why did he drive and keep
me there, his peculiar new token?

I realise my error but he keeps driving
to the mouth of the highway.

I shove my door open—he slams
the brakes. What was private

now public. Caught in the maw
of orange streetlight, the vehicle

half-opened, like the last stutter
of a cricket's one unshackled wing.

I bolt from the carcass.
Keep running.

I write the poem to bury
the endings.

At the Jordan River, by choice

this time, I wait with the others cloaked in white
rented gowns, more concerned with how I would need
to rise clutching the towel wrapped over my underwear.
After the trial and error of the first two baptisms,
it is childish to want another. Back then, the water
could only disappear what it was given: my young,
reluctant self, the ignorance of what would later happen
and happen. The river swells with each surrender.
Hymn rings louder as I approach, quatrains bouncing
over the surface on a feedback loop. When the body displaces
water, it is entombed by viridian, then pulled back, ahistorical,
engulfed by the singing crowd. I ask for my girlhood
to be entombed in a hymn and not a trial. For a colour
to displace memory. The crowd dilutes into a shamble
of dripping gowns. Surrender becomes my reluctant river,
clutching at my ankles. Reminders swell louder. Lucent
strangers clap on the steps. Promising no error
in what becomes when surface breaks.

24

I survive four lifetimes
of a banded ruby-throated
hummingbird. My heart's
reverent labour coursing
ecstatic. In lieu of an after
that will not come:
reminders that still
the rest of my life.
Even when inertia grows a husk
over me, there are parts that keep
moving through the oldest languages
of my blood. Each year
I grow more dangerous
when I do not care
for silence.

Duolingo

When we joy, we die: I'm dead.

I'm dyingggg.

This took me OUT.

When we joy, we live: This gives me life.

I'm living for it.

I'm here for it.

You who pioneer our shining
glossaries of praise:
stay here with me.
There are things we must kill
so we can live to celebrate.

Living Sequence

I don't know how to begin: sunset muted
by the nebulous grey. My hand leaving his

as we walk beneath the eaves of the monastery.
Depending on the legend you believe, they say

Adam's skull is buried beneath these floors—
and from here grew cedar, cypress, pine.

And from these they collected the wood to build the cross
where Jesus was crucified. And He, too, came back.

We are the only ones here to witness a return.
They crumble easy, these structures erected

on the heads of men. I want to hold something
without a burial. I ask the olive trees

what will be made of my love's bones—
cedar, cypress, pine. Let me be one beam

in a great ark, carrying our hushed and thunderous
animals—even the beasts trained for burden.

The future of my love is shapeless.
I do not prepare for death.

Etymology of Care

Late afternoons repeat like this:
I watch strangers walk to the night shift
or to their waiting lovers.

Under changing light,
some of them will reach up
for the single ivory bloom

in my front neighbour's yard.
They will press it to their noses.
Some will beckon the calico

and her kittens, scattered like
capricious pebbles. It is surprising
who stops to bend on their haunches,

hovering by the edge of the lawn,
open palms reaching out. The kittens
bare their furred chests, granting

the brief refuge of touch.
On rush hour, passing cars
are a flurried migration of fish,

the sky slipping down their scales.
Do you see? It helps me forget
I am grieving.

Looming beyond the leaves
are what we must destroy.
Meet me with tenderness on the grass.

Echolocation

At first, it is only us, testing the wind
for what it will carry. Our voices are far
too small, the song dissipating
in its hopeful fiction.

Quiet again.
The dark amphitheatre of sky
smothers.

Then the canopy shivers a lyric.
We feel the hum of roots below,
beings murmuring from mouths
shrouded in soil.
Music wells upwards,
abrupt.

New arrivals stumble into the field,
human and non-human tones mingling.
TNTs come out of hiding, their melodies
joining the high bars of chorus.

We echo into every direction:
swinging the pendulum of treelines,
sounding the hollow of lunar marias.

From unseen waters, song breaches
feather-light. The water in us
shimmers to the invocation.

Our song maps the terrain
of past to future labour.
We trust the others hear us.
They are gathering.

Notes

Sexual Assault Report Questionnaire: Describe your hair.
'Describe your hair' is a field in the Sexual Assault
Reporting Option form from the New South Wales Police.
In the sixth stanza, I paraphrase a quote from poet Alok
Vaid-Menon: 'What feminine part of yourself did you have
to destroy in order to survive in the world?'

Subtle Asian Traits is a Facebook group for people of Asian
heritage to connect over memes, advice, and relevant
news. The poem references the day 'Emily Doe' was
revealed to be Chanel Miller, an Asian-American writer
and artist who survived rape at Stanford University. In the
media coverage of the case, the rapist was often referred to
as the 'Stanford Swimmer'.

In *Pipeline Polyptych,* I make the deliberate choice to
call Palestine as Palestine, against imposed colonial
representations.

Valentine's Day at the Women's Baths uses the structure of
Warsan Shire's poem *Backwards.*

Trick Mirror is entitled after Jia Tolentino's essay
collection *Trick Mirror: Reflections on Self-Delusion*
(Random House 2019).

comfort sequence uses paraphrased and patch-worked

information from Filipino news outlets: Inquirer, Rappler, Panay News, and GMA Network. The links are available on my website: euniceandrada.com

The etymology of 'rape' is a quote from Argentine-Brazilian anthropologist Rita Laura Segato in her interview with Victor M. Uribe-Uran, published in *Hemisphere: A Magazine of the Americas*, Vol. 22 (2013).

comfort sequence also features the findings of Bontok-Igorot anthropologist Dr. June Prill-Brett, who concluded that rape did not exist in Bontoc before its militarisation and exposure to capitalist plunder.

comfort sequence features a reconfigured quote from So Mayer's essay 'Floccinaucinihilipilification' from the anthology *Not That Bad: Dispatches from Rape Culture* (Harper Perennial 2018).

The Yield is inspired by Sonia Feldman's poem '5,000 Prostitutes of Erice'. My poem is informed by the events of late October 1918 in Sampaloc, Manila, when around 170 sex workers from the Gardenia red light district were abducted by the police and transported to Davao to be enslaved as farm labourers.

Uninhabitable refers to Proverbs 21:19 in the New King James Version of the Bible: 'Better to dwell in the wilderness, than with a contentious and angry woman.'

Repatriation refers to the return of 410 Filipino workers from Lebanon during the COVID-19 pandemic. The Department of Foreign Affairs called it 'the largest single mass repatriation flight in Philippine history'.

At the Jordan river, by choice contains a small leap from Daryll Delgado's 'after the body displaces water', from her short story collection of the same name (University of Santo Tomas Publishing House 2012).

Living Sequence was written after a visit to the Monastery of the Cross in Jerusalem. It is inspired by two questions from Bhanu Kapil's *Vertical Interrogation of Strangers* (Kelsey Street Press 2001): 'Tell me what you know about dismemberment' and 'How will you prepare for death?'

Acknowledgements

Thank you to the editors of the following journals and projects, where earlier versions of these poems have appeared: *Australian Poetry Journal, Australian Book Review, Liminal Magazine, Peril Magazine, Portside Review, RUNWAY Journal, The Lifted Brow, DJed Press*, and the *Extraordinary Voices for Extraordinary Times* podcast.

Thank you to the Giramondo team for believing in my work. Eternal gratitude to my first poetry mentor Candy Royalle for helping me find my courage.

Thank you to the friends who keep me hopeful: RJ Dela Rosa, Wendy Xin, Kim Trang, Soo-Min Shim, Del Lumanta. And to the first readers of these poems: The Digital Sala Writers, Danny Soberano, Sara Saleh, Suneeta Peres da Costa, Merlinda Bobis, Gloria Demillo, Brandon Wint—it's a blessing to write alongside you.

Thank you to my inay, my ates, my titas, and my lola for your care. Palangga ta gid ka.

About the author

Eunice Andrada is a poet and educator. Her first poetry collection *Flood Damages* (Giramondo Publishing 2018) won the Anne Elder Award and was shortlisted for the Victorian Premier's Literary Award for Poetry and the Dame Mary Gilmore Award. Born and raised in the Philippines, she currently lives and writes on unceded Gadigal Land.

www.euniceandrada.com